MECHANICS OF
FLIGHT

PLATE I. "MECHANICS OF FLIGHT"
(*By courtesy of "Flight."*)

AN INTRODUCTION TO AERONAUTICAL ENGINEERING

For students engaged in all branches of engineering work

VOLUME ONE

MECHANICS OF FLIGHT

BY

A. C. KERMODE, C.B.E., M.A.

Fellow of the Royal Aeronautical Society
Author of "Flight without Formulae"
and "The Aeroplane Structure"

SIXTH EDITION

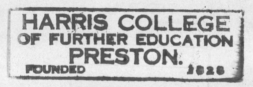

LONDON
SIR ISAAC PITMAN & SONS, LTD.

First published 1932
Second edition 1934
Reprinted 1935
Reprinted 1936
Third edition 1937
Reprinted 1938
Reprinted 1939
Reprinted 1940
Fourth edition 1940

Reprinted 1941
Reprinted 1942
Reprinted 1944
Fifth edition 1945
Sixth edition 1950
Reprinted 1951
Reprinted 1952
Reprinted 1956
Reprinted 1958

Reprinted 1959

SIR ISAAC PITMAN & SONS, LTD
PITMAN HOUSE, PARKER STREET, KINGSWAY, LONDON, W.C.2
THE PITMAN PRESS, BATH
PITMAN HOUSE, BOUVERIE STREET, CARLTON, MELBOURNE
22–25 BECKETT'S BUILDINGS, PRESIDENT STREET, JOHANNESBURG

ASSOCIATED COMPANIES
PITMAN MEDICAL PUBLISHING COMPANY, LTD.
39 PARKER STREET, LONDON, W.C.2

PITMAN PUBLISHING CORPORATION
2 WEST 45TH STREET, NEW YORK

SIR ISAAC PITMAN & SONS (CANADA), LTD.
(INCORPORATING THE COMMERCIAL TEXT BOOK COMPANY)
PITMAN HOUSE, 381–383 CHURCH STREET, TORONTO

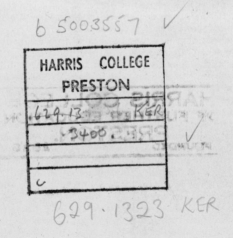
MADE IN GREAT BRITAIN AT THE PITMAN PRESS, BATH
E9—(A.9000)

FOREWORD

PROFESSOR B. MELVILL JONES

Mond Professor of Aeronautics, Cambridge University

THAT it is more difficult to write an elementary book upon a technical subject than to write an advanced treatise upon some abstruse matter may seem to be an obvious mis-statement, but when we consider the remarkable scarcity of good elementary books on any particular subject it becomes apparent that the writing of these books cannot be so easy a matter as may at first sight appear. The writer of the advanced treatise has, of course, to know his subject and make his statements clear and logical, but he is entitled to assume that the reader will be capable of following his most difficult argument and will be willing to make the effort necessary to do so. The difficulties confronting the writer of an elementary book are of an entirely different kind; while keeping his argument sufficiently simple and brief to hold the interest and be within the capacity of the beginner, he has yet to avoid the facile type of statement which too often misleads to the belief that the problem under discussion is much simpler than it really is. His work must successfully face criticism, from two opposing viewpoints; if it is not "sound," the expert will damn it and it will never be widely adopted; if it is not lightly written and easy to follow, the public, for whom it is intended, will not read it, whatever the expert may say about its soundness. Each type of critic is probably unconscious of the requirements necessary to satisfy the other, so that the compromise must be clever indeed if both are to be appeased.

The book to which this is a foreword is a very elementary introduction to the science of aeronautics, and its application to the problem of flight, and the author has therefore had to face these difficulties in their most severe form, but in overcoming them he has been unusually successful; for while the book is written in a simple manner which carries the interest along without effort, it yet manages to convey important elementary principles without misleading the reader into the belief that he understands the whole of matters which can be completely understood only after much closer study. This result has been achieved without giving to the expert critic any serious grounds for grumbling.

Written primarily for pilots and apprentices, many of whom do not intend to proceed more deeply into the theoretical study of the subject, it may yet be read with profit by anyone entering upon the study of aeronautics, whether on the practical or scientific sides. In particular does this apply to the last chapter, where the reader is taken in imagination into the air and his attention is drawn to the actual occurrence of the various phenomena which he has been studying theoretically. Here the author has managed to convey, more clearly than has hitherto appeared in print, the subtle change in point of view which comes to the student of aeronautics when he first experiences in flight the movements, forces, and operations which he has previously studied in the laboratory and lecture room.

v

PREFACE TO THIS VOLUME

THIS work, in its present form, is the result of more than thirty years of experience in various branches of aeronautical work, first as a pilot, secondly as experimental research worker, and lastly as a teacher of aeronautics to apprentices, aeronautical engineers, and pilots. In each of these three capacities, whether as pupil or teacher, the need has been felt of a book outlining the principles of flight in a manner which was neither childish nor so advanced as to be beyond the understanding of the average technical student. It is only when one ventures to supply such a need oneself that one realizes why others have failed to bridge the gap, and thus it is with a feeling of humility and uncertainty that one submits this attempt to the reader for his verdict.

The subject is fascinating, but one must tread carefully lest one falls into the trap of accepting the apparently "obvious" without due consideration of all the factors involved. If this book has any merits in this respect, I must put it down to the bombardment of questions from over ten thousand pupils; their continued insistence on obtaining answers to the why and wherefore of every feature of an aeroplane soon teaches one to see flaws in unsatisfactory replies. Therefore my thanks are due first to my pupils who have often taught me to "think again" about the explanations offered them. Nevertheless the reader must understand that, whereas the main principles on which flight depends are nothing more than the ordinary laws of mechanics, yet, when one gets down to details, the motion of an aeroplane becomes very complex; therefore without making unpractical assumptions, I have been unable to give answers to many of the problems of flight. It is often forgotten that there are many questions to which there can be no direct and simple answer, and in such instances my aim has been to state the problem, secondly to give the practical solutions where such are known, and thirdly to suggest a theory. Thus theory may seem to take a back place, but that is its proper place in a subject in which practice has always led the way.

My thanks are due to those who have helped me with the various editions; to Mr. P. H. Legg, who spared no efforts to produce diagrams to illustrate the original text; to Mr. G. W. Whittaker for reading through the manuscript and proofs; to Mr. J. Parry Jones and Mr. A. I. Ruda for help with the examples and for many useful suggestions; to the publishers for continually revising the text at considerable trouble and expense; and to the proprietors of *The Aeroplane* and of *Flight* and the various aircraft firms who have allowed me to reproduce their photographs. Many others have given me assistance, and I take this opportunity of thanking them also.

Finally, if this book succeeds in convincing the reader that the study of the theory of flight is worth while, and that the practice of flight is even more so, then I shall be fully satisfied. "A little learning" may be "a dangerous thing," but, in this subject at any rate, an absence of learning is even more dangerous. All those whose work brings them into contact with the aeroplane should have some knowledge as to "how it works."

A. C. K.

PREFACE TO SIXTH EDITION

THE first edition of this book was published seventeen years ago, and what years they have been for aviation! The monoplane has come into its own, speeds have increased beyond all expectations, undercarriages have been retracted, the variable pitch propeller has been adopted, methods of construction have altered, and aviation has more than played its part in the greatest war of all history. Even now we are in the midst of yet greater changes—the jet and rocket-propelled aeroplanes, and travel at the speed of sound—these, and other developments, are no longer dreams of the future, they are accomplished facts. In such circumstances it is no easy task to bring up to date a book that was originally conceived and written when flying was, as it now seems, in its infancy. However, I have been encouraged by the continuing demand for the book and I have tried, as it were, to put new wine into a very old bottle, and I hope that it may still be palatable.

In this edition, as in the last, there has been a thorough revision. One has been tempted to start all over again and write anew; that might have been the easier way, but one feels that there must have been something in the original character and features of the book that is worth preserving; and so I have tried to retain that something, while at the same time being fair to my readers by giving them up-to-date information. The book was originally written largely for riggers; in those days riggers had considerable influence, for good or ill, on the flight of an aeroplane, because they could twist it about by tightening and slackening the wires. Nowadays, the flight of an aeroplane depends more on the pilot, who can make adjustments in the air, and less on the rigger, who can do very little about it on the ground. In consequence, throughout the six editions, there has been a tendency to write more and more for the pilot; and in this edition, once again, changes have been made in that direction.

But this time other important changes have also been made. A completely new chapter on mechanics has been inserted at the beginning, and another new chapter, on high-speed flight, at the end. The original chapter on propellers has been amended to include the principles of jet and rocket propulsion and, under the new name of "Thrust," this chapter has been moved to an earlier position in the book. References to the influence of jet and rocket propulsion have also been inserted in other appropriate contexts, notably in connection with performance and range and endurance flying. The numerical examples have been thoroughly revised, greatly increased in number, and brought up to date and more in line with the scope of the book itself. More, and more modern, aerofoil sections have been included in the appendix on aerofoil data, while the appendix on systems of units has been carefully rewritten and a new paragraph on dimensions has been added. New diagrams and photographs have been inserted where required. There are a few omissions from earlier editions—notably out-of-date references to biplanes and a few elementary items such as the description of the parts of an aeroplane which every schoolboy now knows. All these changes

ix

have naturally involved considerable work, but such work will be fully rewarded if, as is confidently expected, they make the book more valuable to its readers.

In all this work I owe a particular debt of gratitude to Mr. K. Ritchley, who has not only given help, criticism and advice, but has undertaken the special task of revising the numerical examples.

This Sixth Edition is presented with a sense of deep gratitude to my readers and friends of the past, for it is they who have given me the encouragement and the courage to tackle the work of revision.

A. C. K.

CONTENTS

xi

LIST OF PLATES

xiii

TO INTRODUCE
OUR AEROPLANE

PLATE II. MONOPLANE

The Avro "Anson XX." An old friend still keeping pace with the times.
(*By courtesy of A. V. Roe & Co. Ltd.*)

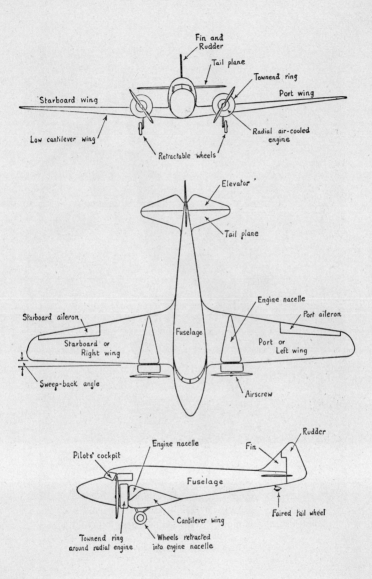

PLATE III. BIPLANE

The Gloster "Gladiator." The last of a long line of biplane
fighting aircraft.

(*By courtesy of "Flight."*)

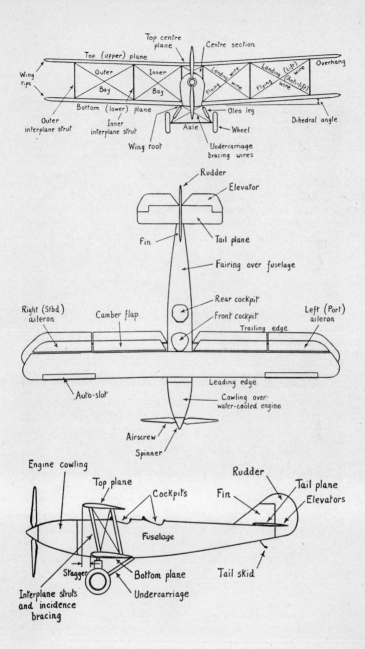

PLATE IV. THE WRIGHT BIPLANE IN FLIGHT, 1903
(*By courtesy of " Flight."*)

PLATE V. THE DH. 108 IN FLIGHT AT THE SPEED OF SOUND, 1948
(*By courtesy of the De Havilland Aircraft Co., Ltd.*)

CHAPTER I

MECHANICS

Flying and Mechanics

THE flight and manoeuvres of an aeroplane provide glorious examples of the principles of mechanics. This fact has never been recognized in school text-books which still rely far too much on the train and the motor car, not to mention the horse and cart, for the illustration of principles and the provision of numerical examples. This is not a book on mechanics; in many ways I wish that it were, for it would then provide me with an opportunity of trying to fill a long-felt want by producing a text-book of a type that would, I believe, be welcomed by the modern generation of both teachers and students. But this is a book on flying. It is an attempt to explain the flight of an aeroplane in a simple and interesting way; the mechanics are only brought in incidentally—as an aid to understanding.

To many people the problems of flying have seemed far more difficult than they really are, simply because the basic mechanical principles underlying the problems are not understood. Bogus theory has been taught, and often believed; theory that had no foundation in fact or principle. Far too frequently there have been fruitless disputes in which both sides have based their arguments on altogether false assumptions. In one way and another the science, and indeed the practice, of flight has suffered through lack of knowledge of mechanics on the part of those who indulge in it. That is the negative side of the picture, but the positive is equally true. The student who takes the trouble to master the mechanical principles will have no difficulty in understanding flying, and will benefit both himself and others by the knowledge that he brings to the subject.

Such a student, if he has not studied the subject at school, will be well advised to read a book on mechanics, and to work through the examples. In this opening chapter I shall try to sum up some of the principles, especially those with which we are most concerned in flying, but the treatment will be sketchy and incomplete, and cannot in itself provide a sure foundation on which to build.

Mass and Inertia

There is a natural tendency for things to continue doing what they are already doing. A body that is at rest, tends to remain at rest. A body that is moving, tends to continue moving—at the same speed and in the same direction.

This is the first principle of mechanics—it is, in effect, what is sometimes called Newton's First Law of Motion. But never mind whose law it is—if, indeed, it is anyone's law except that of God, or nature. And let us not just pay lip service to a law of this kind, let us rather look around us and see it happening—all day and every day.

The book lies on the table; it is at rest, it is **in equilibrium**. Notice the meaning of the words as we go along. It will stay where it is, unless . . . But that is another matter; at the moment it is there, and it tends to stay there.

1

The train is running along the level track at sixty miles an hour; it is not at rest, **but it is in equilibrium,** that is to say it is continuing to run at the same speed in the same direction, and in fact it will continue to do so, unless . . .

Things at rest, and things moving steadily, are both in equilibrium, and they both have a tendency to continue in the same state of rest or motion; in short, they both have the property called **Inertia.**

, Inertia is the Latin word for inaction, or laziness, and this first law is almost like saying that all bodies are by nature lazy. The distinction between every body and everybody being lazy is perhaps unimportant, for true it is that people possess inertia—both mental and physical. What better example of inertia than a habit?

We must beware, however, when we use the same word in ordinary English as in mechanics; work, power and energy are all words used in both, but in rather different senses. So, too, with laziness; and perhaps it is a good thing that in this instance we use the Latin word in mechanics. Few people would believe that after running a hundred yards it is laziness to go on running, but all athletes know that even if they cease to run with their legs, the top portion of their body goes on—owing to inertia. So too if one steps from a moving bus, or train, or if the bus or train suddenly starts or stops, or even when it turns a corner—one tends to go on, or to stay put, or not to turn the corner, quite irrespective of what the bus or train or other things may do; in each case unless, or maybe until—something else happens. We will come to that later.

Inertia is a property, then, of all bodies—it is a quality. We can only measure inertia in terms of **Mass**—which is a quantity. The mass of a body is a measure of how difficult it is to start or stop. It is sometimes described as the "quantity of matter in a body" (in fact Newton himself defined it rather like that!), but just what that is meant to convey it is hard to know—one might just as well simply say that mass is mass.

If mass is a quantity, we must have a unit in which it can be measured. The unit chiefly used in the English-speaking world is the mass of a lump of metal which is carefully preserved in London. All other masses are compared with this one. Strictly speaking, this should be done by measuring the comparative difficulty of starting them from rest up to a given velocity, or of stopping them when they are moving at a given velocity; we could then say that they have a certain number of units of mass. Actually there are short cuts in determining the masses of bodies; the short cuts come to the same thing, but they are more simple and save a lot of time.

Momentum

In the last paragraph it was suggested that in order to compare masses we should measure the difficulty of starting them from rest up to a given velocity; similarly that when stopping the bodies they should all initially be moving at the same velocity. This is because there are really **two** quantities that decide the difficulty of starting or stopping a body, its **mass** and its **velocity. The combined quantity, mass multiplied by velocity,** is called **momentum.**

A body of 10 units of mass moving at 2 units of velocity has 20 units of momentum; so does a body with 5 units of mass moving at 4 units of velocity. The first has the greater mass, the second the greater velocity; but both have the same momentum, both are equally difficult to stop.

A train has large mass, and, compared with a bullet, low velocity; a bullet has a small mass and a high velocity. Both are difficult to stop, and both can do considerable damage to anything that tries to stop them quickly!

Force

We have said that there is a **tendency** for things to continue doing what they are doing. We all know that they don't always continue so to do. **What then compels them to change? What makes them start, or stop, go faster or slower, or even to go round a corner?** The answer is a **Force**; a word with which we are all familiar, far more so indeed than with the words mass and momentum. That perhaps is a pity, because mass and momentum are the more fundamental conceptions, and it will be noticed that we have arrived at this paragraph before the word force was even mentioned.

We are familiar not only with the word force, but in some respects with its physical effects. Every push or pull is a force. The engine exerts a force on the train, to pull it out of the station; the brakes exert a force when they are used to stop it. Now we ourselves are guilty of talking about trains instead of aeroplanes; and, no doubt, we will soon be arguing whether a horse pulls or pushes a cart! Just for this first chapter, however, it may be appropriate to quote as examples objects and happenings with which the student is likely to be most familiar. So, too, our hand exerts a force on a cricket ball when we bowl it, the batsman exerts another force to stop it, or change its direction. And so on in all our life, we exert forces, we experience forces exerted upon us—influences they are often called. What are they all trying to do? **They are all trying to alter things.** They are all trying to change the present state of affairs, to overcome inertia, to alter the momentum. Sometimes they succeed, sometimes they don't. Whether they succeed or not has nothing to do with it, the test of whether they are forces is whether they are **trying** to alter things.

Forces in Equilibrium

When do forces not succeed in altering the existing state of affairs? Surely when they are balanced. The engine is exerting a forward force on the train even when the train is travelling at a steady velocity on a straight and level track. But the train is exerting an exactly equal and opposite force backwards on the engine. In the coupling there are two forces, one forwards, one backwards—they are equal, they are balanced

Direction of Travel
→

Backward Force / Friction & Air Resistance ← → Forward Force / Balancing Friction & Air Resistance

FIG. 1. FORCES IN EQUILIBRIUM

(Fig. 1). So what happens? The train continues to do what it is doing —to go forward at the same speed and in the same direction. It is in equilibrium.

Some people find it very hard to believe that these forces are really

equal, **exactly** equal. Surely, they say, the engine must be pulling
forward just a wee bit harder than the train is pulling backwards;
otherwise, they say, what makes it go forward? Well, what makes it
go forward is the fact that it is going forward, and the law (Newton's
First Law) that it will therefore continue to do so unless there is something to alter that state of affairs. But if the forces are balanced, there
is clearly no net force to upset the balance or state of equilibrium—so
it goes on.

Forces not in Equilibrium

Ah! these people say, so the forces are only equal when the train is
in equilibrium, it will be a very different matter when the engine is
pulling the train out of the station. Yes, indeed, it will be a very different
matter—though not quite so different as they imagine!

We have said that when travelling at a steady speed the engine had to
exert a forward force on the train. Why? If the train tends to go on
of its own accord, why does it need any force at all to pull it along?
Simply because in an imperfect world we cannot altogether eliminate
the force called friction and, what comes to much the same thing, the
air resistance or drag of the train. These, and they are not very large
at normal speeds, tend to hold the train back; it is these, and these
alone, that the pull of the engine must balance.

But what happens when the train starts out of the station? Then a
completely different force is brought into play, the force in fact that we
originally defined. **The train has mass, a large mass; that mass is at
rest when in the station. It requires a force to get it moving, the greater
the mass the greater the force it will require. The more quickly we
wish to get it moving, in other words the greater the rate at which we
wish to give momentum to the train, the greater must be the force.**
This, in effect, is what is sometimes called Newton's Second Law—
perhaps the most important of all the laws of mechanics.

When this force is exerted, the train is no longer in equilibrium, it
gathers speed, **it accelerates.** It will continue to accelerate so long as
the engine exerts a force **over and above** the forces of friction and air
resistance (Fig. 2A). When the pull of the engine again becomes equal
to these combined forces, or when these forces become equal to the
pull of the engine (much the same thing after all), then the acceleration
will cease and the train will be in equilibrium once more.

So a **special force** is required to produce a change of motion, and
when **this force** is being applied the body is **not** in equilibrium.

Inertia Forces

The wording of Newton's Third Law is familiar to every schoolboy—
too familiar, in fact. **" To every action there is an equal and opposite
reaction."** The schoolboy knows that if he over eats there will be an
inevitable reaction, just as the adult knows that a "morning after"
invariably follows a "night before." But the schoolmaster doesn't
quite put it like that—nor did Newton for that matter. The schoolmaster says that the book resting on the table exerts a downward force
on the table, and the table exerts an equal and opposite upward force
on the book. Well, any fool can see that. Or, again, going back to the
engine and the train; the equal and opposite pulls in the coupling when
travelling at steady speed (Fig. 1) provide an example of this law,
though perhaps not quite such an easy one for any fool to see.

To every force there is an equal and opposite force—force and counter-force—somehow or other if we put it that way it seems to bring it home better than when we use the words action and reaction. Notice that there is no "if," or "when," or "but," or "unless" about this law. What then is the state of affairs when a body is **not** in equilibrium? What are the forces on the coupling when the engine is pulling the train out of the station?

Direction of Travel and Acceleration

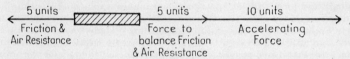

5 units   5 units   10 units
Friction &   Force to   Accelerating
Air Resistance   balance Friction   Force
                     & Air Resistance

Fig. 2A. Forces not in Equilibrium

Well, the engine must pull on the train for **two** reasons; first, because the train is a mass which must be given momentum—this is the special force—secondly, because of the friction and air resistance. Now suppose for the sake of argument that, at a certain moment during the acceleration of the train, the special force is 10 units, and the combined forces of friction and air resistance are 5 units, then clearly the engine must be pulling with a total force of 15 units. With what force is the train pulling back on the engine? And what is the force in the coupling? (Note that we are now using **units of force** which are quite different from the units of mass previously used.)

Direction of Travel and Acceleration

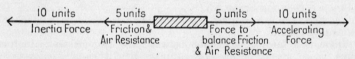

10 units   5 units   5 units   10 units
Inertia Force Friction&   Force to   Accelerating
              Air Resistance   balance Friction Force
                               & Air Resistance

Fig. 2B. Forces not in Equilibrium

The answers seem rather startling—until we think them over. Just as the engine is pulling forward for two reasons, so the train is pulling backward for two reasons—the same two reasons, in fact. The engine must accelerate the train—hence the **special forward force** of 10 units. But the train objects to be accelerated, owing to its inertia—and it shows its objection by exerting a **special backward force** of exactly 10 units! Also, of course, it is held back by the friction and air resistance to the extent of 5 units. So the train is pulling back the engine with a total force of 15 units (Fig. 2B).

So the forces are equal? Yes, in a sense they are.

Think of the pull in the coupling—there is certainly a forward force of 15 units, and equally certainly a backward force of 15 units. So the total pull is—no, **not** 30 units, but 15 units. After all, what can a pull of 15 units mean except that there is a pull of 15 units in **both** directions?

But if the forces are equal, what is causing the acceleration?

The special forward force.

Yes, but if this force is balanced by an equal and opposite backward force, how can it produce an acceleration? That, of course, is the crux of the whole matter, and it must be admitted that it takes a little understanding. The point is that **the backward force is only there because of the acceleration.** It is a special kind of force, even more special perhaps than the forward force that is causing the acceleration. **It is called an inertia force.**

We have been into this in some detail because it is a problem that occurs throughout mechanics. There are really two ways of teaching, and learning, mechanics. One is to omit inertia forces altogether, and to consider that the force producing the acceleration of a mass is an **unbalanced force** (Fig. 2A). At first that makes it all sound very simple. But we must then say that Newton's Third Law of action and reaction only applies when bodies are in equilibrium. There seems no harm in that, but it does lead us into difficulty when, for instance, we come to consider the tension in that coupling between the engine and the train. The advocates of this method will say that there is a forward force of 15 units, and a backward force of 5 units, leaving a net forward force of 10 units to produce the acceleration. But, of course, they must admit that the tension in the coupling is 15 units—the answer is the same however we look at mechanics—and can we conceive of a tension of 15 units meaning anything but a pull of 15 units in each direction?

The alternative approach is the argument that has been given in this chapter. By putting in the backward inertia force—a very real force, by the way—**we make the forces in each direction appear to be balanced** (Fig. 2B), and we reduce the problem to the same simplicity **as if the system were in equilibrium,** which of course it is not.

Weight

There is one particular force with which we are all so familiar, and which has such a profound effect on our lives—especially when we fly!—that it deserves special mention. **It is known as the force of gravity.**

What is the force of gravity?

Familiar though it may be, it is surprising how few people understand its real significance.

There is a force of attraction between any two masses—a mutual force, mass A pulls on mass B, and mass B pulls equally on mass A. Action and reaction again. **The greater the masses, and the nearer they are together, the greater the force of attraction. It is this force, the attraction between masses, that is called the force of gravity.**

In the study of astronomy we are concerned with this force in so far as it affects all the heavenly bodies and their relative motions. On the earth we need only concern ourselves with the more limited aspect of the force of gravity as the mutual force of attraction between the earth itself and each body on or near the earth's surface. **In this limited form we call it weight.** Notice, however, that it is still a mutual force; the earth attracts a body, but a body also attracts the earth. If one falls out of an aeroplane, one certainly seems to do most of the moving, but actually the earth comes to meet one—though not by any means half way!

The Acceleration of Gravity

Talking of falling out of an aeroplane leads one naturally to think of other falling bodies, and of the old tag that a feather and a lump of lead fall at the same rate—which of course they do not!

Now, all materialistic bodies have mass; they must therefore experience forces of gravity due to all the other masses around them. For a body on or near the earth's surface the only appreciable force of gravity is that between the body and the earth itself, i.e. weight. What, then, will happen if we can so arrange matters that **this is the only force acting on the body?** If it is at rest, it will start to move; whatever it is doing, its motion will be changed, it will accelerate.

Now the rate at which any body gathers momentum, the rate at which it accelerates, depends on two things—the mass acted upon, and the force acting upon it. The greater the mass, the less the effect of any given force; the greater the force, the greater the effect on any given mass—rather obvious now perhaps, but absolutely fundamental in our understanding of the subject, so we make no apology for rubbing it in.

Now bodies at the same distance from the centre of the earth may have different masses, but they will have correspondingly different forces of gravity acting upon them—so all will accelerate at the same rate, provided that only the force of gravity acts upon them.

The reason why the feather and the lump of lead do not in fact accelerate at the same rate is of course given in the important proviso that **only** the force of gravity should act upon them. When bodies fall in real air they experience air resistance, and this, of course, acts against the force of gravity. The feather, in proportion to its weight, experiences more air resistance than the lump of lead, and so the resultant force on it is small and it accelerates at a low rate; after a very short fall the air resistance will have become as great as the weight, there will be no nett or resultant force, and the feather will no longer accelerate, but just carry on at the same speed in accordance with the first law. All falling bodies reach this state of affairs in time, and the velocity which they then reach is called the **terminal velocity.** The terminal velocity of the lump of lead is, of course, much higher than that of the feather.

This is what happens in air, but in order to get the principles clear, let us consider for a moment what happens to a falling body when there is no air, that is in a vacuum. Careful experiment has revealed the fact that in a vacuum all bodies do accelerate at the same rate. **We call this the acceleration of gravity, usually abbreviated to the symbol " g."**

Mass, Weight and " g "

If we move a body to different distances from the centre of the earth, its mass does not change; it will still be equally difficult to start or stop.

But since the force of gravity depends on the distance from the centre of the earth, the weight of the body will, of course, change—becoming less and less as it is removed from the earth's centre. So the weight of a body is not constant, it varies even as between London and New York, since the earth is not exactly spherical in shape.

The acceleration of gravity depends on both the mass and the weight; since the mass is constant, and the weight varies, it will be clear that the acceleration of gravity also varies and in the same proportion as the weight.

Units of Measurement

We have succeeded in getting thus far without using any specific units of measurement for mass, force, g or anything else. It is unfortunate that we cannot continue this delightful state of affairs throughout the book—if we could, it would remove most of the terrors of mechanics, and the mistakes that we shall make. But, alas, we have to live in a practical world and, what is more, a world that is as divided about its systems of units as it is about anything else.

The problem is not merely as between the metric system and the British system—that is a comparatively clear-cut issue. It is the sub-systems within each system that cause the real trouble, and which divide teachers and learners of mechanics into rival camps. In this chapter I shall give only the system that we shall use throughout this book, it is the one that is commonly used in aeronautical work in most of the English-speaking world—and it is for that reason, rather than for its other advantages or disadvantages, that we shall use it. The reader who is interested may like to turn to Appendix II in which the problem has been gone into in rather more detail.

For units of distance and time we shall normally use the **foot** and the **second,** and so it follows that the unit of velocity will be the **foot per second,** and of acceleration the **foot per second per second.** These we shall always use in formulae, but it may sometimes be necessary in the examples and in the answers to convert from and to miles and miles per hour, or even nautical miles and knots (nautical miles per hour). The nautical mile and the knot are now used almost exclusively in air navigation, so it will pay us to become accustomed to them.

It is in choosing units for mass and force that the real fun starts. We have seen that the acceleration produced is greater according to the force, i.e. is proportional to the force ; and is less if the mass is greater, i.e. is inversely proportional to the mass.

This means that Acceleration is proportional to Force/Mass, or Force is proportional to Mass $\times$ Acceleration, or in symbols, $F \propto M \times a$.

It is always more convenient to get rid of the proportion sign and replace it by an equal sign and a coefficient, thus—

$$F = kMa$$

This equation will be even further simplified if we can so arrange the units of F, M and a that $k = 1$ and so can be omitted altogether.

This means that our units must be chosen so that when **one unit of force** acts on **one unit of mass** we will get **one unit of acceleration,** i.e. 1 ft./sec./sec.

Now we have already said that the unit of mass is the mass of a certain lump of metal which is kept in London. Unfortunately this unit is called a pound-mass. We shall soon see why it is unfortunate.

If we were to drop this pound-mass in a vacuum in London we would find it accelerated at about 32·2 ft./sec./sec.—in other words, the value of the acceleration of gravity (g) in London is approximately 32·2 ft./sec./sec. In other parts of the world it will vary slightly from this figure.

Now this one pound-mass accelerates because it is acted upon by its weight, and we can define as our unit of force the weight of the one pound-mass when it is in London, and we can call its weight one **pound-weight. So one pound-weight,** or one **pound-force,** is **the weight of one pound-mass when it is in London.**

Thus the same word, pound, is used for measuring two completely different quantities, mass and weight, and, what makes it worse, one of these (the mass) is constant while the other (the weight) varies. So one pound-mass does not always weigh one pound-weight!

Further, if we use these two units we shall not achieve the result of unit force acting on unit mass producing unit acceleration because when one pound-force acts on one pound-mass we get an acceleration of 32·2 ft/sec./sec.

Clearly then we should get unit acceleration if we made the unit of force equal to $\frac{1}{32 \cdot 2}$ of the pound-weight, or alternatively if we made the unit of mass 32·2 times as great as the pound-mass. It is the latter system that we shall use in this book. **The unit of mass, which is equal to 32·2 pounds-mass, is called a slug. Forces will be measured in pounds-weight.**

One pound-weight acting on **one slug of mass** produces an acceleration of **one ft./sec./sec.**, and, if we use these units the formula—

$$F = Ma \text{ will always hold good.}$$

Numerical Questions

The reader will be well advised at this stage to work out for himself some numerical examples (page 336). Only in this way can he become really familiar with the symbols and units and, what is more important, with the principles involved.

Here is a typical example—

EXAMPLE. The mass of an aeroplane is 4,000 lb.-mass. What force, in addition to that required to overcome friction and air resistance, will be needed to give it an acceleration of 8 ft./sec./sec. during take-off?

ANSWER. Mass of aeroplane $= \dfrac{4,000}{32 \cdot 2} = 124$ slugs.

$$\begin{aligned} \text{Force} &= Ma \\ &= 124 \times 8 \\ &= 992 \text{ lb.-force.} \end{aligned}$$

(Note that in ordinary life we do not often talk of the mass of an aeroplane, or anything else, but rather of its weight. In fact, though, we often mean mass but call it weight. It is the mass of a boxer, or of a tug-o'-war team, that really matters, and most certainly our rations should be measured in mass. Strange though it may seem, when we "weigh" an object on a see-saw type of balance, or on a steelyard or weighbridge, we are actually measuring its mass, because we are comparing the force of gravity on it with the force of gravity on a standard mass on the other side of the balance. On a spring balance, on the other hand, we are just measuring the force of gravity, or weight of the object itself.)

Since, in future, we shall use the slug as the unit of mass, and the pound as the unit of force, there will be no need to qualify the pound by writing lb.-force or lb.-weight. If, however, we wish to write of a pound-mass we shall write it as lb.-mass.

If the reader finds that he still gets into difficulties over units he may find it helpful to read the principles of dimensions given at the end of Appendix II. These principles provide the best way of getting down to the fundamentals, and once the fundamentals are understood there should be no difficulty about the details.

Many numerical examples on the relationship between forces and masses involve also the principles and formulae of simple kinematics, and the reader who is not familiar with these should read the next paragraph before he tackles the examples.

Kinematics

If the reader has arrived so far without floundering he has done well. In comparison, much of what follows is plain sailing. It will help us in working examples if we summarize the relations which apply in kinematics, that is, the study of the movement of bodies irrespective of the forces acting upon them.

We shall consider only the two simple cases, those of uniform velocity and uniform acceleration.

Symbols and units will be as follows—

Time $= t$ (sec.)
Distance $= s$ (feet)
Velocity (initial) $= u$ (feet per sec.)
Velocity (final) $= v$ (feet per sec.)
Acceleration $= a$ (feet per sec. per sec.)

Uniform Velocity. If velocity is uniform at u ft./sec. clearly—

Distance travelled $=$ Velocity $\times$ Time

$$\text{or } s = ut$$

Uniform Acceleration. Final velocity $=$ Initial velocity $+$ Increase of Velocity.

$$\text{or } v = u + at$$

Distance travelled $=$ Average velocity $\times$ Time

$$= \left(\frac{v + u}{2}\right) \times t \text{ (but } v = u + at)$$

$$= \left(\frac{u + at + u}{2}\right) \times t$$

i.e. $s = ut + \tfrac{1}{2}at^2$

If we eliminate t from $v = u + at$, we get $t = \dfrac{v - u}{a}$, and putting this

value into s $\left(\dfrac{v + u}{2}\right) \times t$ we get—

$$s = \frac{(v + u)(v - u)}{2a}$$

$$= \frac{v^2 - u^2}{2a}$$

$$\text{or } v^2 = u^2 + 2as$$

With the aid of these simple formulae—all of which are founded on first principles—it is easy to work out problems of uniform velocity or uniform acceleration. For instance—

EXAMPLE 1. If, during a take-off run an aeroplane starting from rest attains a velocity of 60 m.p.h. in 10 seconds, what is the average acceleration?

ANSWER. Initial velocity $u = 0$
Final velocity $v = 60$ m.p.h. $= 88$ ft./sec.
Time $t = 10$ sec.
$a = ?$

Since we are concerned with u, v, t and a, we use the formula—

$$v = u + at$$
$$88 = 0 + 10a$$

$$\therefore a = \frac{88}{10} = \textbf{8·8 ft./sec./sec.}$$

EXAMPLE 2. How far will the aeroplane of the previous example have travelled during the take-off run?

$u = 0, v = 88$ ft./sec., $t = 10$ sec., $a = 8\cdot8$ ft./sec./sec.

To find s, we can either use the formula—

$$s = ut + \tfrac{1}{2}at^2$$
$$= 0 + \tfrac{1}{2} \times 8\cdot8 \times 10^2$$
$$= 440 \text{ ft.}$$
$$\text{or } v^2 = u^2 + 2as$$
$$88 \times 88 = 0 + 2 \times 8\cdot8 \times s$$
$$\therefore s = \frac{88 \times 88}{2 \times 8\cdot8}$$
$$= \mathbf{440 \text{ ft.}}$$

EXAMPLE 3. A bomb is dropped from an aeroplane which is in level flight at 200 knots at a height of 10,000 ft. Neglecting the effect of air resistance, how long will it be before the bomb strikes the ground, and how far horizontally before the target must the bomb be released?

ANSWER. To find the time of fall we are concerned only with the vertical velocity, which was zero at release.

$\therefore \quad u = 0$

$a = $ acceleration of gravity $= 32\cdot2$ ft./sec./sec.

$s = $ vertical distance from aeroplane to ground $= 10,000$ ft.

$t = ?$

We need the formula connecting u, a, s and t, i.e.—

$$s = ut + \tfrac{1}{2}at^2$$
$$\therefore 10,000 = 0 + \tfrac{1}{2} \times 32\cdot2 \times t^2$$
$$\therefore t^2 = \frac{10,000}{32\cdot2} \times 2 = 622$$
$$\therefore \mathbf{t = 25 \text{ sec.}} \text{ (approx.)}$$

Since we are neglecting the effect of air resistance the horizontal velocity of the bomb will, throughout the fall, remain the same as it was at the moment of release, i.e. the same as the velocity of the aeroplane namely 200 knots or $\dfrac{200 \times 6,080}{60 \times 60} = 338$ ft./sec.

Therefore the distance that the bomb will travel forward during the falling time of 25 sec. will be 338×25 ft.

This, of course, is the distance before the target that the bomb must be released.

(Note that in this example we have neglected air resistance. Since we are interested in flying this may seem rather a silly thing to do, because we are only able to fly by making use of the same principles that are responsible for air resistance. In fact, too, the effects of air resistance on bombs are of vital importance and are always taken into account when bombing. Our justification for neglecting the effects of air resistance at this stage is that it is always better to learn things in their most simple form first, then gradually to add the complications. As these complications are added we get nearer and nearer to the real truth, but if we are faced with them all at once the whole picture becomes blurred and the fundamental principles involved fail to stand out clearly.)

Other examples on kinematics will be found on page 335, and the reader who is not familiar with examples of this type is advised to work through them.

Motion on Curved Paths

It has already been emphasized that bodies tend to continue in the same state of motion, and that this involves direction as well as speed. It is clear, therefore, that **if we wish to make a body change its motion by turning a corner or travelling on a curved path, we must apply a force to it in order to make it do so,** and that this will apply even if the speed of the body does not change. This is a special force exactly similar to the one that is required to accelerate the train out of the station, that is to say **the force must be proportional to the mass of the body and to the acceleration which it is desired to produce.** But what is the acceleration of a body that is going round a corner? Is there, in fact, any acceleration at all if the speed remains constant? And another rather important question—in what direction is the acceleration?

Let us deal with the last question first. There is another part of Newton's Second Law which has not so far been mentioned, namely that **the rate of change of momentum of the body will be in the direction of the applied force.** If the mass of the body does not change as it goes round the corner—and this applies to solid bodies such as trains, motor cars or aeroplanes—**the acceleration must be in the direction of the force.** But is there any acceleration if the speed does not change? Yes—because velocity is what we call a vector quantity, that is to say, it has both magnitude and direction, while speed has only magnitude. Thus if the direction of motion changes, the velocity changes even though the speed remains unaltered. But at what rate does the velocity change?—in other words, what is the acceleration? and in what direction is it?

Centripetal Force and Centripetal Acceleration

Here we are going to cheat. The reader who is not familiar with the answer, and who doesn't like cheating, must consult books on mechanics. To save space and time let us take a short cut by saying that we all know the direction of the force as a result of practical experience. Swing a stone round on the end of a piece of string. **In what direction does the string pull on the stone to keep it on its circular path? Why, towards the centre of the circle, of course.** Yes, and since force and acceleration are in the same direction, the **acceleration must also be towards the centre.**

We know too that **the greater the velocity of the stone, and the smaller the radius of the circle on which it travels, the greater is the pull in the string,** and **therefore the greater the acceleration.** It is true that this does not tell us the exact value of the acceleration, but if we are slightly more sensitive to forces we may have realized that the velocity is more important than the radius or, if we have learnt text-book mechanics, that the **acceleration is actually given by the simple formula** v^2/r, where v is the velocity of the body and r the radius of the circle.

The force towards the centre is called Centripetal Force (Centre-seeking Force), and will be equal to the Mass of the body × the Centripetal Acceleration, i.e. to $M \times v^2/r$ (Fig. 3).

We have made no attempt to prove that the acceleration is v^2/r— the proof will be found in any text-book on mechanics and in many mathematical ones—but since it is not easy to conceive of an acceleration towards the centre as so many feet per second per second when the body never gets any nearer to the centre, it may help if we translate the algebraic expression into some actual figures. Taking the simple example of a stone on the end of a piece of string, if the stone is whirled round so as to make one revolution per second, and the length of the string is 3 ft., the distance travelled by the stone per second will be—

$$2\pi r, \text{ i.e. } 2\pi \times 3 \text{ or } 18\cdot84 \text{ ft.}$$
$$\therefore v = 18\cdot84 \text{ ft./sec., } r = 3 \text{ ft.}$$
$$\therefore \text{ Acceleration towards centre} = v^2/r$$
$$= \frac{18\cdot84 \times 18\cdot84}{3}$$
$$= \text{(approx.) } 118 \text{ ft./sec./sec.}$$

Notice that this is nearly four times the acceleration of gravity, or nearly $4g$. Since we are only using this example as an illustration of principles, let us simplify matters by assuming that the answer is $4g$, i.e. $128\cdot8$ ft./sec./sec.

This means that the velocity of the stone towards the centre is changing at a rate 4 times as great as that of a falling body. Yet it never gets any nearer to the centre! No, but what would have happened to the stone if it had not been attached to the string? It would have obeyed the natural tendency to go straight on, and in so doing would have departed further and further from the centre. The acceleration of $4g$ may, in a sense, be taken as the rate at which it is being prevented from doing this.

What centripetal force will be required to produce this acceleration of $4g$? The mass of the stone $\times 4g$.

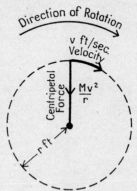

FIG. 3. CENTRIPETAL FORCE

As explained previously we will probably know the weight of the stone and not the mass.

If the weight is 1 lb. the mass will be $1/g$ slug.

So the centripetal force will be $1/g \times 4g = 4$ lb.

$\therefore$ The pull in the string is 4 lb. in order to give the weight of 1 lb. (i.e. mass of $1/g$ slug) an acceleration of $4g$.

Notice the figures, and notice the units, because all this is going to crop up again.

Notice, particularly, that the **force is 4 lb.**, the **acceleration is 4g.** There is a horrible tendency to talk about "g" as if it were a force; it is not, it is an acceleration.

Now this is all very easy provided the centripetal force is the only force acting upon the mass of the stone—but is it? Unfortunately, no. There must, in the first place, be a force of gravity acting upon it.

If the stone is rotating in a **horizontal circle** its weight will act at right angles to the pull in the string, and so will not affect the centripetal force. But of course a stone cannot rotate in a horizontal circle, with the string also horizontal, unless there is something to support the weight of the mass. So let us imagine the mass to be on a table— but it will have to be smooth, frictionless table or we shall introduce yet more forces. We now have, at least in imagination, the simple state of affairs illustrated in Fig. 4.

Now suppose that we rotate the stone in a **vertical** circle, like an aeroplane looping the loop, the situation is rather different. Even if the

stone were not rotating, but just hanging on the end of the string, there
would be a tension of 1 lb. in the string; if it must also rotate with an
acceleration of $4g$ the string must also provide a centripetal force of
4 lb. So when the stone is at the bottom of the circle, D, the total pull
in the string will be 5 lb. When the stone is in the top position, C, its
own weight will act towards the centre and this will provide 1 lb., so
the string need only pull with an additional 3 lb. to produce the total

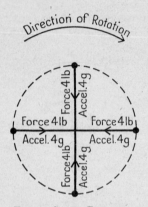

FIG. 4. STONE ROTATING
IN A HORIZONTAL CIRCLE,
E.G. ON A TABLE

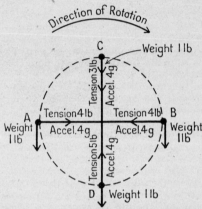

FIG. 5. STONE ROTATING IN A VERTICAL
CIRCLE

of 4 lb. for the acceleration of $4g$. At the side positions, A and B, the
weight of the stone acts at right angles to the string and the pull in the
string will be 4 lb.

To sum up: the pull in the string varies between 3 lb. and 5 lb.,

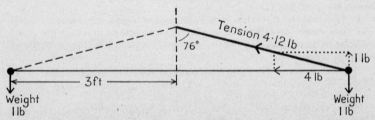

FIG. 6. STONE ROTATING IN A HORIZONTAL CIRCLE WITH
STRING SUPPORTING STONE

but the acceleration is all the time $4g$ and, of course, the centripetal
force is all the time 4 lb. From the practical point of view what matters
most is the pull in the string, which is obviously most likely to break
when the stone is in position D and the tension is at the maximum value
of 5 lb.

To complicate the issue somewhat, suppose the stone rotates in a
horizontal circle, but relies on the pull of the string to hold it up (Fig.
6), we will imagine that the string has been lengthened so that the radius
on which the stone is rotating is still 3 ft. The string cannot of course be

horizontal since the pull in it must do two things—**support the weight of the stone** and **provide the centripetal force.**
Here we must introduce a new principle.
A force of one pound, vertically, is required to support the weight.
A force of four pounds, horizontally, to provide the centripetal force.
Now one plus four does not always make five!—it does not in this example, and for the simple reason that they are not pulling in the same direction. We must therefore represent them by vectors (Fig. 6), and the diagonal will represent the total force which, by Pythagoras' Theorem, will be—

$$\sqrt{4^2 + 1^2} = \sqrt{17} = 4 \cdot 12 \text{ lb.}$$

The tangent of the angle of the string to the vertical will be $4/1 = 4 \cdot 0$. So the angle will be approx. $76°$.
Expressing the angle, θ, in symbols—

$$\textbf{tan } \theta = \frac{\text{Centripetal Force}}{\text{Weight}} = \frac{M \times v^2/r}{W}$$
$$= \frac{W/g \times v^2/r}{W}$$
$$= \frac{v^2}{rg}$$

and this angle θ represents the correct angle of bank for any vehicle, whether it be bicycle, motor car or aeroplane, to turn a corner of radius r feet, at velocity v ft./sec. if there is to be no tendency to slip inwards or to skid outwards.

Centrifugal Force

Whether by accident or design, I am not quite sure, but we have managed to arrive so far without mentioning the term **Centrifugal Force.** This is rather curious because centrifugal force is a term in everyday use, while centripetal force is hardly known except to the student of mechanics.
Consider again the stone rotating, on a table, in a horizontal circle. We have established the fact that there is an **inward** force on the stone, **exerted by the string,** for the set purpose of providing the acceleration **towards the centre**—yes, centripetal force, however unknown it may be, is a real, practical, physical force. But is there also an outward force on the stone?
Some people avoid the issue by saying that there is an outward force on one's hand, or whatever it is that is holding the string at the other end. That, of course, is true, rather obviously so, and that may be called Centrifugal Force if you like, but notice that in that case it is not acting on the stone at all. So I repeat—is there an outward force on the stone?
Yes, certainly there is, and it is called **Centrifugal Force, but it is an inertia force, it represents the resistance of the mass to the centripetal acceleration ;** it is equal and opposite to the centripetal force, it corresponds exactly to the **special** backward force of the train on the engine during the acceleration out of the station. Some teachers object to the term Centrifugal Force altogether, they even say that it does not exist. But that is going too far ; as an inertia force it certainly does exist and after the previous explanation of inertia forces there should not be any difficulty in understanding it now. What should be emphasized is

surely that the force we hear so little of—Centripetal Force—is, of the two, the most real, and incidentally, the most easily understood. It corresponds to the forward force with which the engine accelerates the train out of the station, and there is no difficulty in understanding that.

To sum up motion on curved paths. **There is an acceleration** (v^2/r) **towards the centre, necessitating a Centripetal Force of** Mv^2/r**, and there is an equal and opposite inertia force called Centrifugal Force.** As in straight motion we can either think of the inward force only, or we can reduce the system to apparent equilibrium by putting in the inertia or outward force.

Bodies travelling on curved paths, especially aeroplanes, do not usually maintain a constant radius, but this fact makes no difference to the principles involved. At any particular moment any curve on which a body is travelling may be considered as a circle of a certain radius with a centre somewhere, even if a moment later the body may be on a different circle with different radius and centre.

At this stage, the reader is advised to try some numerical questions on motion on curved paths (page 337).

Work, Power, and Energy

These three terms are used frequently in mechanics, and perhaps nowhere more than in the mechanics of flight, so we must understand their meaning. This is especially important because they are common words too in ordinary conversation, but with rather different shades of meaning.

A force is said to do Work on a body when it moves the body in the direction in which it is acting, and the amount of work done is measured by the product of the Force and the Distance moved in the direction of the force. Thus if a force of 10 lb. moves a body 2 ft. (along its line of action), it does 20 ft. lb. of work. That is all there is to it. Notice that, according to mechanics, you do no work at all if you push something without succeeding in moving it—no matter how hard you push or for how long you push. Notice that you do no work if the body moves in the opposite direction, or even at right angles to the direction in which you push. Someone else must be doing some pushing—and some work ! Notice that brain-work does not count—according to mechanics— unless perhaps some pen-pushing is required !

Power is simply the Rate of doing Work. If the force of 10 lb. moves the body 2 ft. in 5 sec. then the power is 20 ft. lb. in 5 sec. or 4 ft. lb. per second. Note the importance of the time, i.e. of the rate at which the work is done ; the word power, or powerful, is apt to give an impression of size and brute force, but the word as used in mechanics explains the great power of a small aero-engine as compared with its bigger, but slower running, brother of say the Diesel type. The unit of 1 ft. lb. per second is small for practical use, and is usually converted into **Horse Power.** The horse power is defined as **550 ft. lb. per second** (or 33,000 ft. lb. per minute), so that the power in the example given is only a small fraction of a horse power.

A body is said to have Energy if it has the ability to do work, and the **amount of Energy is reckoned by the amount of work that it can do.** The units of energy will therefore be the same as those of work. The amount of work a body can do **should** be the same as the amount that has been done on it, that is to say, it should be able to give back what it has been given. Unfortunately it usually cannot do so, but that is beside the point at the moment. We know that petrol can do work by driving a motor car or an aeroplane, a man can do work by propelling a bicycle or even by walking, a chemical battery can drive an electric motor which can do work on a train, an explosive can drive a shell at high speed from the muzzle of a gun, and atoms—well, atoms can do almost anything if we learn how to manage them. All this means that **energy can exist in many forms, heat, light, sound, electrical, chemical, magnetic, atomic —and, most useful of all, mechanical.** A little thought will convince us how much of our time and energy is spent in converting, or trying to convert, other forms of energy into mechanical energy, the eventual form which enables us to get somewhere. The human body is simply a form of engine—not a simple form of engine—in which the energy contained in our food is converted into useful, or useless, work. Unfortunately there is a tendency for energy to slip back again, we might almost say deteriorate, into other forms, and our efforts to produce mechanical energy are not always very efficient.

Even mechanical energy can exist in more than one form; a weight that is high up can do work in descending, and it is said to possess **Potential Energy** or Energy of Position; a mass that is moving rapidly can do work in coming to rest, and it is therefore said to have **Kinetic Energy** or Energy of Motion; a spring that is wound up, a gas that is compressed, even an elastic material that is stretched, all can do work in regaining their original state, and all possess energy which is in a sense potential but which is given various names according to its application.

In figures, a weight of 50 lb. raised to a height of 2 ft. above its base has 100 ft. lb. of potential energy. This was the work done to raise it to that position, and it is the work that it should be able to do in returning.

In symbols, **W lb. at height h ft. has—**

Wh ft. lb. of energy.

What is the kinetic energy of a mass of M slugs moving at v ft./sec.?

We don't know, of course, how it got its kinetic energy, but as this should not matter very much, let us suppose it was accelerated uniformly at a ft./sec./sec. from zero velocity to v ft./sec. by being pushed by a constant force of F lb.

If the distance it travelled during the acceleration was s ft.

Then the work done, i.e. its kinetic energy, will be Fs ft. lb.

But what is this in terms of M and v?

Well, Force = Mass × Acceleration

or $F = Ma$

To find s, the distance, $v^2 = u^2 + 2as$ (but $u = 0$)

$$\therefore v^2 = 2as$$
$$\therefore s = v^2/2a$$

So K.E. $= Fs = Ma\,v^2/2a = \tfrac{1}{2}Mv^2$ ft. lb.

Thus the kinetic energy of 2 slugs moving at 10 ft./sec.

$$= \tfrac{1}{2}Mv^2$$
$$= \tfrac{1}{2} \times 2 \times 10^2$$
$$= 100 \text{ ft. lb.}$$

If we know the weight, W lb., instead of the mass, M slugs, we can always write W/g instead of M, and the formula then becomes—

$$\text{K.E.} = Wv^2/2g$$

Similarly we can work out the energy possessed by a wound-up spring, or a compressed gas, or an elastic material under stress; it is all interesting and important, particularly perhaps the compressed gas, but what we have covered will be sufficient for the understanding of the remainder of this book.

Energy and Momentum

Let us be sure that we understand the difference between Energy and Momentum, because we will be concerned with the difference later on.

Energy is $\frac{1}{2}Mv^2$. Momentum is Mv.

So our mass of 2 slugs, moving at 10 ft./sec. has 100 units of energy (ft. lb.), but 2×10, i.e. 20 units of momentum (slugs $\times$ ft./sec.).

Yes, but there is more to it than that.

Consider two bodies colliding, e.g. billiard balls.

The total momentum after the collision is the same as the total momentum before; the momentum lost by one ball is exactly the same as the momentum gained by the other. This is the principle of the **Conservation of Momentum.** (In considering this it must be remembered that momentum has **direction,** because velocity has direction.) The law will apply whether the balls rebound, or whether they stick together, or whatever they do.

But the total mechanical energy after the collision will not be the same as before; energy will be dissipated, it will go into the air in the form of heat, sound, etc.; the total energy of the universe will not be changed by the collision—but that of the balls will be.

So momentum is a more permanent property than energy, the latter is often wasted and we shall sometimes find it unfortunate that in order to give a body momentum we must also give it energy.

Pressure

The words Pressure and Force are often confused, which is unfortunate,

FIG. 7. PRESSURE ACTS EQUALLY IN ALL DIRECTIONS

and what is worse we sometimes give figures of pressure in units of force, e.g. an engine boost pressure may be spoken of as $+ 5$ pounds when we mean pounds per square inch. This is just laziness. For **Pressure means Force per unit Area.** If the force is evenly distributed we need only divide the force by the area over which it acts to get the pressure. Thus a force of 10 lb. distributed over an area of 2 square feet, gives a pressure of 5 lb. per sq. ft. More often than not we speak of pressures in pounds per square inch, which is a pity because pounds per square foot fits in more naturally with other units.

Fluid Pressure

In the mechanics of flight we shall be chiefly concerned with fluid pressure, that is the pressure exerted by a liquid or gas. The reason why a fluid exerts pressure is because its molecules are in rapid motion and bombard any surface that is placed in the fluid; each molecule exerts a tiny force on the surface but the combined effect of the bombardment of millions upon millions of molecules results in an evenly distributed pressure on the surface.

All that we can give here is a summary of the main principles and laws of fluid pressure with which we will be concerned later in the book.

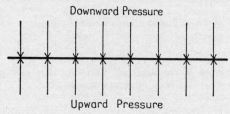

FIG. 8. AIR PRESSURE ON A THIN TABLE

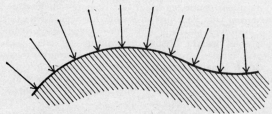

FIG. 9. PRESSURE ACTS AT RIGHT ANGLES TO THE SURFACE

In a fluid at rest the pressure at any point acts equally in all directions. If a **small** ball is completely immersed in a fluid (Fig. 7) there will be an equal pressure to the right and to the left, upwards and downwards. On a **very thin** table (Fig. 8) the air pressure will act equally upwards and downwards. This only applies if the body is at rest relative to the

FIG. 10. PRESSURE INCREASES WITH DEPTH BELOW THE SURFACE

fluid; if the body moves through the fluid, or the fluid moves past the body, there will be a very different state of affairs. Furthermore the ball must be small; strictly speaking, so small that it is just a point. The table must be thin; strictly speaking, so thin that it has no thickness.

The pressure in a fluid at rest acts at right angles to any surface with which the fluid is in contact (Fig. 9). This, it will be noticed, has been assumed in the figures. Again, it will not be true if there is any relative motion between the body and the fluid.

The pressure in a fluid increases with the depth below the surface.
If the thickness, or density, of the fluid is constant—as is very nearly true in a liquid because it is practically incompressible—the increase of pressure will be proportional to the depth (Fig. 10). In a gas there will be an increase of density with depth because the lower layers are compressed by the weight of the gas above them.

Density

Density is defined as the mass per unit volume of a substance (slugs per cu. ft.). Notice that **it is mass and not weight.**
Newton actually used density as the fundamental conception and defined the mass of a body as the quantity of matter in it obtained by multiplying the density by the volume. Be that as it may, the forces experienced by bodies moving through the air are largely reactions caused by the mass of air being forced to change its motion, and it is therefore essential that we think of density in terms of mass. It must be admitted, however, that there are times when it is convenient to use the conception of **weight divided by volume**—in fact, that is really how the word density arose in the previous paragraph—and this is sometimes called **Weight-Density.** If we do this, we must realize that we are thinking of a fundamentally different property of the fluid, measured in different units, i.e. pounds per cu. ft. instead of slugs per cu. ft.

Pressure Head

The fact that the pressure of a liquid increases almost uniformly with depth is often made use of in talking of **pressure in terms of the height or head of a liquid** (Fig. 11). Thus we may speak of 30 inches of mercury, or 20 feet of water, instead of so many pounds per square inch or square foot. How many? Well, let us see.

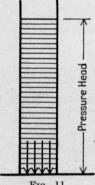

First, let us realize that the pressure, i.e. the force per unit area, will be the same whatever the area of the column that we consider, so, for convenience, let us take a column of 1 sq. ft. area. Then the volume of the mercury column, 30 in. or 2 ft. 6 in. high and 1 sq. ft. in area will be $2\frac{1}{2}$ cu. ft.

The weight-density of mercury is 13·6 × that of water, i.e. about—

$$13\cdot6 \times 62\cdot4 = 848 \text{ lb. per cu. ft.}$$

So the total weight on 1 sq. ft. at the bottom of the column is—

$$848 \times 2\frac{1}{2} = 2,120 \text{ lb.}$$

Fig. 11.
Pressure Head

∴ the pressure = 2,120 lb. per sq. ft. or 14·7 lb. per sq. in.

which is well-known as being approximately the normal atmospheric pressure at sea-level.

Similarly 20 ft. of water, of 1 sq. ft. column, weighs

$$20 \times 62\cdot4 \text{ lb.} = 1,248 \text{ lb.}$$

and the pressure is 1,248 lb. per sq. ft. or 8·7 lb. per sq. in.

Archimedes' Principle

When a body is immersed in a fluid it experiences an upthrust, or apparent loss of weight, equal to the weight of the fluid displaced by the body (Figs. 12A and B).

This important principle is really only an extension of the idea of the increase in the pressure of a fluid with depth, which means that there is a greater pressure pushing up on the body from underneath than there is pushing down on it from on top (that is why the ball had to be so small, and the table so thin, when we were saying that the pressure was the same in all directions).

This principle is the clue to the floating of balloons and airships and of ships and submarines, but we are not much concerned with it in the

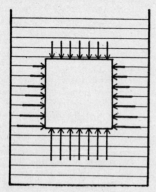

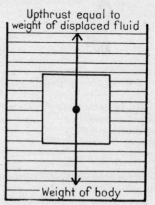

Fig. 12A. ARCHIMEDES' PRIN-
CIPLE: PRESSURE ON A BODY IN
A FLUID

Fig. 12B. ARCHIMEDES' PRIN-
CIPLE. EFFECT OF PRESSURES ON
A BODY IN A FLUID

mechanics of flight of an aeroplane. Students sometimes ask whether it would be worth while to make the body and wings of an aeroplane airtight and fill them with a light gas such as hydrogen so as to supplement the lift obtained from the wings. The answer is quite definitely in the negative. The volume enclosed in a medium sized aeroplane would probably be not much more than 200 cu. ft., and even if exhausted of all air this would only give a lift of about 16 lb. at sea level and less and less at altitude as the air becomes thinner. The extra weight involved in the gas bags, valves and so on would be far more than this—and the inconvenience caused would be intolerable.

The Gas Laws

If we increase the pressure on a gas its volume will decrease, and if we can manage to effect the compression without the temperature rising—not at all an easy thing to do—the decrease in volume will be proportional to the increase in pressure or, as it is usually expressed in **Boyle's Law**—

The volume of a given mass of a perfect gas is inversely proportional to the pressure provided the temperature remains constant.

Expressed in symbols, $PV = \text{constant}$.

But what is a perfect gas? To be honest, one that obeys this and the following, or Charles' Law—which no gas does, exactly.

If a gas is compressed or expanded according to Boyle's Law, i.e. without change of temperature, the compression or expansion is called **Isothermal.**

Charles' Law. The volume of a perfect gas increases by 1/273 of its value at 0° C for every degree Centigrade rise in temperature provided the pressure remains constant (in symbols V/T = constant).

Or, alternatively,

the pressure of a perfect gas increases by 1/273 of its value at 0° C. for every degree Centigrade rise in temperature provided the volume remains constant (in symbols P/T = constant).

In practice, when a gas expands or contracts, the pressure, volume and temperature all change and then we can combine these laws into the form—

$$\frac{PV}{T} = \text{constant}$$

(Note that in these formulae it is essential that T should be expressed in absolute temperature, i.e. degrees Centigrade $+$ 273.)

If we pursue this subject any further we shall land ourselves into the whole subject of thermodynamics, and that will take a book larger than this one, so we will put discretion before valour and retreat gracefully while there is still time!—not, however, without mentioning that there is another ideal way in which a gas can be expanded or compressed, and one which comes much nearer to the truth than the isothermal of Boyle's Law; it is called **Adiabatic, and means that the compression or expansion takes place without any heat going into or coming out of the gas.**

Strange as it may seem, if this happens the temperature of the gas will rise during compression and will fall during expansion—as we all know it does in practice—so that Boyle's Law is not exactly true.

Dynamics of Fluid Flow

We have so far dealt with fluids at rest, and we do not at this stage intend to go any further because the remainder of the book is concerned almost entirely with fluids in motion, and we should therefore be trespassing on other chapters. Even that most important of all the principles of fluid pressure—Bernoulli's Theorem—will be deferred until the next chapter.

Statics

It may seem rather inconsistent that, whereas in this chapter we have dealt with fluids at rest and omitted fluids in motion, in the mechanics of solid bodies our emphasis has been on moving bodies rather than on bodies in equilibrium. There is, however, method in our madness for our object in this chapter has been to prepare the ground for what is to follow. Experience shows that the main difficulty of students in understanding the flight of an aeroplane is caused by confused ideas about the Dynamics of solid bodies, in particular the inter-action of forces, masses and accelerations, and for this reason we have concentrated on that part of the subject. The majority of students, even if they have not learnt mechanics at school, find little or no difficulty in understanding Statics. Much of the subject is, after all, common sense; some of it rather painfully obvious; and there is nothing like the same difficulty or confusion over units. The main principles of Statics that we shall require later are summed up in the following paragraphs and if any student is not familiar with them he is advised to work through the examples (page 339)

Composition and Resolution of Forces, Velocities, etc.

A Force is a vector quantity—that is to say, it has magnitude and direction. and can be represented by a straight line, passing through the point at which the force is applied, its length representing the magnitude

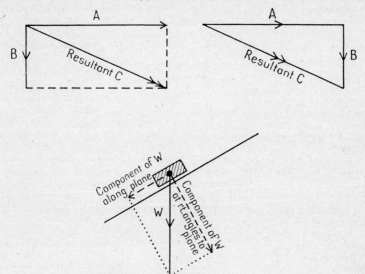

FIG. 13. COMPOSITION AND RESOLUTION OF VECTOR QUANTITIES

of the force, and its direction corresponding to that in which the force is acting.

As vector quantities, **forces can be added, or subtracted, to form a resultant force, or they can be resolved,** that is to say, split up into two or more component parts, by the simple process of drawing the vectors to represent them (Fig. 13).

Velocity and Momentum are also vector quantities and can be represented in the same way by straight lines. Mass, on the other hand, is not; a mass has no direction, and this is yet another distinction between a force and a mass.

The Triangle, Parallelogram, and Polygon of Forces

If three forces which act at a point are in equilibrium, they can be represented by the sides of a triangle taken in order (Fig. 14). This is called the principle of the **Triangle of Forces,** and the so-called **Parallelogram of Forces** is really the same thing, two sides and the diagonal of the parallelogram corresponding to the triangle.

If there are more than three forces, the principle of the **Polygon of Forces** is used—**when any number of forces acting at a point are in** equilibrium, the polygon formed by the vectors representing the forces and taken in order will form a closed figure, or, conversely, **if the polygon is a closed figure the forces are in equilibrium.**

Moments, Couples and the Principles of Moments

The **moment** of a force about any point is the **product of the force**

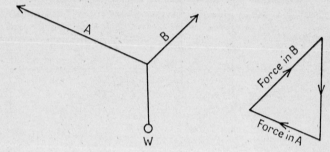

FIG. 14. TRIANGLE OF FORCES

and the perpendicular distance from the point to the line of action of the force.

Thus the moment of a force of 10 lb. about a point whose shortest distance from the line of action is 3 ft. is $10 \times 3 = 30$ lb. ft. (Fig. 15).

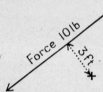

(Note the subtle distinction between a moment in lb. ft. and the work done by a force in ft. lb. Both are forces multiplied by distances, yet it is useful to distinguish between them as they are really quite different quantities. The distance in the moment is merely a leverage and no movement is involved.)

FIG. 15. MOMENT OF A FORCE (ANTI-CLOCK-WISE)

A moment about a point may act in a clockwise, or in an anti-clockwise direction.

If a body is in equilibrium under the influence of several forces in the same plane, the sum of the clockwise moments about any point is equal to the sum of the anti-clockwise moments about that point, or, what amounts to the same thing and is much shorter to express, **the total moment is zero.** This is called the **Principle of Moments,** and applies whether the forces are parallel or not.

When considering the forces acting on a body, the weight of the body itself is often one of the most important forces to be considered. The weight may be taken as acting through the **Centre of Gravity** which is defined as the point through which the resultant weight acts whatever position the body may be in.

Two equal and opposite parallel forces are called a **Couple.** The moment of a couple is one of the forces multiplied by the distance between the two, i.e. by the arm of the couple. Notice that the moment is the same about any point (Fig. 16), but a couple has no resultant.

Mechanics of Flight

We do not pretend, in this chapter, to have covered all the principles of mechanics, nor even to have explained fully those that have been

covered. All we have done has been to select some aspects of the
subject which seem to form the chief stumbling blocks in the understanding of how an aeroplane flies; we have attempted to remove them
as stumbling blocks, and perhaps even so to arrange them that, instead,
they become stepping stones to the remainder of the subject. But the

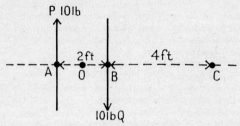

Fig. 16. A Couple

Moments about O. P 10 × 1 = 10 clock. Q 10 × 1 = 10 clock. Total 20 clock.
Moments about A. P zero   Q 10 × 2 = 20 clock. Total 20 clock.
Moments about B. P 10 × 2 = 20 clock. Q zero   Total 20 clock.
Moments about C. P 10 × 6 = 60 clock. Q 10 × 4 = 40 anti. Total 20 clock.

reader has had enough of preliminaries, let us turn now to our real
subject—the Mechanics of Flight.
    No! just a moment while the reader tries to answer some of these.
They are questions—and some of them are puzzling ones too—about
mechanics.

_____

WHAT DO YOU KNOW?

    These questions are tests not so much of mechanical knowledge as
of mechanical sense. Try to puzzle them out. Some of them are easy,
some difficult; some have definite answers, to some the answers are
vague; the answers to some have been given in the text of Chapter I,
others are left entirely to the reader to think out for himself.
    1. What is a vector? Is speed a vector quantity?
    2. A car A is moving at 30 m.p.h. Another car B is moving at
40 m.p.h. in the same direction. What is the velocity of A relative to
B, and in what direction is it?
    3. A lift is descending, and is stopping at the ground floor. In
what direction is the acceleration?
    4. What is the difference between—
        (a) Pressure and Force?
        (b) Moment and Momentum?
        (c) Work and Energy?
    5. What is the cause of Tides?
    6. A billiard player is potting the red ball. In doing so he can make
his own ball follow on, or stop after it has struck the red ball, or rebound
from the red ball. How does he achieve each of these effects, and which
will impart the greatest velocity to the red ball?
    7. Why does it require less force to pull a body up an inclined plane
rather than lift it vertically? Is the same work done in each case?
    8. Distinguish between the mass and weight of a body.
    9. Why is the water pressure greater at the taps on the ground floor
of a building than on the top floor?

10. A cotton reel rests on the floor and is pulled by the cotton which is so wound round it that it comes from the bottom of the reel. Will the reel come towards or go away from the person pulling it?

11. What is (a) a Poundal? (b) a Dyne? (c) a Slug? (d) a Millibar?

12. Why are passengers not allowed to stand on the upper deck of a bus?

13. If the drag of an aeroplane is equal to the thrust of the propeller in straight and level flight, what makes the aeroplane go forward?

14. Is the thrust greater than the drag during take-off?

15. What is a cantilever?

16. What is the difference in principle between a pair of nutcrackers and a pair of sugar tongs?

17. If one must step off a moving bus, why should one do so in the forward direction rather than backwards?

18. Distinguish between mass and inertia?

19. The weight of a motor car is increased by 20 per cent by the addition of extra loads. Will the pressure in the tyres be increased by 20 per cent?

20. Can the centre of gravity of a body be outside the body itself?

21. A heavy ball is thrown horizontally across a railway carriage and out of the window on the opposite side. Describe its motion as seen (a) by an observer in the carriage, and (b) as seen by an observer watching the train go past.

22. What difference will it make to the answers of Question 21, if a ping-pong ball is used instead of a heavy ball?

23. Is the pull in a bicycle chain more or less than the force exerted by the foot of the rider on the pedal?

24. What is a couple? How is the couple applied to the steering wheel of a motor car when only one hand is used for steering?

25. Is the value of "g" the same at all parts of the earth's surface? If not, why not?

26. Is an aeroplane in a state of equilibrium during—

    (a) A steady climb?

    (b) A steady turn?

    (c) A spin?

    (d) Take-off?

27. Are the following the same, or less, or more, on the surface of he moon as on the surface of the earth—

    (a) The weight of a given body as measured on a spring balance?

    (b) The weight of a given body as measured on a weigh-bridge (using standard set of weights)?

    (c) The time of fall of a body from 100 ft.?

    (d) The time of swing of the same pendulum?

    (e) The thrust given by a rocket?

28. In a tug-o'-war does the winning team exert more force on the rope than the losing team?

29. Why is it more important to save weight in the pistons of an engine than to save weight in the crank-case?

30. Why is it impossible to throw bombs outwards by doing a sharp turn? Or is it possible?

31. A cyclist finds some difficulty in riding a light tricycle for the first time. Why?

32. A weight is suspended from the ceiling by a piece of string;

another piece of string of the same strength hangs below the weight. Will the string break above or below the weight—

    (a) if the lower piece of string is pulled with a gradually increasing force until the string breaks?

    (b) if the lower piece of string is jerked until the string breaks?

33. A lump of lead is allowed to fall freely in air. Approximately how far will it fall from rest in 1 sec.?

34. A motor cycle and sidecar is turning a corner with the sidecar on the inside of the turn. What is liable to happen and why?

35. Can the same kind of thing happen if a motor cycle and sidecar turns a corner with the sidecar on the outside of the turn?

36. Suppose you were sitting in the middle of a perfectly frictionless surface. How would you get off it?

37. A barge, containing a quantity of scrap iron, is floating on a small pond. If the scrap iron is taken out of the barge and is allowed to sink in the pond, will the level in the pond rise, or fall, or stay the same?

38. What energy changes are involved in the following processes—

    (a) When coal is used to drive a steam locomotive?

    (b) When water power is used to make electric light?

    (c) When an electrical accumulator is charged?

    (d) When a wireless message is transmitted and received?

    (e) When a bomb explodes?

39. A watch spring is wound up tightly and placed in a glass tube in which it just fits. If the spring is now dissolved in acid, what happens to the energy stored in the spring?

40. A toy balloon is blown up and released without closing the nozzle. What happens and why?

41. What are the two reasons why a body weighs less at the equator than at the poles?

42. Why is the level of water lowered as it flows through the arches of a bridge?

43. What causes an automatic sprinkler used for watering a lawn to rotate?

44. Are the following in equilibrium—

    (a) A book resting on a table?

    (b) A train ascending an incline at a steady speed?

    (c) A rotating flywheel on a stationary engine?

45. Is there an outward force acting on a body that is travelling on a curved path?

46. An engine is pulling a train along a level track at constant speed. In what direction is the resultant force in the coupling between engine and train?

47. If the centrifugal force is equal to the centripetal force what makes a body travel on a curved path?

48. Approximately how much is the centrifugal force at the equator acting on a man weighing 12 stone?

49. What will the centrifugal force on the man be at the North Pole?

50. A flag is flying from a vertical flag pole mounted on the top of a large balloon. If the balloon is released in a strong east wind, in what direction will the flag point?

CHAPTER II

AIR AND AIRFLOW

The Atmosphere

"FLIGHT" begins when we leave the ground and ends when we return to earth again. During the intervening period we have been, as it were, in a new world—a world which, although so near to our own Mother Earth, has very different properties. This world is the **Atmosphere** which surrounds the earth like a huge ocean. The Atmosphere is composed of **air** and this is the medium to which we entrust ourselves when we fly, whether by aeroplane, airship, or balloon, and therefore we must learn something about this atmosphere before we can properly understand the problems of flight.

Invisibility of the Atmosphere

Air is invisible, and this fact in itself makes flight difficult to understand. When a ship passes through water we can **see** the "bow wave," the "wash" astern, and all the eddies and whirlpools which are formed; when an aeroplane makes its way through the atmosphere nothing appears to happen—yet in reality even more commotion has been caused than by the ship (Fig. 17).

If only we could see this commotion, many of the phenomena of flight would need much less explanation. Never was the well-known

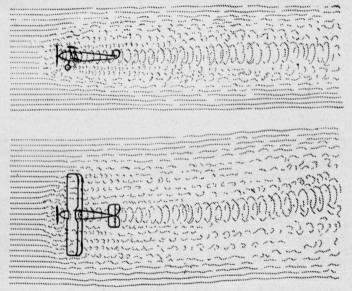

FIG. 17. "SEEING THE AIR," OR "WHAT THE EYE DON'T SEE, THE HEART DON'T GRIEVE OVER"

proverb more true, "What the eye don't see, the heart don't grieve over," and certainly if the turbulence formed in the atmosphere were visible no one could have doubted the improvement to be gained by such inventions as streamline wires and slotted wings. After some experience it is possible to cultivate the habit of "seeing the air" as it flows past bodies of different shapes, and the ability to do this is made easier by introducing smoke into the air or by watching the flow of water, which exhibits many characteristics similar to those of the air.

Density of the Air

Another property of air which is apt to give us misleading ideas when we first begin to study flight is its low density. The air feels thin, it is difficult for us to obtain any grip upon it, and if it has any weight at all we usually consider it as negligible for all practical purposes. Ask anyone who has not studied the question what is the weight of air in any ordinary room—you will probably receive answers varying from "almost nothing" up to "about ten pounds." Yet the real answer will be nearer 300 lb., and in a large hall may be over one ton! Again, most of us who have tried to dive have experienced the sensation of coming down "flat" on to the surface of water; since then we have treated water with respect, realizing that it has substance, that it can exert forces which have to be reckoned with. We have probably had no such experience with air, yet if we ever try it we will find that the opening of a parachute after a long drop will cause just such a jerk as when we encountered the surface of the water. It is, of course, true that the density of air—i.e. the **mass per unit volume**—is low compared, for instance, with water (**at ground level the weight of a cubic foot of air is roughly 0·08 lb.**—about $1\frac{1}{3}$ oz.—making the density about 0·00238 slug per cu. ft., whereas a cubic foot of water weighs $62\frac{1}{2}$ lb., nearly 800 times as much); yet it is this very property of air— its density—which makes all flight possible. The balloon, the airship, the kite, the parachute, and the aeroplane—all of them are supported in the air by forces which are entirely dependent on its density; the less the density, the more difficult does flight become; and for all of them flight becomes impossible in a vacuum. So let us next realize the fact that, however thin the air may seem to be, it possesses, like other substances, the properties of weight, of mass, and of density.

Inertia of the Air

It will now be easy to understand that **air must possess,** in common with other substances, **the property of Inertia and the tendency to obey the laws of mechanics** as outlined in Chapter I. Thus air which is still will tend to remain still, while air which is moving will tend to remain moving and will resist any change of speed or direction (First Law); secondly, if we wish to alter the state of rest or uniform motion of air, or to change the direction of the airflow, we must apply a force to the air, and the more sudden the change of speed or direction and the greater the mass of air affected, the greater must be the force applied (Second Law); and, thirdly, the application of such a force upon the air will cause an equal and opposite reaction upon the surface which produces the force (Third Law).

Pressure of the Atmosphere

Now the weight of air above any surface will produce a pressure at that surface—i.e. a force of so many pounds per square inch of surface. **The average pressure at sea-level due to the weight of the atmosphere is about 14·7 lb. per sq. in.**, a pressure which causes the mercury in a barometer to rise nearly 30 in. This pressure is sometimes referred to as "one Atmosphere," and high pressures are then spoken of in terms of "Atmospheres." The higher we ascend in the atmosphere, the less will be the weight of air above us, and so the less will the pressure become.

Decrease of Pressure and Density with Altitude

The rate at which the pressure decreases will be much greater near the earth's surface than at greater altitudes. This is easily seen by reference to Fig. 18: between sea-level and 10,000 ft. the pressure has been reduced from 14·69 lb. per sq. in. to 10·10 lb. per sq. in., a drop of 4·59 lb. per

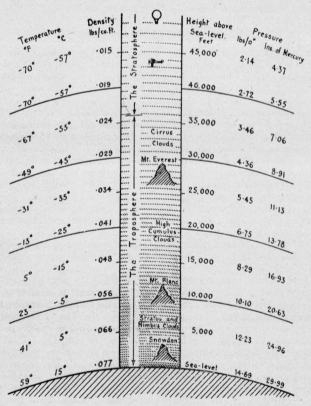

FIG. 18. THE INTERNATIONAL STANDARD ATMOSPHERE

NOTE. In the above table the density of the air has been given in pounds-mass per cu. ft.; to convert into slugs per cu. ft. the values should be divided by 32·2. Height records (1949); balloon, 72,395: aeroplane, 59,446.

sq. in., whereas for the corresponding increase of 10,000 ft. between 20,000 ft. and 30,000 ft. the decrease of pressure is from 6·75 lb. per sq. in., to 4·36 lb. per sq. in., a drop of only 2·39 lb. per sq. in. This difference is easily explained by the fact that **air is compressible,** so that the air near the earth's surface is compressed by the pressure of the air above it, and as we climb higher and higher the pressure becomes less, the air is free to expand and becomes less dense, so that if we could see a cross-section of the atmosphere it would not appear homogeneous—i.e. of uniform density—but it would become thinner and thinner from the earth's surface upwards, the final change from the atmosphere to space being so gradual as to be indistinguishable. In this respect air is different from liquids such as water ; in the first place, there is a definite dividing line or surface at the top of the water ; and, secondly, if we go down beneath the surface of the water the pressure will increase in direct proportion to the depth because the water, being practically incompressible, will remain of the same density at all depths.

Temperature Changes in the Atmosphere

Another change which takes place as we travel upwards through the atmosphere is the gradual drop in temperature, a fact which unhappily disposes of one of the oldest legends about flying—that of Daedalus and his son Icarus, whose wings were attached by wax which melted because he flew too near the sun. The reason for the falling off of temperature is that the radiant heat direct from the sun passes through the atmosphere without appreciably raising the temperature ; the earth, however, absorbs the heat, the temperature of the earth is raised and the air in contact with it absorbs some of this heat, therefore expands, decreases in density, and commences to rise, setting up convection currents in the atmosphere. The rising column of air will expand as it reaches lower pressure, and this expansion will in itself cause a falling off of temperature in accordance with Charles's Law. But quite apart from convection currents, the denser air near the earth's surface will absorb more heat than the thinner layers at greater altitudes, and so even in still air the temperature will fall off with height at a rate of about 1° F. for every 300 ft. This rate of fall does not alter until we reach about 36,000 ft. (this height varies at different parts of the earth, being greater at the Equator), and then quite suddenly the temperature ceases to fall and remains practically constant for further increases in altitude. That portion of the atmosphere below the height at which the sudden change takes place is called the " **troposphere,**" and the portion above is called the " **stratosphere.**" Although most flying takes place in the troposphere, the stratosphere is within the reach of modern aeroplanes, and it will be realized from Fig. 18 that the temperatures likely to be reached, such as − 70° F., are so low as to necessitate special precautions being taken for the comfort of the crew and the cooling systems of water-cooled engines.

Effect of Temperature on Density

The decrease in temperature with altitude should cause the air to contract and tend to become denser, but this effect is more than counteracted by the drop in pressure.

Although air is not quite a "perfect gas," it is found to obey the gas laws within reasonable limits, and if the temperature and pressure are known at any height, it is possible to estimate the density at that height from the formula derived from these two laws—i.e.

$$\frac{PV}{T} = \text{constant or } \frac{P_1V_1}{T_1} = \frac{P_2V_2}{T_2},$$

P_1, V_1, T_1 being the Pressure, Volume, and Absolute Temperature of a certain mass of air at, say, sea-level, and P_2, V_2, T_2 the corresponding values for the same mass of air at the given height.

EXAMPLE. If the Density of air at sea-level is 0·00238 slug per cu. ft. when the Temperature is 15° C. and the Pressure 14·7 lb. per sq. in., find the Density of air at 20,000 ft. where the Temperature is – 24° C. and the Pressure 6·6 lb. per sq. in.

Data: $P_1 = 14\cdot7$ lb. per sq. in. $P_2 = 6\cdot6$ lb. per sq. in.
$\quad\quad\ T_1 = 15°$ C. $= 15 + 273$ $T_2 = -24°$C. $= -24 + 273$
$\quad\quad\quad\quad = 288°$ Abs. $\quad\quad\quad\quad = 249°$ Abs.

Take a volume, V_1, of 1 cu. ft.; find the volume of this same mass of air at 20,000 ft.

$$\frac{P_1V_1}{T_1} = \frac{P_2V_2}{T_2}$$

$$\therefore \frac{14\cdot7 \times 1}{288} = \frac{6\cdot6 \times V_2}{249}$$

$$\therefore V_2 = 1\cdot92 \text{ cu. ft.}$$

Hence 1 cu. ft. at sea-level expands to 1·92 cu. ft. at 20,000 ft., but its mass is still 0·00238 slug.

$\therefore$ at 20,000 ft. the mass of 1·92 cu. ft. is 0·00238 slug

$\therefore$ Mass of 1 cu. ft. is $\dfrac{0\cdot00238}{1\cdot92} = 0\cdot00124$ slug.

$\therefore$ Density of air at 20,000 ft. is 0·00124 slug or 0·0416 lb. per cu. ft. (compare with Fig. 18).

This method is useful because both the Temperature and Pressure of the air can be read direct from instruments, whereas the Density cannot.

Since the density is inversely proportional to the volume of a given mass the working of similar examples can be simplified to some extent by writing the formula in the form—

$$\frac{P_1}{\rho_1 T_1} = \frac{P_2}{\rho_2 T_2}$$

where ρ_1 and ρ_2 represent the densities at sea-level and at height respectively.

Laws of Fluid Pressure

Air, in common with other fluids, will, of course, obey the ordinary laws of fluid pressure (see Chapter I)—e.g. in still air the pressure at any point will be the same in all directions, the pressure will act at right angles to any surface with which the air is in contact, and Archimedes' Principle is true.

Viscosity

An important property of air in so far as it affects flight is its **viscosity.** This means the tendency of one layer of air to move with the layer next to it; it is rather similar to the property of friction between solids. It is owing to viscosity that eddies are formed when the air is disturbed by a body passing through it, and these eddies are responsible for many of the phenomena of flight. Viscosity is possessed to a large degree by fluids such as treacle and certain oils, and although the property is much less noticeable in the case of air, it is none the less of considerable importance.

Winds and Up-and-Down Currents

Air will flow from regions of high pressure to regions where the pressure is lower, and this is the cause of wind, or bodily movement of large portions of the atmosphere. Winds vary from the extensive trade winds caused by belts of high and low pressure surrounding the earth's surface to the purely local gusts and "bumps," caused by local differences of temperature and pressure. On the earth's surface we are usually only concerned with the horizontal velocity of winds, but when flying the rising convection currents and the corresponding downward movements of the air become of considerable importance. The study of winds, of up-and-down convection currents, of cyclones and anti-cyclones, and the weather changes produced by them—all these form the important science of Meteorology, and the reader who is interested is referred to books on that subject.

In the lower regions of the atmosphere conditions are apt to be very erratic; this is especially so within the first few hundred feet. It often happens that as we begin to climb the temperature rises instead of falling—called an **inversion** of temperature. This in itself upsets the stability of the air, and further disturbances may be caused by the sun heating some parts of the earth's surface more than others, causing thermal up-currents, and by the wind blowing over uneven ground, hangars, hills, and so on. On the windward side of a large building, or of a hill, the wind is deflected upwards, and on the leeward side it is apt to leave the contour altogether, forming large eddies which may result in a flow of air near the ground back towards the building or up the far side of the hill, that is to say in the opposite direction to that of the main wind. Even when the surface of the ground is comparatively flat, as on the average aerodrome, the wind is retarded near the ground by the roughness of the surface, and successive layers are held back by the layers below them—due to viscosity—and so the wind velocity gradually increases from the ground upwards. This phenomenon is called **wind gradient.** When the wind velocity is high it is very appreciable, and since most of the effect takes place within ten feet or so of the ground it has to be reckoned with when landing. This will be explained later.

Quite apart from this wind gradient very close to the ground, there is often also a wind gradient on a larger scale altogether. Generally speaking it can be said that on the average day the wind velocity increases with height for many thousands of feet, and it also tends to veer, i.e. to change in a clockwise direction (from north towards east, etc.); at the same time it becomes more steady and there are fewer bumps.

Air Speed and Ground Speed

But our chief concern with the wind at the present moment is that we must understand that when we speak of the speed of an aeroplane we mean its speed relative to the air, or " **airspeed** " as it is usually

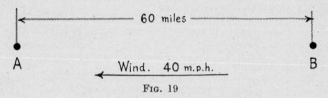

Fig. 19

termed. Now the existence of a wind simply means that portions of the air are in motion relative to the earth, and although the wind will affect the speed of the aeroplane relative to the earth—i.e. its ground speed—it will not affect its speed relative to the air. For instance, suppose that an aeroplane is flying from A to B (60 miles apart), and that the normal speed of the aeroplane (i.e. its air speed) is 100 m.p.h. (see Fig. 19).

If there is a wind of 40 m.p.h. blowing from B towards A, the ground speed of the aeroplane as it travels from A to B will be 60 m.p.h., and it will take one hour to reach B, but the air speed will be 100 m.p.h. (Fig. 20). If, when the aeroplane reaches B, it turns and flies back to A, the ground speed on the return journey will be 140 m.p.h. (Fig. 21); the time to regain A will be less than half an hour, but the air speed will still remain 100 m.p.h.—that is, the wind will strike the aeroplane at the same speed as on the outward journey. Similarly, if the wind had been blowing across the path, the pilot would have inclined his aeroplane several degrees towards the wind on both journeys so that it would have travelled crabwise, but again, on both outward and homeward journeys the air speed would have been 100 m.p.h. and the wind would have

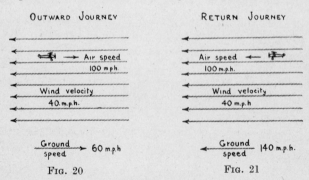

Fig. 20   Fig. 21

been a head-wind straight from the front as far as the aeroplane was concerned.

Imagine a model aeroplane flying inside a railway carriage; the model may fly in the same direction as the train, in the opposite direction, or at right angles to the motion of the train—in each case the speed relative to the train will be the same and the air would always strike the model from the front. But imagine an observer outside the train to whom the train itself was invisible; to him the motion of the model would appear to be very different. The model corresponds to the real aeroplane and the train to the wind; the observer inside the train only notices the air speed, the observer outside the train the ground speed. An aeroplane which encounters a head wind equal to its own air speed will appear to an observer on the ground to stay still, yet in reality it is moving with considerable velocity. A free balloon flying in a wind appears to travel over the ground, yet it has no air speed—a flag on the balloon will hang vertically downwards.

All this may appear simple, and it is in fact simple, but it is surprising how long it often takes a student of flight to grasp the full significance of air speed and all that it means. There are still pilots who say that their engine is overheating because they are flying "down wind"! It is not only a question of speed, but of direction also; a glider may not lose height in a rising current of air (it may, in fact, gain height), yet it is all the time descending relative to the air. In short, the only true way to watch the motion of an aeroplane is to imagine that one is in a balloon floating freely with the wind and to make all observations **relative to the balloon.**

Ground speed is, of course, important when the aeroplane is changing from one medium to another, such as in taking-off and landing, and also in the time taken and the course to be steered when flying cross-country from one place to another—this is the science of Navigation, and once again the reader who is interested must consult books on that subject.

Chemical Composition of the Atmosphere

We have, up to the present, only considered the physical properties of the atmosphere, and, in fact, we are hardly concerned with its chemical or other properties. Air, however, is a **mixture of gases, chiefly Nitrogen and Oxygen,** in the proportion of approximately four-fifths Nitrogen to one-fifth Oxygen. Of these two, Nitrogen is an inert gas, but Oxygen is necessary for human life and also for the proper combustion of the fuel used in the engine, therefore when at great heights the air becomes thin it is necessary to provide more oxygen. In the case of the pilot, this is usually done by supplying him with pure oxygen from a cylinder, whereas extra air is fed into the engine by the process known as "supercharging." Air also contains small and varying quantities of carbon dioxide and the rarer gases helium, argon, and neon, but the presence of these has no practical effect on the phenomena of flight.

There is always a certain amount of **Water Vapour** present in the atmosphere, and this causes a slight decrease in the density as compared with "dry" air. The proportion of water vapour varies from time to time and from place to place, and therefore the effect on the density will also vary, but it is never very appreciable.

The International Standard Atmosphere

The reader will have realized that there is liable to be considerable variation in those properties of the atmosphere with which we are concerned—namely, temperature, pressure, and density. Since it is true to say that the whole performance of the engine, the aeroplane, and the propeller is dependent on these three factors, it will be obvious that the

actual performance of an aeroplane does not give a true basis of comparison with other aeroplanes, and for this reason an **International Standard Atmosphere** has been adopted. (The properties assumed for this standard atmosphere are those given in Fig. 18.) If, now, the actual performance of a certain aeroplane is measured under certain conditions of temperature, pressure, and density, it is possible to deduce **what would have been** the performance of this aeroplane under the conditions of the Standard Atmosphere, and thus it can be compared with the performance of some other aeroplane which has been similarly reduced to standard conditions. This procedure is particularly important where such things as height records are concerned, and it is interesting to note that the height which is counted is not the height actually achieved, but a hypothetical height which might have been reached had the conditions been those of the Standard Atmosphere! This system is not so unreasonable as it sounds, for the very simple reason that there are no reliable means of finding out the actual height reached, however much one might wish to do so.

The Altimeter

The instrument normally used for measuring the height of an aeroplane is the **Altimeter,** which is merely an aneroid barometer graduated in thousands of feet instead of inches of mercury. As a barometer it will, of course, record the **pressure** of the air, and, since the pressure is dependent on the **temperature** as well as the height, it is only possible to graduate the altimeter to read the height if we assume certain definite conditions of temperature. If these conditions are not fulfilled in practice, then the altimeter cannot read the correct height. Altimeters used to be graduated on the assumption that temperature remained the same at all heights. We have already seen that such an assumption is very far from the truth, and the resulting error may be as much as 3,000 ft. at 30,000 ft., the altimeter reading too high owing to the drop in temperature. Altimeters are now calibrated on the assumption that the temperature drops in accordance with the International Standard Atmosphere; this method reduces the error considerably, although the reading will still be incorrect where standard conditions do not obtain.

As a barometer the altimeter will, of course, be affected by the ordinary changes in the pressure of the atmosphere, and therefore an adjustment is provided, so that the scale can be set (either to zero or to the height of the aerodrome above sea-level) before the commencement of a flight, but in spite of this precaution, atmospheric conditions may change **during** the flight, and it is quite possible that on landing on the same aerodrome the altimeter will read too high if the pressure has dropped in the meantime, or too low if the pressure has risen.

Modern altimeters are much more sensitive than the old types; instead of having one pointer they may have as many as three, and these are geared together like the hands of a clock so that the longest pointer makes one revolution in 1,000 ft., the next one in 10,000 ft., and the smallest one in 100,000 ft. The difference between the old and the new types might be likened to a watch with only an hour hand and one with hour, minute, and second hands. But the more sensitive watch is of little use unless it can be made free from error, and can be read correctly—so too the altimeter. In the modern types, if the pilot sets the altimeter to read zero height, which he can do simply by turning a knob, a small opening on the face of the instrument discloses the pressure of the air at that height—in other words, the reading of the barometer. Conversely—and this is the important point—if, while in the air, he finds out by radio the barometric pressure at the aerodrome at which he wishes to land, he can adjust the instrument so that this pressure shows in the small opening, and he can then be sure that his altimeter is reading the correct height above that aerodrome, and that when he "touches down" it will read zero. The altimeter may be used in this way for instrument flying and night flying, that is to say when the height above the ground in the vicinity of the aerodrome is of vital importance, but for ordinary cross-country flying during the day it is preferable to set the **sea-level atmospheric pressure** in the opening. Then the pilot will always know his height above sea-level and can compare this with the height, as shown on the map, of the ground over which he is flying. If this method is used, instead of the altimeter reading zero on landing, it will give the height of the aerodrome above sea level.

Air Resistance or Drag

Whenever a body is moved through air, or other viscous fluid, there is produced a definite resistance to its motion. In aeronautical work this resistance is usually referred to as "Drag."

" Drag " is the enemy of Flight, and every effort must be made to reduce the resistance of every part of an aeroplane to an absolute minimum, provided strength and other essential factors can be maintained. For this reason many thousands of experiments have been carried out to investigate the problems of Air Resistance; in fact, in this, as in almost every branch of this subject, our knowledge is founded simply on the mean results of accumulated experimental data.

Until recent years pure theory has been of very little help in solving the problems of flight. Real progress in aviation has been so rapid and so much experimental work has been carried out that theory has appeared to lag behind and has been unable to do more than attempt to explain practical phenomena, and in some cases it must be admitted that it has not been very successful in this respect. But it is sometimes necessary to beware of jumping to conclusions even in experimental work—the conditions of the experiment do not always reproduce the true state of affairs; experimental errors may be large in comparison with the forces measured, and in consequence the results of apparently similar tests are often confusing and sometimes contradictory.

Experiments and Air Resistance

The investigation of the problems of Air Resistance has been carried out in two ways—

1. **By the study of the nature of the flow of air and other fluids past solid bodies.**

2. **By measuring the actual forces produced on the bodies by the passage of the fluid.**

The data produced by these two methods definitely go to show that there is a direct connection between the two, and, generally speaking, it can be said that the greater the formation of eddies, or turbulence as it is usually called, the greater will be the resistance. This agrees well with the similar conclusion that the resistance to the passage of ships and floats through water is dependent on the amount of wave motion produced.

In experimental work it is usual to allow the fluid to flow past the body rather than to move the body through the fluid. The former method has the great advantage that the body is at rest, and consequently the measurement of any forces upon it is comparatively simple. Furthermore, since we are only concerned with the **relative** motion of the body and the fluid, the true facts of the case are fully reproduced

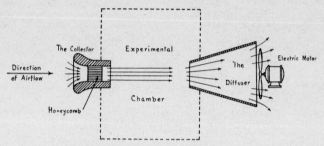

FIG. 22. OPEN JET TUNNEL

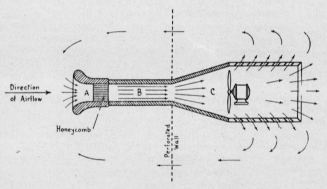

FIG. 23. CLOSED TYPE TUNNEL

provided we can obtain a flow of the fluid which would be as steady as the corresponding motion of the body through the fluid.

Wind Tunnels

Most aeronautical experiments are carried out on models in a **Wind Tunnel.** There are two main types of Wind Tunnel—

1. **The open jet type.**
2. **The closed type.**

In both types the airflow is created by a fan driven by an electric motor, but the essential difference is that in the former type (Fig. 22) the air is drawn across an experimental chamber which is considerably larger than the tunnel itself, whereas in the closed tunnel (Fig. 23), the working section is completely enclosed by the tunnel walls. The air is sucked in through the collector *A* and remains confined while it

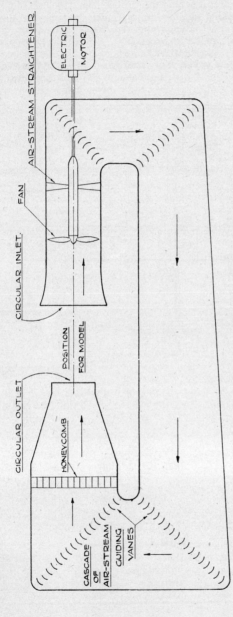

Fig. 24. Open Jet Tunnel with Return Circuit

passes through the working portion *B* to the expanding cone *C*. Only
the model to be tested is placed in the tunnel, the observers and instruments being situated outside. In the open jet type the observers are,
of course, outside the jet itself, but even while the wind is on, they have
free access to the model if necessary. A honeycomb is usually fitted
at the inlet end to straighten the airflow. It has also been found that
in order to obtain a steady flow of air through the tunnel it is necessary
to break up and evenly distribute the air on its return journey through
the room to the mouth of the tunnel; this has been accomplished by

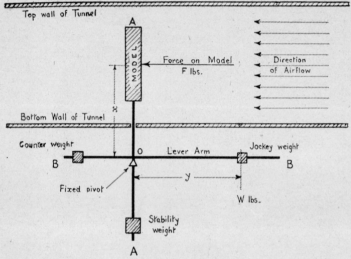

FIG. 25. PRINCIPLE OF THE WIND TUNNEL BALANCE: SIDE ELEVATION

allowing the air to escape from the tunnel through a series of laths
instead of discharging it in one stream from the fan, and also by dividing
the room into two halves by a perforated wall, through which the air
must return.

For many years the closed type of tunnel was almost universally
used in England and in most other countries except France, where the
original Eiffel type of open jet tunnel was very popular. Later,
however, the open jet tunnel came into favour all over the world;
but in the type now used there is an enclosed return flow (Fig. 24),
which makes the tunnel more efficient than an ordinary closed tunnel,
yet at the same time there are all the advantages of the open jet
tunnel, as for instance easy access to the model (Plate VI).

Wind Tunnel Balance

The forces exerted by the air on the model are measured by means
of a **Balance** (Fig. 25). A simple form of Balance consists of three arms,
mutually at right angles, resting at their intersection on a conical steel
pivot, *O*.

The vertical arm *AA* projects into the tunnel through an oil seal and
carries the model; it also continues below the pivot, having a stability
weight which can be screwed up and down to regulate the sensitivity

of the balance, and an oil dashpot which damps out any pulsations. The other two arms BB and CC (Fig. 26) are horizontal and at right angles to each other, BB lying along the axis of the tunnel—i.e. parallel to the airflow—and CC at right angles to the tunnel axis and so to the airflow. These lever arms act like an ordinary weighing machine, carrying a counter-weight at one end and on the other a jockey weight moving along a graduated scale so calibrated as to read the force on the model directly. The counterweight is simply used to balance the long

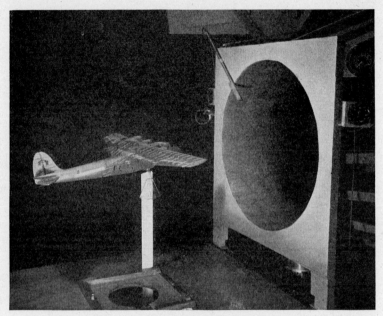

PLATE VI. AN OPEN JET WIND TUNNEL

The photograph gives a good idea of the accessibility of this type of tunnel. The jet opening is on the right and the collector is just out of view on the left. The model in the open jet has tufts of wool on the wings to show the gradual spread of burbling as the angle of attack is increased.

lever arm on which the jockey weight rides; it may also be useful to balance the weight of the model if the latter cannot be supported at its centre of gravity.

As will be seen from the illustration, by the principle of moments $Fx = Wy$, so that if W is a constant weight and x is a fixed distance there is a direct connection between the force F and the distance y when the system is in equilibrium. The jockey weight on BB will measure the force on the model parallel to the airflow—i.e. its Drag or Resistance—whereas the weight on CC will measure the force at right angles to the airflow. There is, in addition, a device which measures the torsion or turning effect about the vertical axis.

A balance of this type, although modified to suit varying requirements, has been found to be both sensitive and accurate, and is still sometimes employed in its original form. It is more usual now, however,

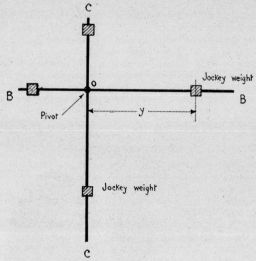

Fig. 26. Wind Tunnel Balance: Plan View

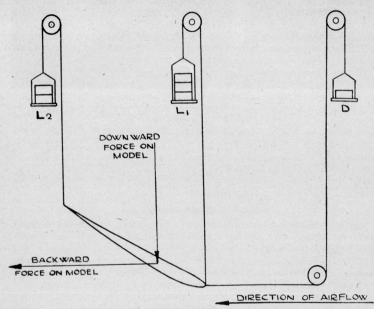

Fig. 27. Wind Tunnel Balance: Principle of Overhead Type

to suspend the model on wires from the roof of the tunnel, the **principle** of this method being shown in Fig. 27. After subtracting the weight of the model, the two weights L_1 and L_2 together measure the total downward force or "Lift," while the weight D measures the backward force, or "Drag." By a simple calculation, the position of the "Centre of Pressure" can be found from the relative value of L_1 and L_2. In actual practice, lever arms pivoted on knife edges or on spring supports are used instead of pulleys. The reason for the upside down suspension is that the weight and lift act in the same directions, i.e. downwards, so that it is only necessary to measure forces in one direction.

Sources of Error

It should perhaps be mentioned here that the wind tunnel experiments on models are liable to three main sources of error when used to forecast full-scale results. These are—

1. **Scale Effect.** It has been found that laws of resistance can be framed which apply well to bodies whose sizes are not very different, but that **these laws become less accurate when there is a great difference in size between the model and the full scale.**

A similar effect is noticed when the velocity of the model test differs largely from the full-scale velocity.

Experiments have shown that definite corrections can be applied to model tests which will allow for a "scale effect" and enable more accurate forecasts to be made.

Readers who are interested will find an explanation of scale effect, and of the advantages of the compressed air tunnel, if they refer to Appendix III. They will also be introduced to the important term "Reynolds' Number."

2. **Interference from Wind Tunnel Walls.** The second error is due to the fact that in the wind tunnel the air stream is confined to the limits of the tunnel, whereas in free flight the air round the aeroplane is, for all practical purposes, unlimited in extent.

In this case also corrections may be applied which reduce the error considerably, unless the models are very large in comparison with the size of the tunnel, in which case the interference is so great that the wind tunnel tests can give little indication of what would happen in free air (Fig. 28).

3. **Errors in Model.** The smaller the scale of the model, the more difficult does it become to reproduce every detail of the full-scale body, and as very slight changes of contour may considerably affect the airflow round a body, and thus its resistance, errors must always be introduced due to the discrepancies between the model and the full-scale body.

Other Experimental Methods

Provided these three limitations are fully realized, and due allowances made for them, wind tunnel results can provide us with some very useful experimental data.

In addition to wind tunnel tests, resistance experiments have been carried out in the following ways—

1. **On "whirling arms,"** the model being attached to one end of a long arm, which is rotated about the other end.

2. **By experiments in water** instead of air.

3. **By experiments in actual flight.**

All these methods have their advantages, but none of them can be made completely free from sources of error.

Streamlines

Lines which show the direction of the flow of the fluid at any particular moment are called **Streamlines,** and a body so shaped as to produce the least possible eddy motion is said to be of **Streamline Shape.**

By introducing smoke into the airflow in wind tunnels, and coloured jets into water tank experiments, it has been possible to study and photograph streamlines and eddy motion.

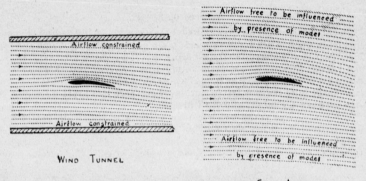

WIND TUNNEL

FREE AIR

FIG. 28. INTERFERENCE FROM WIND TUNNEL WALLS

The results of all these varied experiments seem to show that we may divide the resistance of a body passing through a fluid into two parts—

1. **Form Drag.**
2. **Skin Friction.**

These two between them form a large part of the total Drag of an aeroplane—at high speeds, the major part. The sum of the two is sometimes called **Profile Drag** but this term will be avoided in this book since it is apt to give an impression of being another name for Form Drag, whereas it really includes Skin Friction.

The total Drag of an aeroplane is sometimes divided in another way in which the Drag of the wings or lifting surfaces is separated from the Drag of those parts which do not contribute towards the lift, the Drag of the latter being called **Parasite Drag.** Plate VII illustrates an old type of aeroplane in which Parasite Drag formed a large part of the total. Plate VIII tells another story.

The significance of dividing Drag into Wing Drag and Parasite Drag will be apparent later on; at present let us confine our attention to Form Drag and Skin Friction which will be considered in turn.

1. **Form Drag.** This is the portion of the resistance which is due to the fact that when a viscous fluid flows past a solid object, eddies are formed, and we no longer get a smooth streamline flow. The extreme example of this type of resistance is the case of a flat plate placed at **right angles** to the wind. The resistance is now very large and is almost entirely due to the formation of eddies, the skin friction being negligible in comparison (Fig. 29).

PLATE VII. PARASITE DRAG

The Vickers "Virginia," descendant of the "Vimy," the first aeroplane to make a non-stop flight across the Atlantic (1919).

(By courtesy of "Flight.")

Experiments show that not only is the pressure in front of this plate greater than the atmospheric pressure, but that the pressure behind is less than that of the atmosphere, causing a kind of "sucking" effect on the plate.

Streamline Shapes

It is essential that this form drag should be reduced to an absolute minimum in all those parts of the aeroplane which are exposed to the air.

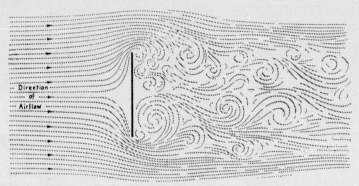

Fig. 29. Form Drag

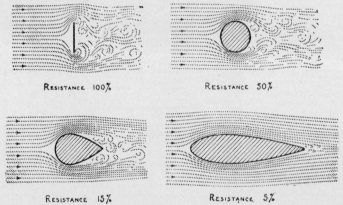

Resistance 100%   Resistance 50%

Resistance 15%   Resistance 5%

Fig. 30. The Effect of "Streamlining"

This can be done by so shaping those parts that the flow of air past them is as smooth as possible, and much experimental work has been carried out with this in view. The results show the enormous advantage to be gained by the "streamlining" of struts and wires; in fact, the figures obtained are so remarkable that they are difficult to believe without a practical demonstration. At a conservative estimate it can be said that a round tube has not much more than half the resistance of a flat plate, while if the tube is converted into the best possible streamline shape the resistance will be only one-tenth that of the round tube or one-twentieth that of the flat plate (Fig. 30).

The Streamline shapes which have given the least resistance have had a fineness ratio—i.e. a/b—of between 3 and 4 (see Fig. 31), and the maximum value of b should be about one-third of the way back from the nose. These dimensions, however, may vary considerably without increasing the resistance to any great extent.

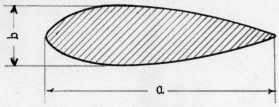

FIG. 31. FINENESS RATIO

It should be mentioned that although we now have a fair idea of the ideal shape for any **separate** body, it by no means follows that two bodies of this shape—e.g. a fuselage and a wing—will give the least resistance when **joined together**; in fact the best way of fairing one body into another is still the subject of investigation, and may prove a very profitable means of reducing the resistance and so increasing the speed of aeroplanes.

Another consideration is that as we learn to decrease the Form Drag the Skin Friction becomes of comparatively greater importance.

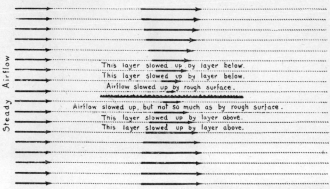

FIG. 32. SKIN FRICTION

2. **Skin Friction.** This is the resistance which would be present on a thin, flat plate placed **edgewise** to the wind (see Fig. 32). In effect, we have already considered one case of skin friction, i.e. wind gradient. The surface of a flat plate, or of an aeroplane wing, is certainly more smooth than that of an aerodrome; but, even so, the air is slowed up, if not actually brought to a standstill, very close to the surface. (If there is dust on an aeroplane wing before flight, it is usually still there after flight, even though the wing may have been travelling through the air at a hundred miles per hour or more.) The layers of air near the surface retard the layers farther away—owing to the friction between the layers, i.e. the viscosity—and so there is a gradual increase in

PLATE VIII. STREAMLINING: THE BRISTOL "BRABAZON"

(By courtesy of the Bristol Aeroplane Co. Ltd.)

velocity as the distance from the surface increases. The maximum velocity—i.e. that of the free airflow—will be reached sooner over a smooth surface than over a rough surface, and since it is the shearing action between the layers which causes the resistance it follows that a smooth surface will have less resistance than a rough surface. Over a smooth surface like that of a wing or strut most of the increase in velocity may occur within a fraction of an inch of the surface as compared with the ten feet or more which we mentioned earlier in connection with an aerodrome surface.

This portion of the resistance is sometimes very considerable, and though it has been found difficult to establish any exact mathematical formula on which it depends, it is obvious that the chief factor producing it must be the "roughness" of the surface, and therefore it is most important that all the surfaces of an aeroplane should be made as smooth as possible, in some cases even to the extent of polishing. Skin friction is also dependent on the area of the surface over which the air flows, the speed of the flow, and the viscosity of the air.

Boundary Layer

The layer or layers of air in which the shearing action is taking place, that is to say between the surface and the full velocity of the air flow, is called the **Boundary Layer.** Owing to the great importance of Skin

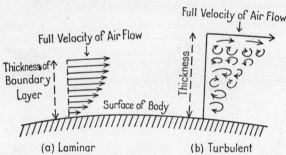

FIG. 33. LAMINAR AND TURBULENT BOUNDARY LAYERS
Thickness of layer greatly exaggerated

Friction, and necessity of keeping it within reasonable limits, particularly at high speed, much patient research work has been devoted to the study of the Boundary Layer. As can well be imagined this has not been easy if only for the reason that the thickness of the layer may sometimes be no more than one-hundredth of an inch.

Now the Boundary Layer, like the main air flow, may be either **Laminar** (Streamline) or **Turbulent** (see Fig. 33), and the difference that these two types of flow make to the total Skin Friction is of the same order as the effect of streamlining the main flow. It has been stated that if we could ensure a laminar boundary layer over the whole surface of a wing the Skin Friction would be reduced to about one-tenth of its value on a conventional type of wing.

The usual tendency is for the Boundary Layer to start by being laminar over the surface near the leading edge of a body, but there comes a point, called the **Transition Point,** when the layer tends to break **away from the surface and become turbulent and thicker** (Fig. 34). **As**

the speed increases the Transition Point tends to come further forward, so more of the Boundary Layer becomes turbulent and the Skin Friction becomes greater.

If this much is understood it will be obvious that the main purpose

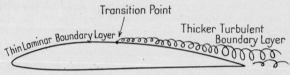

Transition Point

Thin Laminar Boundary Layer

Thicker Turbulent
Boundary Layer

FIG. 34. TRANSITION POINT

of research work has been to discover why the Transition Point moves forward, and how its movement can be controlled so as to maintain laminar flow over as much of the surface as possible.   Since most of this research has been in connection with aerofoils, further discussion will be deferred until the next chapter.

Resistance Formula

Attempts have been made to express the Air Resistance or Drag of a body in terms of a simple mathematical formula.

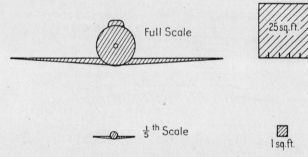

Full Scale

25 sq. ft.

$\frac{1}{5}$ th Scale

1 sq. ft.

FIG. 35. FRONTAL AREA

Our experiments show that, within certain limitations, it is true to say that the total resistance of a body passing through the air is dependent on the following factors—

    (a) **The shape of the body.**
    (b) **The " frontal area " of the body.**
    (c) **The square of the velocity.**
    (d) **The density of the air.**

Of these the "velocity squared" law is probably not strictly true at any speeds and is definitely untrue at very low and very high speeds : when the speeds are low it is truer to say that the resistance is proportional to the velocity, while the problem is complicated at extremely high speeds by the fact that the air may be compressed instead of merely divided by the passage of the body.

It is sometimes thought that the air is compressed in front of a body which is moving quite slowly through the air. We know, of course, that air is compressible, and is also to a large extent elastic, which means that after being compressed it will tend to return to its former position. But these properties of air do not come into play at the speeds with which we normally have to deal in ordinary flight; at such speeds air behaves very like an almost incompressible liquid such as water. The passage of sound is, of course, caused by compression in the air, and it is only when speeds are reached in the neighbourhood of the velocity of sound (about 1,100 ft. per sec.) that appreciable compression of the air begins to take place. High-speed aircraft are now able to fly in this region, and speeds reached by the extreme tips of propeller blades may be even greater than the velocity of sound. It is also interesting to note that the velocity at which sound travels depends on the temperature of the air and becomes appreciably less at high altitudes, and thus the problem of reaching this critical velocity has become an important consideration in high-altitude flying. In such conditions there may be considerable departure from the "velocity squared" law, but for the speeds of ordinary flight—say, 30 m.p.h. to 300 m.p.h.—this law can be taken as accurate enough for practical purposes, so that we can say that if we double the speed we will get four times the resistance, or if we treble the speed we will get nine times the resistance. The problems of high-speed flight are covered more fully in Chapter X.

In the case of (b) when we are considering bodies of very different dimensions we must remember the scale effect to which we have already referred; we should also notice that, if we have a one-fifth scale model of a body, the "frontal area" of the full-sized body will be twenty-five times that of the model (Fig. 35).

[NOTE. The term "frontal area" means the maximum projected area when viewed in the direction of normal motion, e.g. the frontal area of an airship is the maximum cross-sectional area when viewed from the front. If an airship is not pointing exactly in the direction in which it is travelling, then, strictly speaking, the projected frontal area will be changed, but it is often more convenient in experimental work to refer the results to the original frontal area. The same difficulty arises when considering the resistance of wires or struts inclined to the direction of motion and there are other cases where the **surface** area would be a more sensible area to take—no general rule can be laid down, and the student should remember that the chief object of experiments on resistance is to compare the resistance of bodies of a similar kind. We are not very much concerned with how the resistance of a wing compares with the resistance of a wheel, but we do wish to compare the resistance of wings of different sizes and shapes, and also the resistances of different types of wheels. Therefore, if we choose one method to measure the area of wings and another to measure the area of wheels (as indeed we do), it does not matter very much. It is all a question of **convenience.**]

The law of the variation of the resistance with the density of the air is found to be very nearly correct at ordinary densities, and on first investigation seems to point to the advantages of flight at high altitudes, when the air density is less, so resistance will be less, and high speed should be easier to attain. Unfortunately, however, the problem is complicated by other factors such as the effects of altitude on the Thrust of the Propeller, the Power of the Engine, and the Lift of the Wings.

Assuming (a), (b), (c), and (d) to be true, we can express the result by the following formula—

$$R \propto \rho S V^2 \text{ for bodies of the same shape,}$$

or the general formula—

$$R = K \rho S V^2,$$

where K is a coefficient depending on the shape of the body and found entirely by experiment,

ρ represents the Density of the air,

S the Frontal Area of the body,

and V the Velocity.

The units in this formula will, of course, correspond to those adopted in Chapter I, i.e. the Resistance (R) will be in **pounds,** the Density (ρ) in **slugs per cubic foot,** the Area (S) in **square feet,** Velocity (V) in **feet per second,** and K, a coefficient, **merely a number.**

We will therefore write the formula in its simplest form—

$$\text{Resistance} = K \rho S V^2$$

and the student must always remember that the density of the air, ρ, must be measured in slugs per cu. ft., e.g. if the density is given in lb. per cu. ft. the value must be divided by 32.2 before using in the formula.

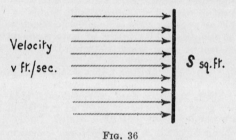

Velocity
v ft./sec.

S sq. ft.

FIG. 36

Theoretical Value of K

The formula given above is the fundamental connection between the flow of air past a body and the force created thereby. In one form or another the student will repeatedly come across this law in his study of flight. We have already emphasized the fact that in aeronautical experiments there is apt to be a wide divergence between Theory and Experiment. This formula provides a very interesting example. The reader, when studying ordinary mechanics, may have worked out examples in which he found the pressure caused by a jet of water impinging on a wall at right angles to the direction of the jet. From Newton's Second Law, the rate at which the momentum of the jet is changed will give the force exerted on the wall. Suppose we apply this method in the case of air. Let the velocity of the air stream be V ft. per sec., and the area of plate be S sq. ft. (Fig. 36.) **Now assuming that all the air which is moving towards the plate actually strikes it, and assuming that the air particles are quite inelastic**—i.e. that they do not rebound but simply drop away from the plate parallel to the surface, and **assuming that nothing happens behind the plate,** then the volume of air striking the plate per second will be VS cub. ft., and if ρ is the density or mass of 1 cu. ft., then the mass of air per second will be ρVS lb.

The momentum of this air is $\rho VS \times V = \rho SV^2$

$\therefore$ Momentum lost by air per second $= \rho SV^2$

$\therefore$ By Newton's Second Law the Force on plate $= \rho SV^2$ lb.

Thus, **on these assumptions,** the value of K should be 1. If we had assumed that the air was perfectly elastic and rebounded at the same velocity after striking the plate, then the change of momentum of the air would have been double and the Force on the plate $2\rho SV^2$ —i.e. the value of $K = 2$. In both cases the error is considerable as compared with practical experiment which gives a value of K for a flat plate of approximately 0·6. The source of the error is not in the theoretical laws concerned, but in our assumptions as to what takes place, **all of which are totally incorrect!** It is noticeable that the theoretical value of K is higher than that found by experiment, and therefore the assumption causing most error is, without doubt, that all the air approaching the plate actually strikes it and is brought to rest; airflow experiments show that, on the other hand, most of the air escapes round the edges of the plate and the flow then becomes turbulent.

The reader may well ask why, if Theory gives us such incorrect results, we do not content ourselves with experimental facts. The answer is that in the study of Aeronautics we **do** rely almost entirely on the results of Experiment, but that, as in this case, Theory often gives us the **nature** of the law, leaving the constants or coefficients to be supplied by experiment. Thus Theory indicates that the force on the plate is **proportional** to ρSV^2 while **Experiment provides the important coefficient of proportionality,** K.

Bernoulli's Theorem

Another very interesting approach to this problem is via Bernoulli's Theorem which states that in the streamline flow of an ideal fluid, i.e. one which is not viscous—the sum of the **Energy of Position** (or Potential Energy) plus the **Energy of Motion** (or Kinetic Energy) plus the **Pressure Energy** will remain constant. In the cases in which we are concerned there is not sufficient change in the height of the fluid to make any appreciable change in the first term of this sum, i.e. in the Energy of Position—therefore the sum of the last two terms should remain constant, which means that if all the Energy of Motion is lost on striking the plate it should be completely converted into Pressure Energy. Now the Kinetic Energy of a mass of M slugs moving at V ft. per sec. is $\frac{1}{2} M V^2$ ft. lb.

$\therefore$ the Kinetic Energy of 1 cu. ft. of air is $\frac{1}{2} \rho V^2$ ft. lb.

$\therefore$ if all this becomes Pressure Energy, the Pressure will be $\frac{1}{2} \rho V^2$ lb. per sq. ft., or if the area of the plate is S sq. ft., the total force on the plate will be $\frac{1}{2} \rho SV^2$. Once again we notice that Theory indicates the nature of the law, but gives us the wrong coefficient. In this case the chief error probably lies in the assumption that the fluid is not viscous, and thus the theory does not allow for the eddies formed behind the plate, which may quite easily increase K from the theoretical value of $\frac{1}{2}$ to 0·6 or other experimental values. This idea is rather confirmed by the fact that in the case of the Pitot tube, which will be mentioned later in this chapter, the value of $K = \frac{1}{2}$ is obtained in practice to an extraordinary degree of accuracy.

Measurement of Air Speed

We have talked a great deal about "Air Speed," but up to the present we have avoided any attempt to explain the methods by which it is usually measured. If, however, the actual method has been omitted, the principle has been established and it will now be very much easier for us to understand the method. The Resistance of a body placed in an air stream depends, **among other things,** on the velocity of the stream—it is not a simple proportion, but that does not matter: the fact remains that there is a connection between the Resistance and the velocity, and therefore, if we can eliminate the "other things," we

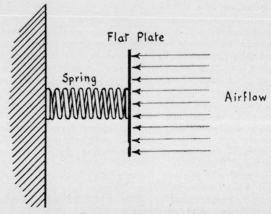

FIG. 37. CRUDE PRESSURE PLATE AIR SPEED INDICATOR

should be able to devise an instrument which by measuring Resistance would give, if suitably calibrated, readings of velocity.

Suppose, for instance, that we were to place a flat plate at right angles to the airflow and behind this plate we fitted a compression spring balance (Fig. 37), then there would be a direct connection between the velocity of the airflow and the reading of the spring balance, provided that the Area of the plate and the Density of the air remained constant. As regards the Area, there is not much difficulty except that we must remember that it is the "frontal" Area facing the airflow which matters, and therefore we must ensure that the plate is at all times at right angles to the airflow. The question of the Density, however, is not quite so simple; in fact, it is true to say that the ordinary method of measuring air speed is dependent on the Density of the air and therefore readings of air speed can only be correct when the Density is of some definite value.

Pitot-Static Tube

Our flat plate apparatus is very crude, but in a slightly modified form it has actually been used as a simple means of registering the air speed. The system, however, which is almost universally employed in Great Britain is the Pitot-Static head. This consists of two metal tubes fixed to some exposed part of the aeroplane and facing directly into the airflow. One of these, the **Pitot** (or pressure) tube, has an open end facing the wind, while the other tube, called the **Static,** is closed at the end but pierced with small holes or slits farther back (Fig. 38).

Sometimes the Pitot tube is a short distance below the Static (as in the figure), but on modern aircraft the tubes are more usually concentric, the Pitot tube forming the centre and being surrounded by the Static. The other end of each tube is connected by metal tubing to the **Air Speed Indicator** in the cockpit.

Old types of Air Speed Indicator consisted of two chambers separated by a rubber, metal, or oiled-silk diaphragm, one tube being connected to each chamber, which was otherwise airtight. In modern types the

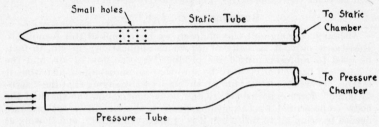

FIG. 38. PITOT–STATIC TUBE

Pitot tube is connected to the inside of a capsule (a flat circula box of corrugated metal such as is used in an altimeter or aneroid barometer), while the Static tube is connected to the casing of the instrument. In each type the principle is the same: when there is no air speed the normal atmospheric pressure will be communicated to both sides of the diaphragm or capsule, but when the air blows up against the open Pitot tube the extra pressure due to the air velocity plus the normal atmospheric pressure will act on one side, while the Static tube still conveys the ordinary atmospheric pressure to the other. The difference in pressure causes a deflection of the diaphragm or capsule, which, by suitable gearing, makes a pointer move round the scale, which is marked off in air speeds.

Dynamic Pressure

It might be expected that the open Pitot tube would effectively bring the air to rest, and practical experiment proves this to be true to a remarkable degree of accuracy; in other words, the value of K for the extra pressure due to the airflow striking the Pitot tube is almost exactly one-half, i.e. the theoretical value of K according to Bernouilli's Theorem.

Thus the extra force on the open end of the Pitot tube is $\frac{1}{2}\rho S V^2$, where S is the area of the opening. Therefore the **intensity of pressure** on the open end due to the airflow will be the force divided by the area, i.e. $\frac{1}{2}\rho V^2$ **lb. per sq. ft.**

This value of the pressure, $\frac{1}{2}\rho V^2$, will always be experienced when a moving stream of air is brought to rest, and it is convenient to use it as a kind of **unit of pressure**; it is, as it were, the **dynamic pressure** of the air, as distinct from the ordinary **static pressure.**

It should be noted that both the dynamic and static pressure act on the pitot tube, while only the static pressure acts on the static tube. The Air Speed Indicator therefore reads the difference between the two, i.e. the dynamic pressure.

So important is the conception of dynamic pressure that instead of writing our resistance formula in the form

$$R = K\rho S V^2,$$

we separate out the unit of dynamic pressure $\frac{1}{2}\rho V^2$, which would leave it as

$$R = 2K \times \tfrac{1}{2}\rho V^2 \times S,$$

which can be simplified if we use a new coefficient C, the value of which will be twice the value of K. Thus we arrive at the form

$$\text{Resistance} = C . \tfrac{1}{2}\rho V^2 . S.$$

Although, throughout this chapter, we have applied this formula to Resistance only, it is really of far wider application; it can, in fact, be used to represent any force produced by the flow of air, and the reader will be well advised to be sure that he understands just what it means. Therefore, let us sum up the position by saying that **the " aerodynamic " force** experienced by any body depends on the **shape of the body** (represented by the coefficient C in the formula), **the pressure needed to bring air to rest when it is of the given density, and flowing at the given velocity** (represented by $\frac{1}{2}\rho V^2$), and the **frontal area** (represented by S).

Because of the wider applications of this formula (to Lift, and so on), the coefficient used for Resistance or Drag is usually distinguished by the suffix D and written C_D, thus

$$D = C_D . \tfrac{1}{2}\rho V^2 . S.$$

From our formula we are now in a position to estimate the resistance of bodies moving through the air, provided we know the value of C_D for the particular shape concerned. This is usually found by experiment, but in the absence of more accurate information, the following values may be used—

For a flat plate	$C_D = 1\cdot2$
For a circular tube . . .	$C_D = 0\cdot6$
For a streamline strut . . .	$C_D = 0\cdot06$

EXAMPLE. Find the Resistance of a flat plate, 6 in. $\times$ 4 in., placed at right angles to an airflow of velocity 60 m.p.h. (Assume sea-level air density.)

Density of air $= 0\cdot08$ lb. per cu. ft. $= \dfrac{0\cdot08}{32\cdot2}$ or $0\cdot00248$ slugs per cu. ft.

Data: $C_D = 1\cdot2$

$\rho = 0\cdot00248$ slugs per cu. ft.

$V = 60$ m.p.h. $= 88$ ft. per sec.

$S = 6 \times 4 = 24$ sq. in. $= \dfrac{24}{144} = \tfrac{1}{6}$ sq. ft.

$\therefore$ Resistance $= C_D \tfrac{1}{2}\rho V^2 S = \dfrac{1\cdot2 \times 0\cdot5 \times 0\cdot00248 \times 1 \times 88 \times 88}{6}$

$= 1\cdot92$ lb.

Calibration of Air Speed Indicator

To return to our Air Speed Indicator, the dynamic pressure, $\frac{1}{2}\rho V^2$, which is the difference in pressure on the two sides of the diaphragm,

can, for calibration purposes, be balanced against a difference in height
of water in the two sides of a U-tube.

As an example, suppose a certain air speed produces a difference of
1 in. of water.

A column of water 1 in. in height and 1 sq. ft. in cross-section has a
volume of $\frac{1}{12}$ cu. ft. and weighs $\frac{62\cdot4 \text{ lb.}}{12} = 5\cdot2$ lb.

$$\text{(62·4 lb. being the weight of 1 cu. ft. of water)}$$

$$\therefore \tfrac{1}{2}\,\rho V^2 = 5\cdot2 \text{ lb. per sq. ft.}$$

and ρ (at sea-level) $= 0\cdot077$ lb./cu. ft. $= 0\cdot0024$ slugs per cu. ft.

$$\therefore V^2 = \frac{5\cdot2 \times 2}{\rho} = \frac{10\cdot4}{0\cdot0024} = 4330.$$

$$\therefore V = \sqrt{4330} = 66 \text{ ft./sec. or 45 m.p.h.}$$

In this way the dial of the air speed indicator can be calibrated
over the range of air speed required.

For air speed indicators fitted in modern high-speed aircraft it is
not sufficiently accurate to assume the value of K to be $\frac{1}{2}$ over the
whole range of air speeds marked on the indicator. Whereas the error
of such an assumption is less than 1 per cent at 150 m.p.h. it has
become as much as 5 per cent at 450 m.p.h., which means that although
the instrument would only read about 1·5 m.p.h. too high at 150 m.p.h.
it would read over 20 m.p.h. too high at 450 m.p.h. Fortunately we
know fairly well the changes which take place in the velocity-squared
law at these high speeds, and so we can calculate the errors involved
and allow for them in calibrating the instruments. In order to confirm
or modify our calculations experiments are being made in very high
speed wind tunnels.

"Indicated" Air Speed

The Pitot-Static method of measuring air speed is dependent on the
air density, but, curiously enough, the errors introduced by changes in
density are, from some points of view, an advantage during flight.
This is because the Lift and other forces on an aeroplane wing are
also dependent on the air density, and hence the "Indicated" Air
Speed (the incorrect speed recorded by the Air Speed Indicator) may
sometimes be more useful to the pilot than the True Air Speed would
be. We shall come across this point again later when considering the
"stalling" speed of an aeroplane.

It is easy to calculate the true air speed from the indicated air speed
provided we know the original air density for which the indicator was
calibrated, and also the density at the particular height with which
we are concerned. Suppose at 20,000 ft. the Air Speed Indicator reads
240 m.p.h.—i.e. 352 ft./sec. This means that the pressure on the Pitot
tube is the same as would be produced by a speed of 352 ft./sec. at
standard air density of, say, 0·077 lb. per cu. ft., i.e. $\frac{0\cdot077}{32\cdot2}$, or 0·0024
slugs per cu. ft.; but this pressure is $\frac{1}{2}\rho V^2$, i.e. $\frac{1}{2} \times 0\cdot0024 \times 352^2$.

Now the standard air density at 20,000 ft. is 0·041 lb. per cu. ft.
(i.e. 0·00127 slugs per cu. ft.), and if the true air speed is V ft./sec.,
then the pressure on the Pitot tube will be $\frac{1}{2} \times 0\cdot00127 \times V^2$, which
must be the same as $\frac{1}{2} \times 0\cdot0024 \times 352^2$

∴ it is clear that $0 \cdot 00127 \, V^2 = 0 \cdot 0024 \times 352^2$.

$$\text{or } V = \sqrt{\frac{0 \cdot 0024}{0 \cdot 00127}} \times 352 = 1 \cdot 37 \times 352$$

$$= 482 \text{ ft./sec. or } 329 \cdot 2 \text{ m.p.h.}$$

Thus the Indicated Air Speed is 240 m.p.h., and the True Air Speed approximately 330 m.p.h.

A similar calculation for 40,000 ft. will reveal the interesting result that at that height the true air speed is slightly more than double the indicated air speed!

We have said that the **indicated** air speed **may sometimes be** more useful to the pilot than the true air speed. For purposes of navigation, however, and for bomb dropping, he must estimate his speed over the ground, and in order to find this he must first know his **true** air speed. Instruments can be devised to measure true air speed as, for example, the well-known cup anemometer, which is used for measuring the wind velocity at meteorological stations. Such an instrument is independent of air density, but it is not suitable for the high speeds of flight. Some more complicated instruments use the principle of the Pitot-Static method but have automatic compensating devices to allow for the changes in density; these instruments are too elaborate and expensive for general use, and since the difference between the two speeds may be very appreciable, we must fall back on some means of converting the indicated speed to true. Approximate rules are sometimes quoted whereby some percentage is added for every thousand feet of height. Such rules are most unsatisfactory; they can only be correct for one particular height and become hopelessly incorrect if the actual height differs much from that particular height. You may sometimes hear people arguing as to which is the correct rule—ought one to add 1·5 per cent, or 1·75 per cent, or 2 per cent to the indicated speed for every thousand feet of height? The answer is that **all** such rules are wrong. An alternative would be to make a calculation like the one in the above example, but this would involve having tables available of the density at different heights (even so the answer would not be strictly correct unless allowances were made for the difference between actual temperature and the assumed temperature of the International Standard Atmosphere), nor can it be said that pilots would take kindly to working out square roots in the air! Can one blame them? Simpler than this would be to have a table showing the percentages to add at various heights; here are some of the answers—100 m.p.h. indicated speed means a true speed of 116 m.p.h. at 10,000 ft., 137 m.p.h. at 20,000 ft., 163 m.p.h. at 30,000 ft., 201 m.p.h. at 40,000 ft. (The reader who has followed the argument so far will notice how these figures confirm two points already made—first, that the difference between true and indicated is very considerable; secondly, that none of the approximate rules quoted gives the right answer for more than one height.) Fortunately a solution to this problem has been found in the form of a " **computer,**" one of those little examples of mechanized mathematics which have done much to dispel a pilot's worries. By simple adjustments he can set the height, indicated speed, and temperature, and by even less than the proverbial "turning of a handle" he can read the true air speed!

The pilot talks and thinks in terms of indicated air speed. Quite apart from the convenience it is natural that he should do so; after all, it is what he sees in front of him all the time he is flying—it is the speed he reads "on the clock." It is therefore rather a solemn thought to realize that **it really is not a speed at all**! If the "clock" reads 300 m.p.h. all it means is that the net pressure on the diaphragm in the instrument is the same as it would be if the air speed were 300 m.p.h. at standard sea-level conditions. The real air speed may be anywhere between about 200 m.p.h. and about 700 m.p.h. according to the conditions at the time.

Position Error

Even now we have not by any means disposed of the errors which have to be considered in the measurement of air speed. One of the problems is to decide in what place to put the Pitot-Static head—it is a problem which is more acute on the modern monoplane than it was on the biplane. The difficulty is to find a position where there is a steady flow of air, and where the static pressure is unaffected by the presence of the aircraft itself, its speed, and its attitude to the air. Complete solution of the problem is impossible; it is a question of making the best of a bad job. On biplanes a position on one of the front interplane struts, about two-thirds of the way up, was found to be fairly satisfactory; on monoplanes many positions have been tried, in front of the leading edge, above the plane, below the plane, and, on twin or four-engined aircraft, in front of the nose of the fuselage. Wherever we put it the airflow and the pressure are affected and an error is introduced—called **Position Error.** The degree of error cannot be calculated, as it varies according to the type of aircraft, the position of the head on the aircraft, and with speed and attitude. Attitude is important not only owing to its effect on the pressures around the aeroplane, but because the changes of attitude which occur at different speeds mean different inclinations of the Pitot head to the air flow. The best we can do is to find out the error by experiment on one of each type of aircraft, and then provide the pilot with a table showing the error at various speeds. As a general rule the speed shown on the indicator is too low at low speeds and too high at high speeds, a typical table being as follows: at 80 m.p.h. add 3 m.p.h., at 100 m.p.h. subtract 1·2 m.p.h., at 140 m.p.h. subtract 8 m.p.h., at 160 m.p.h. subtract 10 m.p.h. Owing to the difficulty of finding a suitable position for the Pitot-Static head, position error is usually worse on monoplanes than on biplanes.

It is curious how long we often take to think of a simple idea to remedy a trouble. We long sought, without much success, for a suitable position for the Pitot-Static head. Most of the positions tried were reasonably good so far as the Pitot tube was concerned, but it was the static tube that caused most of the error. This may seem a little puzzling since the static pressure affects both the Pitot and the Static tube, and one would think that it would not matter much if it were incorrect on both sides. The answer to this puzzle will be found in Bernoulli's principle and is fully explained in the next paragraph. It was discovered, however, that there is usually some part of the aeroplane where the pressure is very nearly the static atmospheric pressure in all conditions of flight; this position is unsuitable for the Pitot tube and so the two were separated. In modern aircraft the Pitot head may

be out on one of the wings, and the **static vent,** as it is called, may be a
hole in the side of the fuselage or even at the tail.

The Venturi Tube

One of the most interesting examples of Bernoulli's Theorem is provided by the venturi tube (Fig. 39). This simple but effective instrument is nothing but a tube which gradually narrows to a throat, and
then expands even more gradually to the exit. Its effectiveness as a
means of causing a decrease of pressure below that of the atmosphere
depends very much on the exact shape. If a photograph is taken, or a
diagram made, of the flow of air or water through a venturi tube, it
will be observed that the streamlines are closest together at the throat,

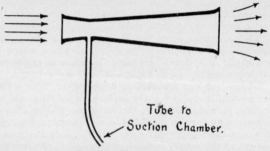

Tube to
Suction Chamber.

FIG. 39. VENTURI TUBE

and this gives an unfortunate impression that the fluid has been compressed at this point. We have avoided giving a diagram of the flow
because at this stage such an impression is the last thing we want to
convey. What we would like to be able to do is to show a cine film,
or, better still, an actual experiment, which would make it quite clear
that while it is true that the streamlines are closer together at the
throat, the velocity of flow is also higher. This is the important point:
the dynamic pressure has gone up and therefore, in accordance with
Bernoulli's principle, the static pressure has gone down. If a tube is
taken from the throat and connected to a U-tube containing water,
the suction will be clearly shown.

An interesting experiment with a venturi tube is to place an ordinary
Pitot tube (**without a static**) facing the airflow at various positions in
the venturi tube. Connect the Pitot tube to a U-tube, and leave the
other side of the U-tube open to the atmospheric pressure outside the
air stream. The Pitot tube will record $p + \frac{1}{2}\rho V^2$, i.e. the static pressure
in the stream plus the dynamic pressure, and the U-tube will therefore
show the difference between this and the atmospheric pressure outside
the stream. It will be found that $p + \frac{1}{2}\rho V^2$ is very nearly constant,
whether the Pitot tube is placed in the free air stream in front of the
venturi, or in the mouth, or the throat, or near the exit. This is a convincing proof of Bernoulli's Theorem. The Pitot tube could, of course,
be connected to an Air Speed Indicator, and if the static side of the
Air Speed Indicator were left open to atmospheric pressure outside the
air stream, a constant reading would be obtained at all parts of the
venturi, but this would **not** mean that the air speed was constant.
Notice again that one must beware of the readings of Air Speed Indicators! The Air Speed Indicator will only record the air speed if one side

is connected to a Pitot tube in the air stream, and the other side to a static tube at the same part of the air stream. If a complete Pitot-static tube is connected to the Air Speed Indicator and inserted at various parts of the venturi, it will be clear that the air speed increases from mouth to throat and then decreases again to the exit. The air speed increases very nearly in the same proportion as the area of cross-section of the venturi decreases, and this suggests that there is little or no change in the density of the air. Even more convincing evidence that the density does not change is provided by the flow of water through a venturi tube; the pattern of flow and the results obtained are very similar to those in air, and we know that water is for all practical purposes incompressible.

Let us illustrate our points by taking a numerical example. Suppose the area of the throat of a venturi tube is a quarter of the area of the mouth, and suppose the speed of air flow at the mouth is 60 m.p.h.

If we neglect any change of density of the air as it flows through the venturi, the speed of flow at the throat will be 240 m.p.h.

Now if a complete Pitot-Static head is placed at the mouth, and is connected to an Air Speed Indicator, the reading will, of course, be 60 m.p.h., which is the air speed at the mouth.

If the complete head is placed at the throat, the reading will be 240 m.p.h. So far, so good.

But suppose a Pitot tube is placed at the throat, where the speed is 240 m.p.h.—and the static side of the Air Speed Indicator is connected to a static tube at the mouth—or, what comes to the same thing, is left open to the atmosphere (the static pressure in the free air stream at the mouth will be practically the same as in the still atmosphere)—**then what will the Air Speed Indicator read?** Not quite so easy?

Let us call the static pressure at the mouth, i.e. the atmospheric pressure, p_a

Velocity at mouth, V_a.

Static pressure at throat, p_b.

Velocity at throat, V_b.

The air density will be the same at both, i.e. $\rho_a = \rho_b$

Then on the Pitot tube at the throat the total pressure will be the sum of the static and dynamic pressures, i.e.

$$p_b + \tfrac{1}{2}\rho V_b{}^2$$

which, by Bernoulli's Theorem, **is the same as**

$$p_a + \tfrac{1}{2}\rho V_a{}^2$$

On the Static tube at mouth pressure will be just p_a.

∴ Pressure on diaphragm in the Air Speed Indicator will be the difference between these two, i.e.

$$p_b + \tfrac{1}{2}\rho V_b{}^2 - p_a$$
$$\text{or } p_a + \tfrac{1}{2}\rho V_a{}^2 - p_a$$
$$\text{which equals } \tfrac{1}{2}\rho V_a{}^2$$

Now when the net pressure on an Air Speed Indicator is $\tfrac{1}{2}\rho V_a{}^2$, ρ being the standard sea-level density, the instrument reads V_a—that is the whole idea of the calibration.

Therefore, in this example, the reading will be **60 m.p.h.**

Notice that the speed recorded is that of the air flow where the static is, and not where the pitot is.

Is this just an accident?

Let us reverse the positions of pitot and static and see what happens. **Place the pitot at the mouth where the air speed is 60 m.p.h. Static at the throat where it is 240 m.p.h.**

Total pressure on pitot $= p_a + \frac{1}{2}\rho\, V_a^2$
$$= p_b + \frac{1}{2}\rho\, V_b^2$$

Pressure on static $= p_b$.

Therefore difference between the two $= p_a + \frac{1}{2}\rho\, V_a^2 - p_b$
$$= p_b + \frac{1}{2}\rho\, V_b^2 - p_b$$
$$= \frac{1}{2}\rho\, V_b^2$$

Therefore the Indicator reads V_b, i.e. 240 m.p.h.—again the speed corresponding to the position of the static and not the pitot.

The explanation is that the total pressure on the pitot tube, the sum of the dynamic and the static pressures, is, in accordance with Bernoulli's Theorem, the same at any part of the air stream. Therefore so long as the pitot tube is in the stream, it makes no difference at what part of the stream it is. The static, on the other hand, must be correct for the place where we wish to measure the air speed.

This fact enables us to play some curious tricks; we can, for instance, measure the air speed at the throat of a double venturi tube without putting a pitot in the tube at all—all we need to do is to put the pitot in the free air stream (outside the venturi altogether), and connect a static to the throat of the double venturi. This is convenient since there will probably be no room for a pitot tube at the throat, whereas the static pressure can be obtained from a small hole in the side of the tube and this causes no obstruction to the air flow.

It should be noted that the pitot must be in the smooth air stream whose velocity we wish to measure—it is no good putting it behind an obstruction, nor in the slipstream from the propeller where there will be greater energy, nor in any place where there is turbulence; because Bernoulli's Theorem is only true for streamline flow. But it can be in a position where the air is flowing at a higher or lower speed than that of the aeroplane, and, provided the static gives the true atmospheric pressure, the Air Speed Indicator will read the correct speed of the aeroplane.

Now try the Examples on page 345, they will surely bring the lesson home.

There are many practical examples of the venturi tube in everyday life, but there is no need to quote them, because we have sufficient examples in flying to illustrate this important principle. The choke tube in a carburettor is one; a wind tunnel is another, the experiments usually being done in the high-speed flow at the throat, and the air speed at this point is often measured by a single static hole in the side of the tunnel. A small venturi may be fitted inside a larger one, and the suction at the throat of the small venturi is then sufficient to drive gyroscopic instruments. But best example of all is the suction on top of an ordinary aerofoil section as explained in the next chapter.

Before reading the next chapter see if you can answer the following questions. If you can do so you have probably understood most of this chapter and you may proceed with confidence. Similarly, you are advised to try the questions given at the end of each chapter before going on to the next.

---

1. Why is it difficult to find out the exact height of the Atmosphere?
2. What is meant by the "Density" of Air?

3. Why does the Density of Air decrease as the height increases?

4. Which falls off more rapidly with height, the density or the pressure? Why?

5. What is the difference between the "Troposphere" and the "Stratosphere"?

6. What is meant by the "International Standard Atmosphere"?

7. State Boyle's and Charles's Laws for perfect gases.

8. What is the cause of winds?

9. How does the wind affect flight?

10. When would you expect the air to be "bumpy"?

11. What is meant by "wind gradient"?

12. Describe any methods which have been employed to enable us to "see" the air.

13. Why does an Altimeter have an adjustment so that it can be set before each flight?

14. Why may it be necessary to re-set an altimeter during flight?

15. Of what gases is the air composed?

16. What are the chief differences between the atmosphere at sea level and at 30,000 ft.?

17. What is Archimedes' Principle?

18. What is the meaning of Viscosity?

19. Draw a graph showing the variation of (i) Temperature, (ii) Density, with Altitude, from sea level up to 45,000 ft.

20. Why is the study of Air Resistance so important?

21. Describe the practical methods by which the problem has been investigated.

22. Sketch an open jet and a closed type of wind tunnel.

23. What do you think are the relative advantages of the two types?

24. What is meant by a return-flow tunnel?

25. What is meant by "Scale Effect"?

26. What are the errors to which wind tunnel experiments are liable, and what measures can be taken to reduce such errors to a minimum?

27. What do you understand by the term "Streamline Shape"?

28. Distinguish between "Skin Friction" and "Form Drag."

29. Show by a sketch the nature of the airflow passing (i) a cylinder, (ii) a body of streamline shape, (iii) a flat plate at right angles to the airflow, and (iv) a flat plate parallel to the airflow.

30. To what extent does Experiment confirm Theory in the study of Air Resistance?

31. Describe the various methods by which Air Speed may be measured.

32. Distinguish between "Indicated" Air Speed and "True" Air Speed.

33. What is the significance of the pressure, $\frac{1}{2}\rho V^2$?

34. What is "Position Error"?

35. What is a "Static Vent"?

36. State Bernoulli's Principle.

37. Why is the position of the Static tube more important than that of the Pitot tube?

38. Give examples of the venturi tube principle—
       (i) in aeronautical work, (ii) in everyday life.

For numerical examples on Air and Airflow see page 340.

CHAPTER III

AEROFOILS

So far we have only considered the Resistance, or "Drag," of bodies passing through the air. In the design of aeroplanes it is our aim to reduce such resistance to a minimum, but, curiously enough, we obtain our Lift from very much the same kind of forces and pressure effects as produce the Drag.

Flapping Wings

All attempts to fly in heavier-than-air machines must embody some means of forcing the air downwards so as to provide the equal and opposite reaction which is to lift the weight of the machine. It was natural that the early experimenters should endeavour to obtain this reaction by forcing the air downwards by "flapping" of wings in imitation of a bird, but machines working on this principle, called "Ornithopters," have never been really successful. It is often argued that "Nature must know best," and that we should still continue to experiment on these lines; but such arguments are no more logical than to suggest that ocean liners should cross the Atlantic by flapping their rudders after the fashion of a fish's tail, or that railway engines or automobiles should be provided with legs instead of wheels. All our mechanical experience has tended to show the advantages of rotary motion over the reciprocating motion which is so often employed by Nature. The foregoing remarks are not intended to imply that nothing has been learnt by the study of the flight of birds; such is very far from being the case, and there still remain problems to be solved in which we may hope that our knowledge of bird flight will come to the rescue.

Aerofoils

But if we reject the idea of flapping wings, we must replace it by some other device which will deflect the air downwards. In the conventional aeroplane this is provided for by wings, or aerofoils, which are inclined at a small angle to the direction of motion, the necessary forward motion being provided by the thrust of a rotating airscrew, or by some type of jet or rocket propulsion. These aerofoils are always slightly curved, but in the original attempts to obtain flight on this system flat surfaces were used.

Flat Plate

If the air flows past a flat plate which is inclined to the direction of the airflow, we find that the pressure of the air on the top surface of the plate is decreased while that underneath it is increased. The result of this is that there is a net pressure on the plate trying to force it both upwards and backwards, e.g. suppose the area of a plate is 100 sq. in. and the average pressure on the top surface could be reduced from the normal atmospheric pressure of 15 lb. per sq. in. to 13 lb. per sq. in., while the pressure underneath was increased from

15 lb. per sq. in. to 16 lb. per sq. in. (Fig. 40), then we would have a
net pressure of 3 lb. per sq. in., or a total force of 300 lb. on the plate.

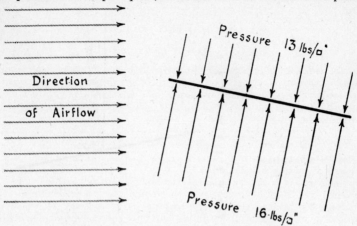

FIG. 40. FLAT PLATE MOVING THROUGH THE AIR

This force is called the **Total Reaction,** and it acts approximately at
right angles to the plate (see Fig. 41).

It will be seen that if the angle of inclination is small, the upward
component will be large in comparison to the backward component;
on the other hand, as the angle becomes small the Total Reaction will
in itself diminish, becoming zero at 0°, so that in our attempt to reduce
the backward component we automatically reduce the upward
component, and in consequence an angle must be chosen which gives
the best compromise.

Lift and Drag

We have referred to these two components as "upwards" and
"backwards," but this will only be so on the assumption that the

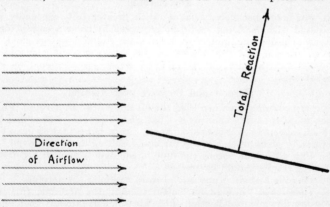

FIG. 41. THE TOTAL REACTION

airflow is horizontal or, what amounts to the same thing, that the plate is moving horizontally through still air.

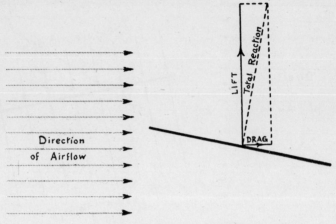

FIG. 42. AIRFLOW HORIZONTAL; PLATE INCLINED AT SMALL ANGLE TO AIRFLOW

In practice the direction of motion of an aeroplane is by no means always horizontal, and it is usual to split up the Total Reaction into its two components **relative to the airflow** as follows—

1. The component at right angles to the direction of the airflow, called **LIFT** (Figs. 42, 43, and 44).

2. The component parallel to the direction of the airflow, called **DRAG** (Figs. 42, 43, and 44).

The use of the term "Lift" in this sense is apt to be misleading, for under certain conditions of flight, such as a vertical nose dive, it may act horizontally, and cases may even arise where the Lift acts vertically downwards.

The Aerofoil

It was soon discovered that a much greater Lift, especially when compared with the Drag, could be produced by using a curved surface instead of a flat one, and thus the modern **Aerofoil** was evolved. The curved surface had the additional advantage that it automatically provided a certain amount of thickness which was necessary for structural strength.

Airflow and Pressure over Aerofoil

Experiments have shown that the air flows over an aerofoil (Fig. 46) much more smoothly than over a flat plate (Fig. 45), less eddies being formed, especially over the top surface. The result is that we get a better decrease in pressure on the top surface, resulting in an improved Lift.

In Fig. 46, which shows the flow of air over a typical aerofoil, the following results should be noticed—

1. There is a slight "upwash" before reaching the aerofoil.

2. There is a "downwash" after passing the aerofoil; this is the necessary downward deflection of the air which has already been referred to. The downwash is important because it affects the direction of the

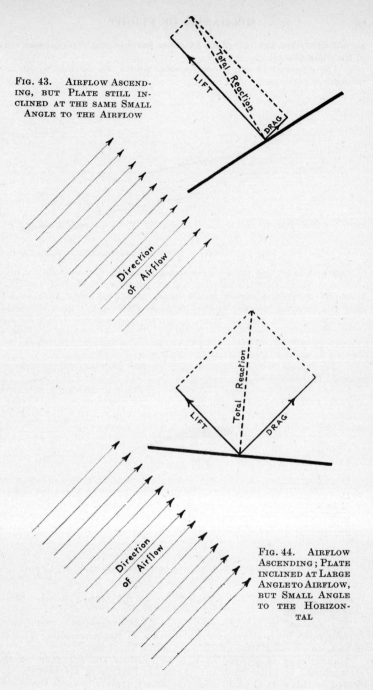

Total Reaction

LIFT

DRAG

Direction of Airflow

Total Reaction

LIFT

DRAG

Direction of Airflow

Fig. 44. Airflow Ascending; Plate inclined at Large Angle to Airflow, but Small Angle to the Horizontal

air which strikes the tail plane or other parts of the aeroplane in rear of the main planes.

3. The streamlines are closer together above the aerofoil where the pressure is decreased.

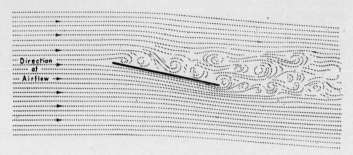

FIG. 45. AIRFLOW OVER A FLAT PLATE

This fact is at first puzzling, because, as in the venturi tube, it may lead us to think that the air above the aerofoil is compressed, and that therefore we should expect an increased pressure. The explanation is that the air over the top surface is passing through a kind of bottle-neck, similar to a venturi tube, and that therefore its velocity must

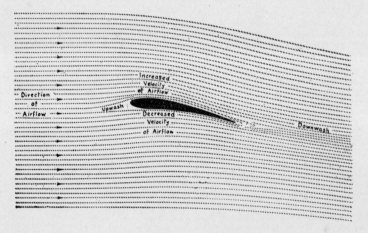

FIG. 46. AIRFLOW OVER AN AEROFOIL INCLINED AT A
SMALL ANGLE

increase at the narrower portions, i.e. at the highest points of the curved aerofoil.

The increase in kinetic energy due to the increase in velocity is accompanied by a corresponding decrease in static pressure. This is, in fact, an excellent example of Bernoulli's Theorem.

Another way of looking at it is to consider the curvature of the streamlines. In order that any particular particle of air may be deflected on this curved path, a force must act upon it towards the centre of the curve, so that it follows that the pressure on the outside of the particle must be greater than that on the inside; in other words, the pressure decreases as we approach the inner streamlines, i.e. the ones near the top surface of the aerofoil. This point of view is interesting because it emphasizes the importance of curving the streamlines downwards, which is the essence of the whole matter.

Chord

It has already been mentioned, when considering the flat plate, that the exact angle of inclination to the airflow is of great importance. In

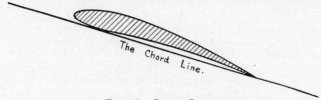

FIG. 47. CHORD LINE

the case of a curved aerofoil it is not particularly easy to define this angle, since we must first decide on some straight line in the aerofoil section from which we can measure the angle to the direction of the airflow. Unfortunately, owing to the large variety of shapes used as aerofoil sections, it is not easy to define this "Chord" line to suit all aerofoils. As this book is intended for the use of practical men, we will adopt the chord line which is in common use among Riggers, namely, **the line formed by a straight edge placed tangential to the under-surface of the aerofoil** (Fig. 47). Even this, however, is only practicable when the straight edge will touch the under-surface at at least two points. This is not always so in the case of modern aerofoils, which often

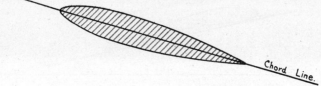

FIG. 48 CHORD LINE: SYMMETRICAL AEROFOIL

have a convex under-surface; in such cases the chord should be specially defined, although it is usually taken as the line joining the Leading Edge to the Trailing Edge. This is the "centre line" in the particular case of symmetrical aerofoils, such as are usually used for tail planes (Fig. 48).

The official definition of the chord line, which is now applied to all shapes of aerofoils, is "The line joining the centres of curvature of the leading and trailing edges." However, we can still stick to our practical definition, provided we make sure what is intended to be taken as the chord line in any particular problem with which we are faced. This applies not only to wind tunnel tests on aerofoils, but to the practical rigging of the wings on an aeroplane.

[NOTE. It is only fair to the reader to point out that the practical definition which we have given of the Chord Line is apt to lead to wrong ideas unless it is clearly understood that it is merely a definition of **convenience**, and not one of theoretical correctness. For instance, we shall discover that, if we accept our practical definition, an aerofoil may provide Lift **even when it is inclined at a slightly negative angle to the airflow.** Now, how can an aerofoil which is inclined at a negative angle deflect the air **downwards?** The idea seems absurd, but the explanation of the riddle is simply that the **aerofoil is not really inclined at a negative angle.** Our curious chord may be at a negative angle, but the curved surfaces of the aerofoil are inclined at various angles, positive

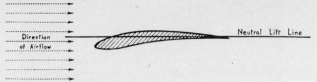

FIG. 49. NEUTRAL LIFT LINE

and negative, the net effect being that of a slightly **positive angle,** which causes a downwash and produces Lift.

Now if we tilt the nose of our aerofoil downwards until it produces **no Lift,** it will be in an exactly similar position to that of a flat plate placed edgewise to the airflow and producing no Lift, and if we now draw a straight line through the aerofoil **parallel to the airflow** (Fig. 49) it will be the inclination of **this line** which settles whether the aerofoil provides Lift or not.

Such a line is called the **Neutral Lift Line,** and would in some senses be a better definition of the chord, but it can only be found by wind tunnel experiments for each aerofoil, and, even when it has been found, it is most awkward from the point of view of practical measurements.]

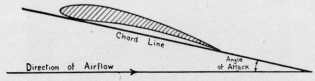

FIG. 50. CHORD LINE AND ANGLE OF ATTACK

Angle of Attack

We will call the angle between the chord of the aerofoil and the direction of the airflow the **Angle of Attack** (Fig. 50).

This angle is often referred to as the "Angle of Incidence," but we purposely avoid the use of this term because it is apt to be confused with the Riggers' Angle of Incidence, which is a definite rigging measurement, being the angle between the chord of the aerofoil and some fixed datum line in the aeroplane.

[NOTE. If we wish to be precise we must be careful in our definition of the term "Angle of Attack," because, as has already been noticed, the direction of the airflow is changed by the presence of the aerofoil itself, so that the direction of the airflow which actually passes over the surface of the aerofoil is not the same as that of the airflow at a considerable distance from the aerofoil. The student will find this distinction of great importance if he wishes to study the modern theory of aerofoils in more advanced books; at present we will be content to consider the direction of the airflow as that of the air stream at such a distance that it is undisturbed by the presence of the aerofoil.]

PLATE IX. PRESSURE PLOTTING

The special aerofoil is mounted vertically in the open jet. In the lower right-hand corner is the multi-manometer on which can be seen the different levels of the liquid in the tubes.

Pressure Plotting

As the Angle of Attack is altered the Lift and Drag change very rapidly, and experiments show that this is due to changes in the distribution of pressure over the aerofoil. These experiments are carried out by the method known as "Pressure Plotting" (Fig. 51), in which small holes in the aerofoil surface (a, b, c, d, etc.) are connected to glass manometer tubes (a, b, c, d, etc.) containing water or other liquid; where there is a "suction" on the aerofoil the liquid in the corresponding tubes will be sucked up, but where there is an increased pressure the liquid will be depressed. Such experiments have been made both on models in wind tunnels and on full-scale aeroplanes in actual flight, and the results are most interesting and instructive.

The reader who is interested in this method of "pressure plotting" is advised to work through Example No. 144 on page 346. In this example the results of an actual experiment are given, together with

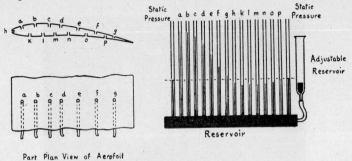

Part Plan View of Aerofoil

FIG. 51. PRESSURE PLOTTING

a full explanation of how to interpret the results. In order to follow through to the end of this example it is necessary to have a knowledge of the Lift formula given later in this chapter, but the actual "pressure plotting" can be done without this.

Pressure Distribution

Fig. 52 shows the Pressure Distribution, obtained in this manner, over an aerofoil at an angle of attack of 4°. Two points are particularly noticeable, namely—

1. The decrease in pressure on the top surface is greater than the increase on the lower surface.

2. The pressure is not by any means evenly distributed, both the decreased pressure on the upper surface and the increased pressure on the lower surface being most marked over the front portion of the aerofoil.

Both these discoveries are of extreme importance to us in our efforts to understand the science of flight.

The first shows that, although both surfaces contribute, it is the **top surface,** by means of its decreased pressure, which provides the greater part of our Lift; at some angles as much as four-fifths of the Lift is obtained from the decrease in pressure on the top surface. The student is at first startled by this fact, as he feels that it is contrary to his ideas of common sense; but, as so often happens, once he has learnt the truth and significance of this top surface lift, he is often inclined to exaggerate it, and to refer to the area above the aerofoil as a "partial vacuum," a "semi-vacuum," or even a "vacuum." Although, by a slight stretch of imagination, we might allow the term "partial vacuum," the other two expressions are hopelessly misleading, as will be seen when we examine the facts. We find that the greatest height to which water in our manometer is sucked up when air flows over an ordinary aerofoil at the ordinary speeds of flight is about 5 or 6 in.; now, if there were a "vacuum" over the top surface, the water would be sucked up about 34 ft. Or looking at it in another way, suppose that there was a "vacuum" over the top surface of an aerofoil and that the pressure underneath was increased from 14·7 lb. per sq. in. to 20 lb. per sq. in., then we would have an average upward pressure on the aerofoil of 20 lb. per sq. in., or 2,880 lb. per sq. ft. The actual average lift obtained from an aeroplane wing is from about 10 up to 20, 30, 40, or 50 lb. per sq. ft. Take a notebook of about 1 sq. ft. area and place a 20 lb. weight on it; lift this up and it will give you some idea of the average

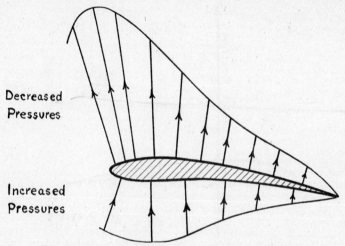

Decreased
Pressures

Increased
Pressures

FIG. 52. PRESSURE DISTRIBUTION OVER AN AEROFOIL

lift provided by a square foot of aeroplane wing, and the type of load which has to be carried by the covering. You will not want to repeat the experiment with 2,880 lb. on the notebook!

[NOTE. The reason why the pressure distribution diagram has not been completed round the leading edge is because the changes of pressure are very sudden in this region and cannot conveniently be represented on a diagram. The increased pressure on the underside will continue until we reach a point head-on into wind where the air is brought to rest and the increase of pressure will be $\frac{1}{2}\rho V^2$ as recorded on a pitot tube; after this there will be a very sudden drop to zero, followed by an equally sudden change to the decreased pressures of the top surface.]

Centre of Pressure

The second thing that we learn from our pressure distribution diagram—namely, that both decreases and increases of pressure are greatest near the Leading Edge of the aerofoil—will mean that if we were to replace all the distributed pressure by a **Single Resultant Force**, this single force would act less than half-way back along the chord. The position on the chord at which this resultant force acts is called the **Centre of Pressure** of the Aerofoil (Fig. 53). The idea of a "Centre of Pressure" is very similar to that of a Centre of Gravity of a body whose weight is unevenly distributed, and it should therefore present no difficulty to the student who understands ordinary mechanics.

The comparison becomes even more close when we realize that we can
find the Centre of Pressure on the aerofoil by finding the Centre of
Gravity of the Area of Pressure Distribution. This can be done by
drawing the pressure distribution curve on a sheet of cardboard, cutting
it out and sticking pins in at various points along the chord until the
cardboard will balance with the chord horizontal.

To sum up, we may say that we have **a decreased pressure or
" suction " above the aerofoil and an increased pressure below,** that **the**

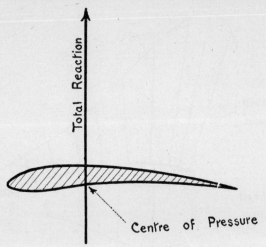

FIG. 53. CENTRE OF PRESSURE

decrease of pressure above is greater than the increase below, and that
in both cases the effect is greatest near the Leading Edge (Fig. 52).

All these facts are of importance when we come to consider the
" Structure " of the Wing; for instance, we shall realize that the top
covering or " skin " must be held **down** on to the ribs, while the bottom
covering will simply be pressed up against the ribs. We see also why
the front portion of the ribs must be much stronger than the trailing
edge portion.

" Pressure Plotting " experiments have also been carried out at various
points along the span of an aerofoil, and they show that, except near
the wing tips, where there is a gradual falling off, the pressures are very
much the same at all parts of the span.

Total Reaction on an Aerofoil

If we were to add up all the distributed pressure over the aerofoil
and replace it by the Total Resultant Force acting at the Centre of
Pressure, we should find that, at certain Angles of Attack, this Total
Resultant Force does not act at right angles to the chord as in the case
of a flat plate, but may act at an even smaller angle to the vertical,
so increasing the proportion of Lift to Drag as compared with a flat
plate.

It must not be thought from this that the Resultant Force can ever
act actually **forwards,** as this would give us a kind of negative drag
and a form of perpetual motion. The truth is that the Total Reaction

must always have a **backward** component when considered relative to the path of flight of the aerofoil, but that it may have a **forward** component when considered relative to the chord of the aerofoil, and thus it may load the anti-drag bracing, i.e. that part of the structure which prevents the wings from folding forward, instead of the drag bracing in flight. Owing to the small angles which are involved, this point is not very easy to understand, but it is important because it explains the advantage of a curved aerofoil compared to a flat plate. It is another

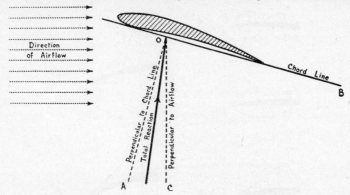

FIG. 54. INCLINATION OF TOTAL REACTION

case where common sense is apt to mislead us and make us think that it must always be the drag bracing which is loaded in flight. Fig. 54 should help to make this point more clear. When the line of the Reaction lies along AO (which is at right angles to the chord BO), neither drag nor anti-drag bracing is loaded; if it lies behind AO it means that the ratio of Lift to Drag is increased and that the anti-drag bracing will be loaded; if it lies in front of AO, then the ratio of Lift to Drag is decreased and the drag bracing will be loaded. In practice the Line of Reaction usually lies in front of AO at small Angles of Attack and behind AO at larger angles; it can never lie behind the vertical, CO.

Movement of Centre of Pressure

Pressure Plotting experiments show that as the Angle of Attack is altered the distribution of pressure over the aerofoil changes considerably, and consequently there will be a **movement of the Centre of Pressure.** The position of the Centre of Pressure is usually defined as being a certain proportion of the Chord back from the Leading Edge. Fig. 55 illustrates typical pressure distribution over an aerofoil at $-4°$, $0°$, $4°$, $8°$, $12°$, $16°$ and $20°$ Angles of Attack. (In these diagrams only the "Lift component" of the total pressure has been plotted. The "Drag component" has hardly any effect on the position of the Centre of Pressure.) It will be noticed that at a negative angle, and even at $0°$, the pressure on the top surface near the Leading Edge is increased above normal, and that on the lower surface is decreased; this causes the "loop" in the pressure diagram, which means that this portion of the aerofoil is being pushed **downwards** while the rear portion is being pushed upwards, so that the whole aerofoil tends to turn over nose first. This is really equivalent to saying that the Centre of Pressure

is a long way back—in other words, the only place where we could put
one force which would have the same effect as the distributed pressure
would be a long way behind the Leading Edge. In some cases the
Centre of Pressure may be so far back as to be many chords' length
behind the Trailing Edge. As the Angle of Attack is increased up to
16°, the Centre of Pressure is seen to move gradually forwards until it
is less than one-third of the chord from the Leading Edge, while above
this angle it begins to move backwards again.

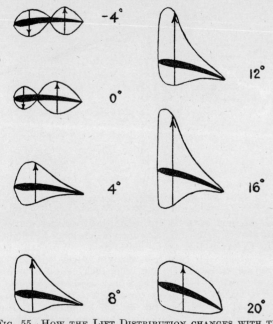

FIG. 55. How the Lift Distribution changes with the
Angle of Attack

Unstable Movement of Centre of Pressure

Now during flight, for reasons which we shall see later, the Angle
of Attack is usually between 2° and 8° and is very rarely below 0°
or above 16°. So that we can come to the conclusion that, **for the
ordinary angles of flight, as the Angle of Attack of the aerofoil is increased,
the Centre of Pressure tends to move forward.**

Lift a poker at its Centre of Gravity and it will lie horizontal; move
the position at which you lift it forwards towards the knob and the rear
end of the poker will drop : this is because the Centre of Lift has moved
forwards as compared with the Centre of Gravity. Therefore the
forward movement of the Centre of Pressure on the aerofoil as the
Angle of Attack is increased will tend to drop still further the Trailing
Edge of the aerofoil; in other words, the Angle of Attack will increase
even more, and this will in turn cause the Centre of Pressure to move
further forward, and so on. This is called **instability,** and it is one of
the great problems of flight.

If we were to take the wing off a model aeroplane and try to make it glide without any fuselage or tail, we would find that it would either turn over nose first or its nose would go up in the air and it would turn over on to its back. This is because the wing is unstable, and although we might be able to weight it so that it would start on its glide correctly, it would very soon meet some disturbance in the air which might raise its nose; this would cause the Angle of Attack to increase, the Centre of Pressure or Lift would move forward, and this would cause the nose to lift still further, and the same cycle of operations would be repeated. The opposite would happen if the initial disturbance caused the nose to drop, but in either case the wing would fail to glide.

Stable Movement of Centre of Pressure

Curiously enough, in the case of a **flat plate, an increase of the Angle of Attack over the same angles causes the Centre of Pressure to move backwards;** this tends to dip the nose of the plate back again to its original position, and so makes the flat plate **stable.** For this reason it is possible to take a **flat** piece of stiff paper or cardboard, and, after properly weighting it, to make it glide across the room. If it meets a disturbance which causes the nose to rise, the Centre of Pressure will move backwards and automatically decrease the angle again so that the paper will resume its original glide. If, on the other hand, the nose drops, the Centre of Pressure will move forwards, and this will automatically increase the angle again. (It should be noted that the flat piece of paper will only glide if it is weighted so that the Centre of Gravity is roughly one-third of the chord back from the Leading Edge. If it is not weighted the Centre of Pressure will always be in front of the Centre of Gravity, and this will cause the piece of paper to revolve rapidly.)

Stationary Centre of Pressure

This unstable movement of the Centre of Pressure is a definite disadvantage of the ordinary curved aerofoil, and in a later chapter we will consider the steps which are taken to counteract it. It might be as well, however, to mention at this stage that attempts have been made to devise aerofoil shapes which have not got this unpleasant characteristic, and, as a result, it has been found possible to obtain an aerofoil in which the Centre of Pressure remains practically stationary over the Angles of Attack used in ordinary flight. The chief feature noticeable in such aerofoils is that the under-surface is usually convex instead of concave, and that there is often a reflex curvature towards the trailing edge (see Fig. 62). Unfortunately, attempts to improve the stability of the aerofoil may often tend to spoil other important characteristics.

Lift and Drag of an Aerofoil

Now the ultimate object of the aerofoil is to obtain the Lift necessary to keep the aeroplane in the air; in order to obtain this Lift it must be propelled through the air at a definite **Velocity** and it must be set at a definite **Angle of Attack** to the flow of air past it. We have already discovered that we cannot obtain a purely vertical force on the aerofoil; in other words, we can only obtain Lift at the expense of a certain amount of **Drag.** The latter is a necessary evil, and it must be reduced to the absolute minimum so that we can reduce the power required to pull the aerofoil through the air, or alternatively increase the velocity which we can obtain from a given engine power. Our next task, therefore, is to investigate how much Lift and how much Drag we will obtain from different shaped aerofoils at various angles of attack and at various velocities. Our task is one of appalling magnitude; there is no limit to the number of aerofoil shapes which we might test, and in spite of thousands of experiments carried out in wind tunnels and by full-scale tests in the air, it is still impossible to say that we have discovered the best-shaped aerofoil for any particular purpose.

In the early days, very few aerofoil shapes were suggested by theory; the usual method was to sketch out a shape by eye, give it a thorough test and then try to improve on it by slight modifications. The result of this method is that we now have a mass of experimental data obtained under varying conditions in the various wind tunnels of the world. The results are interpreted in different ways, and several systems of units and symbols are used, so that it is difficult for the student or practical aeronautical engineer to make use of the data available. It is not the function of this book to give such data, and the reader who requires it for practical purposes must refer to some up-to-date and reliable aeronautical handbook. For our purposes it is only necessary to examine the results obtained for a typical aerofoil and then to see how these may be modified by alteration in the shape of the aerofoil.

The hit-and-miss method of aerofoil design has gradually been replaced by more systematic methods. The first step in this direction was to design and test a "family" of aerofoils by taking a standard symmetrical section and altering the curvature of its chord line. An early example of this system was the R.A.F. series of aerofoils beginning with R.A.F. 30, a symmetrical section from which R.A.F. 31, 32, 33, 34, etc., were evolved by curving the centre line in various ways and according to a definite plan. Then R.A.F. 40 was used as the basic aerofoil of a new family, and so on. There are also now theoretical formulae from which aerofoil sections have been designed for specific purposes. But, whatever the method of the original design, we still rely on wind tunnel tests to decide the qualities of the aerofoil, and it must be admitted that the aerofoils of the old hit-and-miss days are still some of the best in their respective classes.

Methods of Finding Lift and Drag

In wind-tunnel work it is the usual practice to measure Lift and Drag separately, rather than to measure the Total Reaction and then split it up into two components. The Aerofoil is set at various Angles of Attack to the air which can be assumed to travel parallel to the axis of the wind tunnel, and the Lift (or force at right angles to the airflow) is measured on the lever arm CC (Fig. 26) which lies at right angles to the axis of the tunnel, while the Drag is measured on the lever arm BB which lies along the tunnel axis. In addition to the Lift and Drag, the Turning Moment, or tendency of the aerofoil to revolve about its supports, can be measured and in this way the position of the Centre of Pressure is estimated. If the aerofoil is suspended from the top of the tunnel, as in Fig. 27, similar calculations can be made.

Results of Lift and Drag Experiments

The results of the experiments show that within certain limitations both the Lift and Drag of an aerofoil depend on—
(a) **The shape of the aerofoil.**
(b) **The plan area of the aerofoil.**
(c) **The square of the velocity.**
(d) **The density of the air.**

Notice the similarity of these conclusions to those obtained when measuring the ordinary Air Resistance of a body (see page 50), and in both cases there are similar limitations to the conclusions arrived at.

The reader should notice that whereas when measuring Air Resistance we considered the **frontal area** of the body concerned, in the case of aerofoils we take the **plan area.** This is more convenient because the main force with which we are concerned in the case of aerofoils, i.e. the Lift, is at right angles to the direction of motion and very nearly at right angles to the aerofoils themselves, and therefore this force will depend on the plan area rather than the front elevation. The plan area will, of course, alter as the Angle of Attack is changed and therefore it is more convenient to refer all our results to the **maximum plan area** (the area projected on to the plane of the chord), so that the area will remain constant whatever the Angle of Attack may be. Unfortunately it is customary to use the same symbol S both for the plan area of a wing and the frontal area of any other body.

In so far as the above conclusions are true, we can express them as formulae in the forms—

$$\text{Lift} = C_{\text{L}} \cdot \tfrac{1}{2}\rho V^2 \cdot S$$
$$\text{Drag} = C_{\text{D}} \cdot \tfrac{1}{2}\rho V^2 \cdot S$$

Lift Coefficient and Drag Coefficient

The symbols C_{L} and C_{D} are called the **Lift Coefficient** and the **Drag Coefficient** of the aerofoil respectively; they depend on the shape of the aerofoil, and they will alter with changes in the Angle of Attack. They are found entirely by experiment. ρ represents the Air Density in slugs per cubic foot, S the plan area of the wing in square feet, V the velocity, or air speed, in feet per second, and the method of writing the formulae in terms of $\tfrac{1}{2}\rho V^2$ has already been explained in Chapter II.

Other symbols and systems of units are used, but to avoid any confusion only one system is introduced here, as the student of more advanced works should find no difficulty in adjusting his ideas to new units when he comes across them. (See note about units in Appendix II on page 317.)

Aerofoil Characteristics

The easiest way of setting out the results of experiments on aerofoils is to draw graphs showing how
(a) **The Lift Coefficient,**
(b) **The Drag Coefficient,**
(c) **The ratio of Lift to Drag, and**
(d) **The position of the Centre of Pressure**
alter as the **Angle of Attack** is increased over the ordinary angles of flight.

Typical graphs are shown in Figs. 57, 58, 59, and 60.

[NOTE. The graphs shown in the context do not refer to any particular aerofoil; they are intended merely to show the type of curves obtained for an ordinary general purpose aerofoil.

In Appendix I at the end of the book, tables are given showing the values of C_L, C_D, L/D, and the position of the Centre of Pressure for a few well-known aerofoils. The reader is advised to plot the graphs for these aerofoils and to compare them with one another (see examples Nos. 151, 152, 153, and 154). In this way he will be enabled to understand much more clearly the arguments followed in the remaining portion of this chapter.

If further information is required, the reader is referred to any good handbook of aeronautics, or to Government research publications.]

It is much more satisfactory to plot Lift Coefficient and Drag Coefficient than the total Lift and Drag obtained from any particular experiment, because the former will be practically independent of the Air Density, the scale of the aerofoil and the velocity employed for the experiment, whereas the total Lift and Drag will depend on the actual conditions at the time of the experiment. In other words, suppose we take a particular aerofoil section and test it on different scales at different velocities in various wind tunnels throughout the world and also full-scale in actual flight, we should in each case obtain the same curve showing how the Lift Coefficient changes according to the Angle of Attack. An attempt has been made to make this point clear because some students who can understand perfectly a "Lift Curve" obtained from a particular experiment become alarmed when they come across the rather more abstract "Lift Coefficient."

It must be admitted that, in actual practice, the curves of Lift Coefficient obtained by these various experiments will not exactly coincide. This is due to the fact that the theories which have led us to adopt the formula Lift = C_L. $\frac{1}{2}\rho V^2$. S are not exactly true for very much the same reasons as those we mentioned when dealing with Air Resistance in Chapter II—for instance, scale effect and the interference of the wind-tunnel walls. As a result of the large number of experiments which have been performed, it is now possible to make allowances for these errors and so obtain good accuracy whatever the conditions of the experiment; but these corrections are outside the scope of this book, and in any case are so small that we need not worry about them in our endeavour to understand the main principles.

Graphs

Now let us look at these curves to see what they mean. To the uninitiated a graph spells boredom. How many lectures has one listened to during which the lecturer has thrown on to the screen graph after graph in an endeavour to elucidate his points? Yet how rarely has one discovered what one graph is intended to convey before the next one comes along to cause further perplexity until one politely goes to sleep until the next intelligible picture is projected on to the screen. Such must be the experience of many aeronautical students, yet it must be admitted that a graph which is properly understood can convey a great deal of information in a compact and practical form.

Lift Curve

Let us first examine the graph (Fig. 57), which shows how the **Lift**

Coefficient of our imaginary aerofoil changes according to the Angle of Attack.

The first thing we notice is that **when the Angle of Attack has reached 0° there is already a definite Lift Coefficient and therefore a definite Lift;** this is a peculiar property of most cambered aerofoils. A flat plate, or a perfectly symmetrical aerofoil, will, of course, give no Lift when there is no Angle of Attack.

We notice next that **between 0° and about 12° the graph is practically a straight line, meaning that as the Angle of Attack increases there is a**

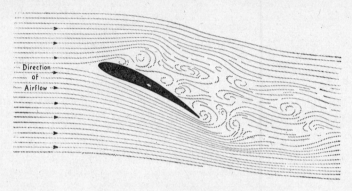

FIG. 56. AN AEROFOIL STALLED

steady increase in the Lift; whereas above 12°, although the Lift still increases for a few degrees, the increase is now comparatively small and the graph is curving to form a top, or maximum, point.

At about 15° the Lift reaches a definite maximum, and above this angle the Lift begins to decrease, the graph now curving downwards.

Stalling Angle of Aerofoil

Now this last discovery is perhaps the most important factor in the understanding of the why and wherefore of flight. It means that whereas at small angles any increase in the angle at which the aerofoil strikes the air will result in an increase in Lift, **when a certain angle is reached any further increase of angle will result in less Lift instead of more Lift.**

This angle is called the "Stalling Angle" of the aerofoil, and, rather curiously, perhaps, we find that the **shape** of the aerofoil makes little difference to the **Angle** at which this "Stalling" takes place, although it may affect considerably the amount of Lift obtained from the aerofoil at that angle.

Stalling

Now, what is the cause of this comparatively sudden breakdown of the Lift of an aerofoil? The student will be well advised to take the first available opportunity of watching, or trying for himself, some simple experiment to see what happens. Although, naturally, the best demonstrations can be given in wind tunnels with proper apparatus for the purpose, perfectly satisfactory experiments can be made by using paper or wooden model aerofoils and inserting them in any fairly steady flow of air or water, or moving them through air or water.

The movement of the fluid is emphasized by introducing wool streamers or cigarette smoke in the case of air and coloured streams in the case of water.

Contrary to what might be expected, **the relative speed at which the aerofoil moves through the fluid makes very little difference to the angle at which stalling takes place;** in fact, an aerofoil stalls at a certain angle, not at a certain speed. (It is not correct to talk about the "stalling speed" of an aerofoil, but it will be seen in a later chapter why we

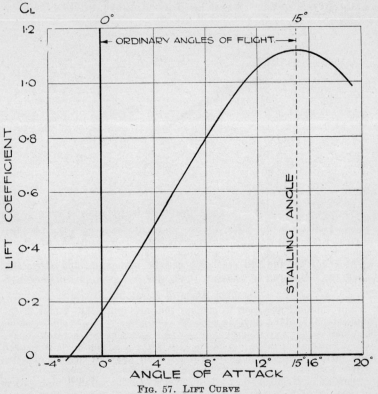

FIG. 57. LIFT CURVE

talk about the stalling speed of an **Aeroplane.**) Now, what happens? While the angle at which the aerofoil strikes the fluid is comparatively small, the fluid is deflected by the aerofoil, and the flow is said to be of a streamline and steady nature (compare Fig. 46); but suddenly, when the critical angle of about 15° is reached, there is a complete change in the nature of the flow, which becomes "**turbulent.**" The airflow breaks away from the top surface forming eddies or whirlpools similar to those behind a flat plate placed at right angles to the wind; there is no even downwash from the trailing edge, and therefore very little Lift due to the downward deflection of the fluid. Some experiments actually reveal the fact that the fluid which has flowed beneath the under-surface doubles back round the trailing edge and proceeds

to flow forward over the upper surface. In short, the streamline flow
has broken down, and what is called "burbling," or turbulence, has
taken its place, with consequent loss in Lift (Fig. 56).

Anyone who has steered a boat will be familiar with the same kind
of phenomenon when the rudder is put too far over, and yachtsmen also
experience "stalling" when their sails are set at too large an angle to
the relative wind. There are, in fact, many other examples of "stalling" in addition to that of the aerofoil.

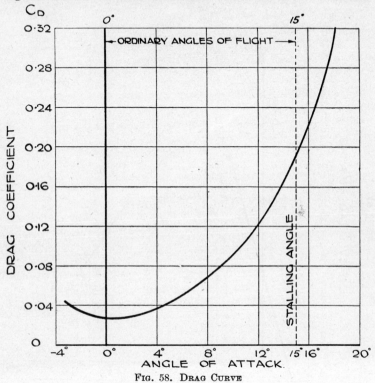

FIG. 58. DRAG CURVE

Perhaps this phenomenon of stalling is made even more clear if we
look once again at the results of Pressure Plotting experiments of Fig. 55.
We notice that up to the critical angles a considerable suction has been
built up over the top surface, especially near the Leading Edge, whereas
as soon as we reach the stalling angle the suction near the Leading
Edge completely disappears, and thus accounts for the loss in Lift,
because it will be noticed that after stalling the pressure on other parts
of the aerofoil remains much the same as before the critical angle. This
fact emphasizes the importance of the front portion of the aerofoil,
especially in connection with stalling.

Some students are apt to think that **all** the Lift disappears after
the critical angle; this, of course, is **not** so, as will be easily seen by
reference to either the Lift Curve or to the Pressure Plotting diagrams.

The aerofoil will, in fact, give a certain amount of Lift up to an angle of attack of 90°, but it is not usual to draw graphs much beyond the critical angle because, for reasons which will be given later, it is extremely difficult, though not impossible, to fly an aeroplane beyond this angle.

The **Stalling Angle**, then, is that Angle of Attack at which the **Lift of an aerofoil is a maximum, and beyond which the Lift will begin to decrease owing to the airflow becoming turbulent instead of streamline.**

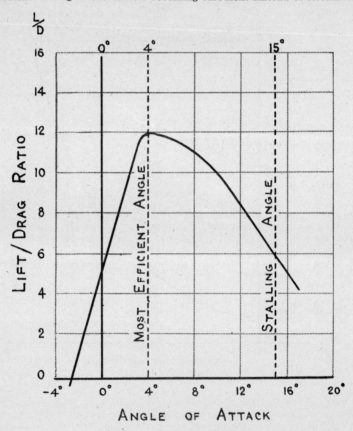

FIG. 59. LIFT/DRAG CURVE

The Drag Curve

Now for the **Drag Curve** (Fig. 58). Here we find much what we might expect. The Drag of the aerofoil is least at about 0° or $\frac{1}{2}$° Angle of Attack, and increases on both sides of this angle. Up to about 8°, however, the increase of Drag is not very rapid, then it gradually becomes more and more rapid, especially after the Stalling Angle when the airflow becomes turbulent.

The Lift/Drag Ratio Curve

Now we come to a very interesting curve (Fig. 59)—that which shows the **relation between the Lift and the Drag** at various Angles of Attack.

In a former paragraph we have come to the conclusion that we want as much Lift, but as little Drag, as it is possible to obtain from our aerofoil. Now from our Lift Curve we find that we will get most Lift at about 15°, from our Drag Curve we get least Drag at about 0°, but both of these are at the extreme range of possible angles, and at neither of them do we really get the best conditions for flight—namely, the **best Lift in comparison to the Drag**, or the **best Lift/Drag ratio.**

If the reader has available the Lift Curve and the Drag Curve for any aerofoil, he can easily plot the Lift/Drag curve for himself by reading the C_L off the Lift Curve at each angle and dividing it by the C_D obtained from the Drag Curve at the same angle. It should be noticed that it makes no difference whether we plot L/D or C_L/C_D, as both will give the same numerical value, since $L = C_L \cdot \frac{1}{2}\rho V^2 \cdot S$ and $D = C_D \cdot \frac{1}{2}\rho V^2 \cdot S$

Therefore $L/D = \dfrac{C_L \cdot \frac{1}{2}\rho V^2 \cdot S}{C_D \cdot \frac{1}{2}\rho V \cdot S} = C_L/C_D.$

We find that the Lift/Drag ratio increases very rapidly up to about 3° or 4°, at which angles the Lift is as much as 12 times the Drag (some aerofoils give a Lift of 16 to 20 times the Drag); the ratio then gradually falls off, because, although the Lift is still increasing, the Drag is increasing still more rapidly, until at the Stalling Angle the Lift may be only 5 or 6 times as great as the Drag, and after the Stalling Angle the ratio will fall still further until it reaches 0 at 90°.

The chief point of interest about this Lift/Drag curve is the fact that this ratio is greatest at an Angle of Attack of about 3° or 4°; in other words, it is at this angle that the aerofoil gives its best all-round results—i.e. it is most able to do what we chiefly require of it, namely to obtain as much Lift as possible consistent with a small Drag or Resistance. It is for this reason that, when an aerofoil is in level cruising flight, the wings will strike the air at about this angle, sometimes called the **Optimum** angle, rather than an angle of 15°, which would give the required Lift at a slow but uneconomical speed, or, say, $\frac{1}{2}°$, which would give the required Lift at a high but uneconomical speed. This explains why when an aeroplane is placed in "Rigging Position," for purposes of inspection or overhaul, the wings are inclined to the horizontal at 3° or 4°. This is the "Riggers' Angle of Incidence" and the aeroplane is in the attitude of normal level flight. When, however, the tail wheel is on the ground, the wings are inclined at 15° or 16°—the aeroplane is in the landing, or stalling, attitude. The modern tendency, especially on high-speed aircraft, is to set the wings for level flight at an angle less than that which gives the best L/D, but this is simply because the designer is out for speed rather than economy.

The Centre of Pressure Curve

Lastly, let us examine the curve (Fig. 60), which shows **how the Centre of Pressure moves** as the Angle of Attack of the aerofoil is increased.

This curve merely confirms what we have already learnt about the movement of the Centre of Pressure on an ordinary aerofoil. At

0° the Centre of Pressure is rather more than half-way back—i.e. 0·52 of the chord from Leading Edge to Trailing Edge; at 4° it is 0·4 of the chord back, and at 12° 0·28 of the chord back; in other words, the Centre of Pressure gradually moves forward as the angle is increased over the ordinary angles of flight. The curve shows that after 12° the Centre of Pressure begins to move back again, but this fact is not of great importance as these angles are not often employed in ordinary flight.

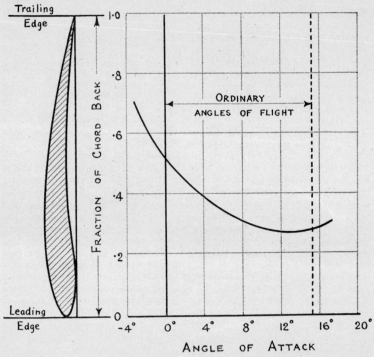

FIG. 60. CENTRE OF PRESSURE CURVE

The Ideal Aerofoil

These four curves will tell us all we want to know about any particular aerofoil; they give us the "characteristics" of the aerofoil.

What characteristics do we want in the ideal aerofoil? We cannot answer that question fully until a later stage, but briefly we may say that we need the following—

1. **A High Maximum Lift Coefficient.** In other words, the top part of our Lift Curve must be as high as possible. In our imaginary aerofoil it is only about 1·12, but we should like a maximum Lift Coefficient of 1·6 or even more. Why? Because we shall find that the higher the maximum Lift Coefficient which we can obtain from our aerofoil, the lower will be the Landing Speed of our aeroplane, and nothing perhaps will contribute more towards the safety of our aeroplane than that it shall land at a low speed.

2. A Low Minimum Drag Coefficient. In other words, the bottom part of our Drag Curve must be as low as possible. Why? This will mean that, as far at any rate as the wings are concerned, our aeroplane will have a low Resistance and will therefore be able to attain high speed, and it is by virtue of its high speed that the aeroplane has advantage over other means of transport; in fact, without high speed there is very little to be said for our aeroplane. It is important that the minimum Drag Coefficient should not only be low at a certain angle of attack, but that it should remain small over a large range of angles.

In addition to these first two characteristics we want a high value of $C_L$max./$C_D$min. This sounds very much the same thing as saying that we want a high $C_L$max. and a low $C_D$min. If we can find them both in the same aerofoil—yes. But it does not follow that an aerofoil which has a very high maximum C_L will have a good value of $C_L$max./$C_D$min., nor that one which has a low minimum C_D will have a high value of $C_L$max./$C_D$min. This is only another way of saying that neither an aerofoil which is most suitable for low speed, nor one that is most suitable for high speed, will give the best **range of speed.** We might almost call $C_L$max./$C_D$min. the "speed range factor." Our aerofoil gives a $C_L$max. of 1·12, $C_D$min. of 0·034, so the speed range factor is 1·12/0·034, i.e. about 33 (not at all a good value, as the reader will soon discover if he takes the trouble to work out the corresponding figure for the aerofoils given in Appendix I).

3. A Good Lift/Drag Ratio. This requirement must not be confused with that given above. $C_L$max. and $C_D$min. affect the extreme ends of the speed range, but the greatest value of C_L/C_D or, what comes to the same thing, L/D, concerns more the speeds and angles of **normal flight.** High Lift/Drag ratio spells efficiency, good weight-carrying capacity, less fuel consumption for distance covered, and less expense. At its best, our aerofoil shows a Lift of only about 12 times the Drag (see Fig. 59). A mere glance at the tables in Appendix I will show that this, too, is a very poor value—our aerofoil does not seem to have **any** of the characteristics of an ideal aerofoil.

4. A High Maximum Value of $C_L^{\frac{3}{2}}/C_D$. This sounds a little involved, and if the reader thinks it is getting beyond him he need not hesitate to skip this paragraph. From the design point of view it is important, but we are not all going to be designers. The Power required to propel an aeroplane is proportional to Resistance × Velocity, i.e. to DV. For an aeroplane of given Weight, the Lift for level flight must be constant (being equal to the Weight). If L is constant, D must vary inversely as L/D (or C_L/C_D). From the formula $L = C_L \cdot \frac{1}{2}\rho V^2 S$ it can be seen that if L, ρ and S are constant (a reasonable assumption), then V is inversely proportional to $\sqrt{C_L}$ (or $C_L^{\frac{1}{2}}$). Thus Power required is proportional to DV, which is inversely proportional to (C_L/C_D) × $C_L^{\frac{1}{2}}$, i.e. to $C_L^{\frac{3}{2}}/C_D$. In other words, the greater the value of $C_L^{\frac{3}{2}}/C_D$, the less the power required, and this is especially important from the point of view of climbing and staying in the air as long as possible on a given quantity of fuel. If the reader likes to work out the value of this fraction for different aerofoils at different angles, and then compares the best value of each aerofoil, he will be able to decide the best aerofoil from this point of view.

5. A Small Movement of Centre of Pressure. The Centre of Pressure of our aerofoil moves between 0·28 and 0·52 of the chord during ordinary flight; we would like to restrict this movement so as to improve our stability, and also because if we can rely upon the greatest pressures on the wing remaining in one fixed position we can further reduce the weight of the structure required to carry these pressures.

6. **Sufficient Depth to enable Good Spars to be Used.** Here we are up against an altogether different problem. Inside our aerofoil must run the spars, or other internal members, which provide the strength of the structure. Now the greater the depth of a spar, the less will be its weight

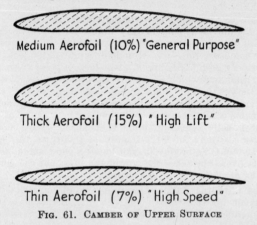

Medium Aerofoil (10%) "General Purpose"

Thick Aerofoil (15%) "High Lift"

Thin Aerofoil (7%) "High Speed"

FIG. 61. CAMBER OF UPPER SURFACE

for a given strength. We must therefore try to find aerofoils which are deep and which at the same time have good characteristics from the flight point of view.

Compromises

So much for the **ideal aerofoil.** Unfortunately, as in the case of most ideals, we find that no practical aerofoil will meet all our requirements. In fact, it is really worse than this, because in the attempt to improve an aerofoil from one of these points of view we usually find that we make it worse from other points of view, until we are forced either to go "all out" for one characteristic, such as maximum speed, or to take a happy mean of all the good qualities—in other words, to make a **compromise,** and all compromises are bad! It is perhaps well that we have introduced this word "compromise" at this stage, because **the more one understands about aeroplanes the more one realizes that an aeroplane is from beginning to end a compromise.** We want an aeroplane which will do this, we want an aeroplane which will do that; we cannot get an aeroplane which will do both this and that, therefore we make an aeroplane which will half do this and half do that—a "half and half affair," not a "regular right down aeroplane." And of all the compromises which go to make up **that final great compromise, the finished aeroplane,** the shape of the aerofoil is the first, and perhaps the greatest, compromise.

Camber

How can we alter our aerofoil in the attempt to obtain better results?

The main change which we can make is in the curvature, or **Camber,** of the top and bottom surfaces.

In the case of the **top surface** we find that a **large camber will give us good lift,** but high drag, and therefore low speed. Large camber also gives good depth for spars. For general use on monoplanes, the best

CONCAVE UNDER-SURFACE

FLAT UNDER-SURFACE

CONVEX UNDER-SURFACE

SYMMETRICAL AEROFOIL

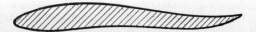

REFLEX CURVE NEAR TRAILING EDGE

FIG. 62. CAMBER OF LOWER SURFACE

top surface camber is probably about 11 per cent of the Chord, but for pure weight-carrying it may be much greater than this; while for high speed and for biplane sections it should not be more than 7 or 8 per cent of the Chord (Fig. 61). For all normal speeds, the position of greatest camber should be approximately one-third of the Chord back from the Leading Edge.

As regards the **under-surface**, alterations in camber have less effect. To get the best Lift a slightly concave camber is probably best, but convex cambers give room for deeper and therefore lighter spars and result in less movement of the Centre of Pressure. Some aerofoils are symmetrical—that is to say, the camber of the bottom surface is the same as that of the top, so that the aerofoil can be used either way up (Fig. 62).

High-speed Aerofoils

The attainment of really high speeds, speeds approaching that at which sound travels in air, is causing new problems in the design and in the flying of aeroplanes. Not the least of these problems is the shape of the aerofoil section.

Speed is a comparative quantity and the term "high speed" is often used rather vaguely; in fact, the problem changes considerably at the

FIG. 63. LAMINAR FLOW AEROFOIL SECTION

various stages of high speed. In general, we may say that we have so far been considering aerofoil sections that are suitable for speeds up to 200 or 300 m.p.h.—and while we must keep abreast of modern progress, we must also remember that while these speeds have been exceeded by a few aeroplanes they can hardly be considered as dawdling speeds for the majority of types. Furthermore all aeroplanes, however fast they may fly, must pass through this important region. At the other end of the scale are the speeds near and above the so-called "sonic" barrier, shall we say from 500 m.p.h. up to—well, what you will! The problems of such speeds will be dealt with in Chapter X. It will be noticed that there is a gap, from say 300 m.p.h. to 500 m.p.h., and this gap has certain problems of its own; among other things, **it is in this region of speeds that the so-called Laminar Flow aerofoil section has proved of most value.**

Laminar Flow Aerofoils

The significance of the Boundary Layer was explained in Chapter II. Research on the subject has led to the introduction of the Laminar Flow or Low Drag Aerofoil, so designed as to maintain laminar flow over as much of the surface as possible. By painting the wings with special chemicals the effect of turbulent flow in the boundary layer can be detected and so the transition point, where the flow changes from laminar to turbulent, can actually be found both on models and in full-scale flight. Experiments on these lines have led to the conclusion that **the Transition Point occurs where the air flow over the surface begins to slow down, in other words at or slightly behind the point of maximum suction.** So long as the velocity of airflow over the surface is increasing the flow in the boundary layer remains laminar, so it is necessary to maintain the increase over as much of the surface as possible. The aerofoil that has been evolved as a result of these researches (Fig. 63) **is thin, the leading edge is more pointed than in the conventional shape, the section is nearly symmetrical** and, most important of all, **the point of maximum camber is much further back than usual**, sometimes more than 50 per cent of the chord back.

The pressure distribution over these aerofoils is much more even, and the airflow is speeded up very gradually from the leading edge to the point of maximum camber.

There are, of course, snags—and quite a lot of them. It is one thing to design an aerofoil section that has the desirable characteristics at a small angle of attack, but what happens as the angle of attack is increased? As one would expect, the Transition Point moves rapidly forward! It has been found possible, however, to design some sections in which the low drag is maintained over a reasonable range of angles. Other difficulties are that the behaviour of these aerofoils near the stall

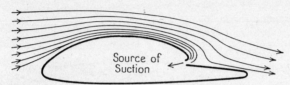

FIG. 64. THICK WING CONTROL OF BOUNDARY LAYER BY SUCTION

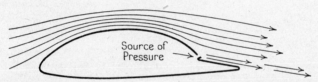

FIG. 65. THICK WING CONTROL OF BOUNDARY LAYER BY PRESSURE

is inferior to the conventional aerofoil and the value of C_L max. is low, so stalling speeds are high. Also, the thin wing is contrary to one of the characteristics we sought in the ideal aerofoil.

But by far the most serious problem has been that wings of this shape are very sensitive to slight changes of contour such as are within the tolerances usually allowed in manufacture. The slightest waviness of the surface, or even dust, or flies, or raindrops that may alight on the surface, especially near the leading edge—any one of these may be sufficient to cause the Transition Point to move right up to the position where the irregularity first occurs, thus causing all the boundary layer to become turbulent and the drag due to skin friction to be even greater than on the conventional aerofoil. This is a very serious matter, and has led to the tightening up of manufacturing and maintenance tolerances, and even to suggestions that it may become necessary to protect a wing by temporary covering during take-off during which it may be affected by dust, mud, flies, etc.

Another and more drastic method of controlling the Boundary Layer is to provide a source of suction near the trailing edge, with the object of "sucking the boundary layer away." This is not merely an idea—it has been tried, and it works, and it has the advantage that a much thicker wing section can be used (Fig. 64). The practical difficulty is in the power and weight involved in providing a suitable source of suction. A possible alternative, and maybe one easier to provide, is a discharge of air backwards from a similar position, thus "blowing away the boundary layer" (Fig. 65). It is rather curious that the decreases of pressure of the suction device, and the increases of pressure of the blast of air, can both be made to serve the same purpose.

Aspect Ratio

Up to the present we have only considered aerofoils from the point of view of their cross-section, and it is now necessary to find out the effect of altering the **plan form** of the aerofoil. Suppose we have a wing of 100 sq. ft. plan area, it may be of 20 ft. **span** and 5 ft. **chord**, or 25 ft. span and 4 ft. chord, or even 50 ft. span and 2 ft. chord. In each case the cross-section of the aerofoil may be the same, although, of

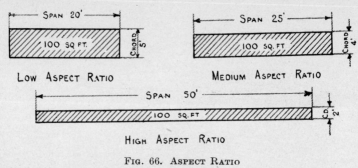

FIG. 66. ASPECT RATIO

course, to a different scale, depending on the chord. Now according to the conclusions at which we have already arrived, the Lift and Drag are both proportional to the Area of the Wing, and therefore since all of these wings have the same area they should all have the same Lift and Drag. Experiments, however, show that this is not exactly true and indicate a definite, though small, advantage to the wings with larger spans, both from the point of view of Lift and Lift/Drag ratio.

The ratio Span/Chord is called **Aspect Ratio** (Fig. 66), and the Aspect Ratios of those wings which we have mentioned are therefore 4, 6·25, and 25 respectively, and the last one, with its "high aspect ratio," gives the best results. Why? It is a long story, and some of it is beyond the scope of this book; but the reader has the right to ask for some sort of explanation of one of the most interesting and, in some ways, one of the most important, problems of flight. So here goes!

Induced Drag

Experiments with smoke or streamers show quite clearly that the air flowing over the top surface of a wing tends to flow **inwards** (Fig. 67). This is because the decreased pressure over the top surface is less than the pressure outside the wing tip. Below the under-surface, on the other hand, the air flows **outwards** (Fig. 67), because the pressure below the wing is greater than that outside the wing tip. Thus there is a continual spilling of the air round the wing tip, from the bottom surface to the top. Perhaps the simplest way of explaining why a high aspect ratio is better than a low one is to say that the higher the aspect ratio the less is the **proportion** of air which is thus spilt and so is ineffective in providing lift—the less there is of what is sometimes called "tip effect" or "end effect." Such an explanation is all right as far as it goes, but it is only a part of the story.

When the two airflows, from the top and bottom surfaces, meet at the trailing edge they are flowing at an angle to each other and cause eddies or **vortices** rotating clockwise (viewed from the rear) from the left wing, and anti-clockwise from the right wing. Apparently all the

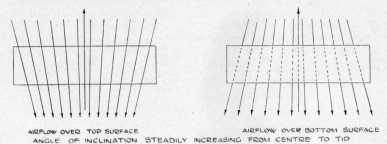

AIRFLOW OVER TOP SURFACE   AIRFLOW OVER BOTTOM SURFACE
ANGLE OF INCLINATION STEADILY INCREASING FROM CENTRE TO TIP

FIG. 67. THE CAUSE OF TRAILING VORTICES

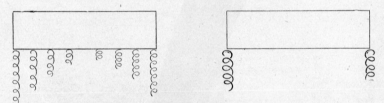

FIG. 68. TRAILING VORTICES WHICH BECOME WING-TIP
VORTICES

vortices on one side join up and form one large vortex which is shed from each wing tip (Fig. 68). These are called **Wing-tip Vortices.**

All this is happening every time and all the time an aeroplane is

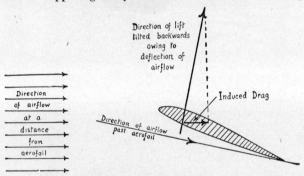

FIG. 69 INDUCED DRAG

flying, yet some pilots do not even know of the existence of such vortices. Perhaps it is just as well, perhaps it is a case of ignorance being bliss. In earlier editions of this book it was suggested that if only pilots could **see** the vortices, how they would talk about them! Well, by now most pilots **have seen** the vortices or, to be more correct

PLATE X.   WING-TIP VORTICES

This picture is remarkable in that it was taken from ground level, and shows visible vortices from the wing tips of a " Beaufighter " during a sharp pull up from a dive.   Notice how the vortices indicate the large angle of attack of the wings during the manoeuvre.

(By courtesy of " The Aeroplane.")

the central core of the vortex, which is made visible by the condensation of moisture caused by the decrease of pressure in the vortex (Plate X). These visible (and sometimes audible!) trails from the wing tips should not be confused with the vapour trails caused by condensation taking place in the exhaust gases at high altitudes (Plate XII).

PLATE XI. HIGH ASPECT RATIO
The Wien sailplane.
(*By courtesy of "Flight."*)

Now if you consider which way these vortices are rotating you will realize that there is an upward flow of air outside the span of the wing, and **a downward flow of air behind the trailing edge of the wing itself.** This downward flow must not be confused with the ordinary downwash. One difference is that the latter is always accompanied by a corresponding upwash in front of the aerofoil, so that the final direction of the airflow is unaffected. But in the case of the wing-tip vortices the corresponding upward flow is outside the wing span and not in front of it, so that **the net direction of flow past the wing is downwards.** Therefore the Lift—which is at right angles to the airflow—is slightly **backwards,** and thus contributes to what we call the Drag (Fig. 69). This part of the Drag is called **Induced Drag.**

In a sense, Induced Drag is **part of the Lift**; so long as we have Lift we must have Induced Drag, and we can never eliminate it altogether, however cleverly we design our wings. But **the greater the Aspect Ratio,** the less violent are the wing-tip vortices, and **the less will**

PLATE XII. EXHAUST TRAILS AT ALTITUDE

These trails are quite different from wing-tip vortices; they are caused by condensation of the water in the exhaust gases, and are only formed at certain heights when the temperature conditions are suitable.

(By courtesy of " The Aeroplane.")

be the Induced Drag. If we could imagine a wing of infinite aspect ratio, the air would flow over it without any inward or outward deflection, there would be no wing-tip vortices, no Induced Drag. (Clearly such a thing is impossible in practical flight, but it is interesting to note that an aerofoil in a wind tunnel may approximate to this state of affairs if it extends to the wind-tunnel walls at each side.) The best we can do in practical design is to make the Aspect Ratio as large as is practicable. Unfortunately a limit is soon reached—from the **structural** point of view. The greater the span, the greater must be the wing strength, the heavier must be the structure, and so eventually the greater weight of structure more than counterbalances the advantages gained. Again it is a question of compromise. In practice, Aspect Ratios vary from 6 to 1 up to about 10 to 1 for ordinary aeroplanes, but considerably higher values may be found on sailplanes, where aerodynamic, or "flight" efficiency must take precedence over all other considerations (see Plate XI).

All the theory of Induced Drag can be worked out mathematically (in fact Dr. Lanchester worked it out before the Wright Brothers flew), and experiment confirms the theoretical results. The full calculation involved would be out of place in a book of this kind, but the answer to it all is quite simple and the reader may like to know it, especially since it helps to give a clearer impression of the significance of this part of the Drag.

The coefficient of Induced Drag is found to be $C_L{}^2/\pi A$, where A is the Aspect Ratio and C_L the Lift Coefficient. This means that the actual Drag caused by the vortices is $C_L{}^2/\pi A$. $\frac{1}{2}\rho V^2 S$, but since the $\frac{1}{2}\rho V^2 S$ applies to all aerodynamic forces, it is sufficient to consider the significance of the coefficient, $C_L{}^2/\pi A$. In the first place, the fact that A is underneath in the fraction confirms our previous statement that the greater the Aspect Ratio, the less the Induced Drag; but it tells us even more than this, for it shows that it is a matter of simple proportion: if the Aspect Ratio is doubled, the Induced Drag is halved. The significance of the $C_L{}^2$ is perhaps not quite so easy to understand. C_L is large when the Angle of Attack is large, that is to say when the speed of the aircraft is low (this will be explained more clearly later); so the Induced Drag is relatively unimportant at high speed (probably less than 10 per cent of the total Drag), more important when climbing (when it becomes 20 per cent or more of the total Drag), and of great importance for taking off (when it may be as high as 70 per cent of the total Drag). In fact, the **Induced Drag is inversely proportional to the square of the speed,** whereas all the remainder of the Drag of an aeroplane is directly proportional to the square of the speed.

It is easy to work out simple examples on Induced Drag, e.g.—

A rectangular monoplane wing has a span of 50 ft. and chord of 8 ft. What is the Induced Drag Coefficient when the Lift Coefficient is 1·2 ?

$$\text{Aspect ratio} = A = 50/8 = 6·25$$

$$\text{Induced Drag Coefficient} = C_L{}^2/\pi A = 1·2^2/6·25\pi = 0·073$$

Perhaps this does not convey much to us, so let us work out the actual Drag involved, assuming that the speed corresponding to a C_L of 1·2 is 60 m.p.h. and that the air density is 0·0024 slugs per cub. ft.

$$\begin{aligned}\text{Induced Drag} &= (C_L{}^2/\pi A) \cdot \tfrac{1}{2}\rho V^2 S\\ &= 0·073 \times \tfrac{1}{2} \times 0·0024 \times 88^2 \times 400\\ &= 271 \text{ lb.}\end{aligned}$$

Let us take it even one step further and find the horse-power required to overcome this Induced Drag—

$$\text{H.P.} = D\,V/550 = 271 \times 88/550 = 43·4$$

These examples will help the reader to realize that Induced Drag
is something to be reckoned with; he is advised to work out for himself
similar examples, which will be found on pages 349 and 350.

Taper and Shape of Wing Tips

In addition to changes of aspect ratio, the plan form of the wing
may be tapered from centre to wing tip; this is often accompanied
by a taper in the depth of the aerofoil section (Fig. 70) and also by a
"wash-out," or decrease of angle of incidence, towards the wing tip.

Wing tapered in elevation.

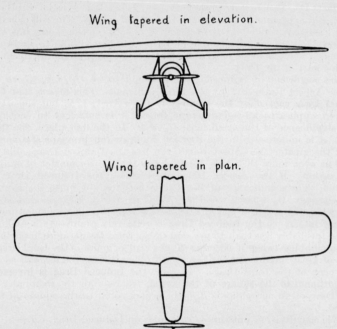

Wing tapered in plan.

FIG. 70. TAPERED WING

The tapered wing has advantages both from the structural and aerodynamic points of view, and has at last come into its own on modern
types of aeroplane. This is a feature in which we were slow to accept
the teachings of Nature, for the wings of most birds have a decided taper.
Where the chord is not constant along the span, the numerical value of
the Aspect Ratio is usually taken as the fraction Span²/Area.

Taper in plan form means a sweep-back of the leading edge, or a
sweep-forward of the trailing edge, or both. Considerable sweep-back
of the whole wing is sometimes used, but this is usually more for consideration of stability or for very high-speed flight, and discussion of the
problem from these points of view is deferred to later chapters.

The actual wing tip may be square, rounded, or "raked" either
backwards or forwards, but, within reason, such changes have very
little effect on the efficiency of the wing (Fig. 71).

PLATE XIII. A TYPICAL BIPLANE

The Gloster "Gladiator," perhaps the best of all the great biplane-fighter aircraft. Though obsolete as a fighter even before the Second World War, it played its part in other roles.

(*By courtesy of "Flight"*)

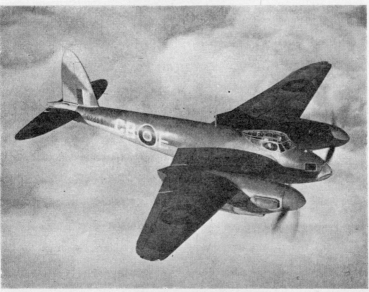

PLATE XIV. A TYPICAL MONOPLANE

The De Havilland "Mosquito." In its day the fastest military aircraft in the world, and one that to this day holds the record for versatility.

(*By courtesy of "The Aeroplane."*)

Monoplane versus Biplane

Up to the present we have not considered the possibility of placing one aerofoil above another in the manner in which they are used, or were used, in a biplane. The argument of monoplane versus biplane is as old as the achievement of heavier-than-air flight, and, until a few years ago, it still remained as undecided, and therefore as interesting, as it was when Langley produced the first successful flying machine, a monoplane; and the Wright brothers built the machine which first

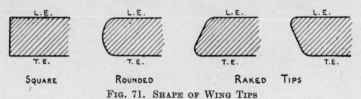

SQUARE   ROUNDED   RAKED TIPS

FIG. 71. SHAPE OF WING TIPS

flew, a biplane. During the first Great War this argument almost became a national one, the Germans, to a large extent, favouring the monoplane, which the British boycotted completely (following a rather hasty decision formed as the result of Army trials held a few months before that war).

Soon after the 1914–18 war, however, the monoplane again entered the field; between the two wars it slowly but surely gained ground,

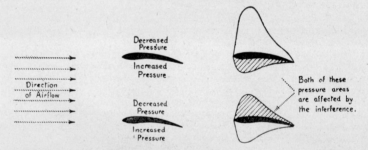

FIG. 72. BIPLANE EFFECT

and perhaps the second Great War decided its final victory. Of course, here again there is a wonderful opportunity for the profound believer that "Nature must know best," for when, he will ask, did you see a biplane bird? Be that as it may, naturalists claim that there are biplane insects.

The pros and cons of each type, monoplane and biplane, cannot be fully discussed at this point because we are at present only concerned with the effect **on the aerofoils** of putting one above another. From this point of view we will very soon find that the monoplane must be an easy winner, but there are many other considerations which have to be taken into account, such as manoeuvrability and the weight and rigidity of the structure, and when we come up against these we soon begin to find that the argument is by no means so one-sided as it at first appears. The erstwhile protagonists of the biplane still claim that the biplane was the better type until improvements in materials of construction, and the acceptance of higher wing loadings and higher landing speeds, made it possible to construct a monoplane that was comparable with a biplane in manoeuvrability.

Biplane Interference

If we place two aerofoils one above the other, as in Fig. 72, the region of higher pressure below the top aerofoil will be in close proximity to the region of decreased pressure above the bottom aerofoil, and it is hardly surprising to find that these two regions of different pressures tend, to a certain extent, to neutralize each other. Although the decrease in pressure above the top aerofoil remains practically unaffected, the increase in pressure below this aerofoil **is partially destroyed by the presence of the lower aerofoil,** and therefore the top aerofoil will lose some of its lift. Similarly, in the case of the lower aerofoil, while the bottom surface remains unaffected, **the decreased pressure on the top surface will be reduced by the presence of the upper aerofoil. Thus both aerofoils will lose Lift,** but it is the top surface which provides most of the Lift and **therefore it is the lower aerofoil** (since its top surface is affected) **which will suffer most by the combination.**

This interference between the two aerofoils is sometimes called "Biplane Effect."

Gap

The biplane enthusiast will, of course, try to find some means whereby he can reduce this interference between two super-imposed aerofoils. The most obvious line of attack is to increase the **Gap**—i.e. the distance between the two aerofoils—and so far to remove the regions of different pressures that they will no longer interfere one with another. This, as might be expected, has the desired effect, and eventually we find that the interference disappears altogether—but only when the Gap is about four times the Chord. Here, again, is the rub; for as we increase the Gap, with the avowed object of reducing interference and so increasing Lift, we increase also the lengths of struts and Wires and hence the weight and air resistance, and so we eventually defeat our own ends by obtaining more extra Weight than gain in Lift. It is another case of "swings and roundabouts," of "happy means"— another **compromise.**

Stagger

Thwarted at any rate in the full attainment of his desire to make two aerofoils as good as one, our biplane enthusiast has not yet exhausted his possibilities. He now tries the expedient of placing one aerofoil slightly in advance of the other. Such an arrangement is called **Stagger.**

If the top plane is in advance of the lower, it is called **Positive** or **Forward Stagger;** if behind the lower, **Negative** or **Backward Stagger.**

By staggering the aerofoils we separate the regions of increased and decreased pressure, and, as we might expect, we obtain better results owing to the decreased interference. We might think that the best results would be obtained from Backward Stagger, which appears to leave the important upper surface of the bottom plane free from interference. Here, however, our reasoning appears to lead us astray because

experiments quite definitely show that Forward Stagger gives the best results, and that Backward Stagger may actually do harm.

The good effect of Stagger from the point of view of the extra Lift obtained is not so great as has often been imagined, and **Stagger causes extra loads in the structure,** which means extra strength needed, and so **extra weight,** which may almost, if not quite, compensate for any increase in efficiency. Why, then, was stagger almost universally employed in biplanes? The answer is that the adoption of the staggered disposition of the two planes was of considerable help to the designer in solving the essentially practical, but none the less important, problems of easy access to cockpits and the angles of view of the pilot.

It cannot be too strongly impressed on the reader that **the field of view of the pilot is of the utmost importance,** that it has often been most seriously neglected, and that any improvement in efficiency in flight which means a sacrifice in the angles of view will probably be a step in the wrong direction.

Gap, stagger and other devices help, in a greater or less degree, to give "monoplane efficiency" to the biplane; if they do not altogether succeed we must remember that the chief advantages which used to be claimed by the biplane enthusiasts were **structural** ones, and therefore outside the scope of this book.

Variable Camber

Many attempts have been made to provide aerofoils with some kind of "variable camber" so that the pilot might be able to alter his aerofoil from a "high-lift" type to a "high-speed" type at will. Owing to the tremendous advantage to be gained by such a device, it is not surprising to find that much ingenuity has been expended, many patents have been taken out, and it is not easy to compare the rival merits of the various slots, flaps, slotted flaps and so on. Fig. 73 shows some of the devices with the increase in maximum lift claimed for each, but we must not take these figures as the only guide to the usefulness or otherwise of each device, because there are other points to be considered besides maximum lift. For instance, we may want an increase in drag as well as lift, the flaps acting as an "air brake," which may be useful in increasing the gliding angle (explained later). Another important consideration is the simplicity of the device; anything which needs complicated operating mechanism will probably mean more weight, more controls for the pilot to work, something more to go wrong. The modern aeroplane is already over-complicated, and, unfortunately, there seems to be every indication that it will become more and more so.

The column in Fig. 73 which gives values of the increase in the ratio of **maximum** C_L to **minimum** C_D gives some idea of the improvement in **speed range** of aircraft fitted with that type of variable camber, the maximum C_L representing the low speed and the minimum C_D the high speed. Speed range is, from many points of view, the most important quality sought in an aeroplane.

Flaps and Slots

The student of flight is apt to become bewildered by the mere multitude and variety of the contraptions which have been devised to improve the ordinary aerofoil. The pilot himself, for whose benefit they were invented, often wonders whether they have made flying any easier—they certainly have not made it simpler—the man on the ground, whether practical or theoretical, complains that he has been given much more to learn and understand. But the pilot must remember that although it may have been easy to fly the aircraft of even a few years back without these devices, **the same is not true of the latest modern aircraft, which would be both difficult and dangerous to fly without them.** To the man on the ground one can only say that it is his job to improve the aeroplane and that, as he does so, he must expect to find more and more complication.

But are these inventions really so complicated? Is it not more true to say that, considering the improvements that have been effected, most of the devices are extremely simple, both in principle and in practical operation? Perhaps it will help if we attempt to classify them. Nearly all of them can be classed as either **Slots** or **Flaps**—or a combination of the two.

Slots may be subdivided into—

(a) **Fixed slots.**

(b) **Controlled slots.**

(c) **Automatic slots.**

Flaps may be subdivided into—

(a) **Camber flaps.**

(b) **Split flaps.**

(c) **Slotted flaps.**

(d) **Lift flaps.**

(e) **Spoilers.**

We can also classify the effects of both slots and flaps on the characteristics of an aerofoil by saying that their use may cause one or more of the following—

(a) **Increase of Lift.**

(b) **Increase of Drag.**

(c) **Change of Stalling Angle.**

(At the moment we are not concerned with the corresponding results on the flight of the aeroplane—that can wait for a later chapter.)

Slots

Quite a fascinating book could be written on the history of slots. Like most histories, such a book would probably be highly coloured by the personal opinions of the author. There are those who have made most exaggerated claims for slots, there are others who have argued that slots were useless—except possibly to improve a specially bad aerofoil shape. Lawsuits have been fought on the subject, even international lawsuits. Such matters are altogether outside our province, but one aspect of the history should be known by all interested in aeronautical work; that is the changes which have taken place in the ideas as to the best ways of manipulating slots and the uses to which they may be put.

But first let us consider what a slot is—and what it does.

If a small auxiliary aerofoil, called a slat, is placed in front of the main aerofoil, with a suitable gap or slot in between the two (Plate XV), the maximum lift coefficient of the aerofoil may be increased by as much as 60 to 100 per cent (Fig. 74). What, perhaps, is even more

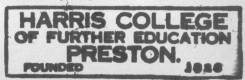

EFFECT OF VARIOUS LIFT INCREASING DEVICES, ON WING CHARACTERISTICS.		ANGLE OF ATTACK OF BASIC AEROFOIL AT MAX. LIFT	PERCENTAGE INCREASE IN MAX.LIFT OVER BASIC AEROFOIL	PERCENTAGE INCREASE IN $\frac{C_L \text{ MAX.}}{C_D \text{ MIN.}}$
	BASIC AEROFOIL	15°	–	–
	SIMPLE FLAP	12°	51%	51%
	SLOTTED FLAP	12°	53%	42%
	FRONT SLOT (AUTOMATIC)	28°	26%	35%
	FRONT SLOT AND SIMPLE FLAP	19°	69%	7 %
	FRONT SLOT AND SLOTTED FLAP	19°	75%	10%
	SPLIT FLAP	14°	70%	63%
	ZAP FLAP	13°	85%	77%
	FOWLER FLAP	15°	90%	83%

Fig. 73. Effects of Various Slot and Flap Devices

(*Note:* The values of $\frac{C_L\text{max.}}{C_D\text{min.}}$ given for the "front slot and simple flap" and "front slot and slotted flap" assume that the slot remains open even at small angles of attack, thus giving large drag. If automatic slots are used in conjunction with a simple flap or slotted flap the results in the last column would be much better, in fact superior to the simple flap, slotted flap or automatic slot used separately.)

PLATE XV. SLOTS

The DH. 108 on the ground, with slot clearly visible at the port wing tip.
This is an example of the use of slots on a modern aircraft to help overcome
the wing tip stalling which is characteristic of swept-back wings.

(By courtesy of the Associated Press Ltd.)

remarkable is that **the stalling angle may be increased from 15° to 25° or more** (Fig. 74).

The reason behind these results is clearly shown in Fig. 75. Stalling is caused by the breakdown of the steady streamline airflow which suddenly becomes turbulent. On a slotted wing the air flows through the gap in such a way as to keep the airflow smooth, following the contour of the surface of the aerofoil, and continuing to provide lift

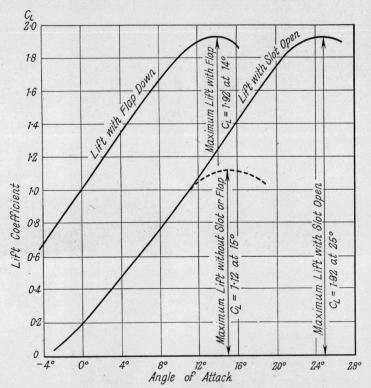

FIG. 74. EFFECT OF FLAPS AND SLOTS ON MAXIMUM LIFT COEFFICIENT AND STALLING ANGLE

until a much greater angle is reached. Numerous experiments confirm this conclusion.

The extra lift provided by the slotted wing enables us to obtain a lower landing speed or stalling speed, and this was the original idea behind it all. It was considered that if the slots were permanently open, i.e. **fixed slots,** the extra drag at high speed would be a greater disadvantage than the advantage gained by the extra lift at low speed, so most of the early slots in commercial use were **controlled slots,** that is to say, the slat could be moved backwards and forwards by a control mechanism attached to a lever in the cockpit; the slot could then be closed for high-speed flight and opened for low speeds. Rumour has it that it was because pilots complained that the slat was difficult to move into the forward position that experiments were made which revealed that, if left to itself, it would do so of its own accord. Be that as it may, **automatic slots** soon came into their own. In these the slat is moved by the action of the air pressure, i.e. by making use of that extraordinary forward and upward suction near the leading edge. Fig. 76 shows how the force on the slat inclines forward as the stalling angle is reached. The opening of the slot may be delayed or hastened by "vents" at the trailing or leading edge of the slat respectively

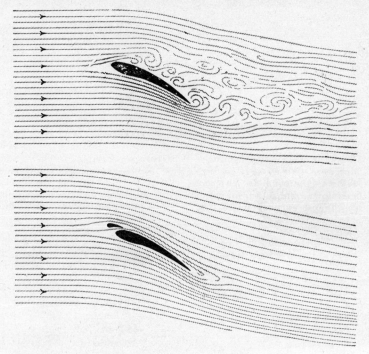

FIG. 75. EFFECT OF THE SLOT ON THE AIRFLOW OVER AN AEROFOIL
AT LARGE ANGLE OF ATTACK

(Fig. 77), and there may be some kind of spring or tensioning device to prevent juddering, which may be otherwise likely to occur.

Before leaving the subject of slots—for the time being, at any rate—there are a few interesting points which may be worth mentioning. First, **there has been some tendency,** particularly on American aircraft, **to return to the fixed slot.** If carefully concealed behind the front portion of the aerofoil, high speed is not seriously affected. Secondly, **slots are not very widely used on modern aircraft,** and, when they are, they are used more for stability and control than for their original purpose of decreasing landing speed. Thirdly, what might be called **the " slot idea " may be extended to other parts of the aircraft.** An early example of this was the "Townend Ring" in which a ring of aerofoil section, acting very like a slat, surrounded a radial engine and, by smoothing the airflow, considerably reduced the resistance. These, and other specially shaped cowlings serving the same purpose, are still in use. Similarly fillets may be used at exposed joints, and other awkward places, to prevent the airflow from becoming turbulent.

Flaps

The history of flaps is longer, and just as varied, as that of slots. The ordinary **camber flap** really works on the same principle as the

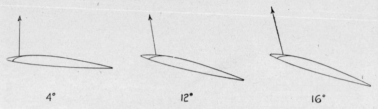

4°   12°   16°

FIG. 76. DIRECTION OF FORCE ON THE AUXILIARY AEROFOIL
AT VARYING ANGLES OF ATTACK

aileron or other control surface: it is truly a "variable camber." Such flaps were used as early as during the 1914–1918 war, and the original idea was the same as with slots, i.e. to decrease landing speed with flaps down, and retain maximum speed with flaps up. Their early use was almost exclusively for deck-landing purposes. It seemed at first

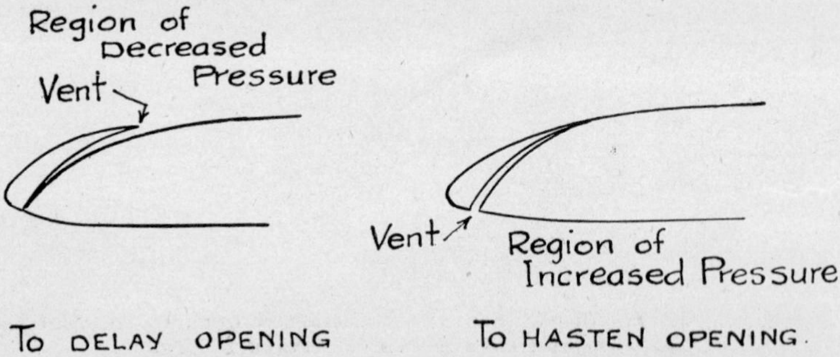

Region of
    Decreased
Vent   Pressure

Vent
Region of
Increased Pressure

To DELAY OPENING   To HASTEN OPENING.
FIG. 77. EFFECT OF VENTS ON OPENING OF SLOTS

as though the invention of slots, which followed a few years after that war, might sound the death-knell of flaps. Far from it—if anything it has been the other way round, especially in recent years, when flaps have become a necessity rather than a luxury on modern high-speed aircraft, while slots (except in the form of the slotted flap) are very rarely used on such aircraft. This is because flaps can do all that slots can do—and more—nor do they suffer from some of the disadvantages of the latter. **Flaps**, like slots, **can increase lift**—honours are about even in this respect. **Flaps can increase drag**—not, like slots, when it is not wanted, i.e. at high speed, but when it is wanted, i.e. at low speed. More than this, by using different degrees of flap angle, and different types of flap, pilot and designer can, to a large extent,

PLATE XVI. FLAPS

The flaps, in the lowered position, on the Avro "Athena II."
(*By courtesy of A. V. Roe & Co. Ltd.*)

PLATE XVII. AIR BRAKES OR SPOILERS

The dive brakes above and below the wing of the "Meteor IV."
(*By courtesy of the Gloster Aircraft Co. Ltd.*)

increase either lift or drag, or both, as and when they wish. But perhaps the greatest advantage of the flap over the slot is that whereas both, in a sense, increase the angle at which the stall occurs, the flap does it **without any increase in the angle of the main portion of the aerofoil.** (See Fig. 74.) Thus the flapped aircraft can fly slowly, and land slowly, at a reasonable attitude to the ground, whereas the slotted aircraft cannot take full advantage of its slots unless its nose is pointing high in the air even in horizontal flight, or for landing. This is clearly shown in Fig. 73; the aerofoils with front slots reach their maximum lift at angles from 19° to 28°, those with flaps from 12° to 15°.

Fig. 73 also gives some idea of the different types of flap. The simple flap, or **camber flap,** gives an increase of both Lift and Drag as it is lowered to about 50°, from 50° to 90° the Lift remains almost constant, while the Drag increases rapidly. The **slotted flap** has much the same characteristics, but, if there is also a front slot, the increase in Lift is greater and continues to a slightly greater angle. The **split flap** gives a greater increase of both Lift and Drag, but otherwise has much the same effects as a camber flap. The Zap flap (a modified type of split flap in which the hinge point moves back as the flap is lowered) is the same, only more so. The Fowler flap, and other similar types like the Gouge flap, are **Lift flaps,** that is to say the main intention and effect is to increase Lift. This they do by providing simultaneously a virtual increase in the wing area and in the wing camber.

The real **Spoiler,** or **Air Brake,** or **Dive Brake** is in a special category of its own, and need not necessarily be associated with the aerofoils. It may be used for various purposes on different types of aircraft; on a high-performance sailplane to spoil the Lift and increase the Drag and so enable it to get down at all; on a medium speed aeroplane to check the speed before turning or manoeuvring or after landing; on really high-speed aircraft to prevent the speed reaching the Critical Mach Number (see Chapter X). The spoiler usually consists of a flat plate, which need not be very large, either above or below the wings, or both above and below, and so arranged that it can be turned at right angles to the airflow.

If you understand aerofoils you have broken the back of the problem of flight—so test yourself with the following questions—

1. Why does an aerofoil provide a better lifting surface than a flat plate?

2. What is meant by the Lift and the Drag of an aerofoil?

3. What is "downwash"?

4. What is the "neutral lift line"?

5. Distinguish between the Angle of Attack and the Riggers' Angle of Incidence of an aerofoil.

6. Why is the Riggers' Angle of Incidence of an aeroplane wing usually in the neighbourhood of 3° or 4°?

7. What do we find out by pressure plotting over the surface of an aerofoil?

8. How does the pressure distribution over an aerofoil change as we increase the angle of attack from negative angles to beyond the stalling angle?

9. What is meant by the "Centre of Pressure" of an aerofoil?

10. What is an "unstable" movement of the Centre of Pressure?

11. Why is it more convenient to speak of the "Lift Coefficient" and "Drag Coefficient" rather than the Lift and Drag of an aerofoil?

12. What do you understand by the "Stalling Angle" of an aerofoil?

13. Sketch the airflow over an aerofoil (a) just before, and (b) just after the stalling angle.

14. What characteristics would we like to obtain in an ideal aerofoil?

15. What is a laminar flow aerofoil?

16. What is meant by the Transition Point?

17. What is meant by Aspect Ratio?

18. Explain how "wing-tip vortices" are formed.

19. What are the advantages and disadvantages of a high aspect ratio?

20. What is "Induced Drag"?

21. What is "Biplane Effect"?

22. What are the advantages of forward stagger?

23. What attempts have been made to increase the maximum Lift of an aerofoil?

24. Explain why an automatic slot opens when a certain angle of attack is reached.

25. What is a "Townend Ring"?

26. How do (a) Slots, and (b) Flaps, alter the characteristics of an aerofoil?

27. Classify the various types of slots and flaps.

28. What are the advantages of the flap over the slot?

Now try the numerical examples on aerofoils on page 345.

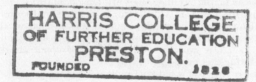

CHAPTER IV

THRUST

Introduction

IN Chapter II we made a study of Drag—the force that tries to hold the aeroplane back. In this chapter we shall deal with **Thrust**—the force that opposes Drag and keeps the aeroplane going forward. **In level flight the Thrust must be equal to the Drag, in order to accelerate the aeroplane it must be greater than the Drag, and in climbing it must also be greater than the Drag because it will have to support some proportion of the Weight.** The actual conditions of balance of the forces will be dealt with in the next chapter; it is sufficient at this stage to realize that we must provide the aeroplane with considerable Thrust, and that the performance that we can achieve from the aeroplane will be largely dependent upon the amount of Thrust that we can provide.

Methods of Providing Thrust

The motor car and the railway engine obtain their Thrust by the force on the circumference of the wheels pushing backwards on the road or rails; there is, or should be, no appreciable slip. The earth reacts by pushing forward on the vehicle. The ship, on the other hand, obtains Thrust by taking some of the water through which it travels, accelerating it and pushing it backwards at a higher velocity than that of the ship forwards. The method of the aeroplane corresponds more closely to that of the ship than that of the motor car or railway engine; once the aeroplane is clear of the ground, the only reasonable way of obtaining Thrust is to push air or something else, backwards and to rely on the reaction to push the aeroplane forwards. This is, in fact, what is done, and to save complication the same system is usually used while still on the ground although it must be admitted that it is not always a very efficient system for this purpose.

The Thrust-provider, of whatever kind it may be, must be supplied with energy. This will usually be in the form of **a fuel, which is fed into some kind of " engine " where, in burning, its chemical energy is changed into heat energy, which in turn is converted into the mechanical work done in propelling the aeroplane against the Drag.** Methods of providing Thrust differ only in the way in which these various conversions are effected, and in the efficiency of the conversion, that is to say in the proportion of useful work got out, or of Thrust provided, to the energy supplied.

The Engine

This is a book on Mechanics of Flight, and it would be out of place to go into any details of thermodynamics or aero-engines. When considering propulsion, however, it is difficult to know where to draw the line, and it is becoming even more difficult as speeds increase and new methods of providing Thrust are evolved. The propeller coupled to the reciprocating or piston engine has had a long innings—and it is not out yet. In this system, whether it be the fixed pitch propeller fitted to the simple 3- or 4-cylinder engine of the early days of flight, or

112

constant-speed variable-pitch contra-rotating propellers fitted to two-speed two-stage supercharged 24-cylinder engines of to-day, there is a clear-cut boundary line between engine and air-frame in the form of the propeller shaft. The propeller is a problem in mechanics of flight, an aerodynamic problem; the engine is a thermodynamic problem. But the probable eventual system of the future, the **athodyd,** is almost

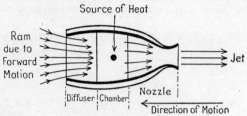

Fig. 78. Principle of the Athodyd or Ram-jet

entirely an aerodynamic problem; in a sense no engine is involved. The various jet and rocket systems of to-day come between the two extremes.

The Athodyd

Let us begin at the end, as it were, by considering for a moment the athodyd—or **aero-thermodynamic-duct** (a long name that is quite out of keeping with the extreme simplicity of the device). This is simply a duct, or tube, shaped possibly in the form of a venturi or other special shape, which faces the airflow caused by the motion of the aircraft through the air (Fig. 78). It relies on the forward speed, or ram effect (it is sometimes called a **ram-jet**) to collect and compress the air which then flows over some source of heat—the Germans actually tried a coal-burning brazier!—from which it gains energy and so flows out of the duct at a higher speed than that at which it entered. There are no moving parts, neither reciprocating nor rotary, no need for lubrication of any kind, nothing in fact except a tube, a source of heat and a fuel. Once the thing is going there will probably be sufficient heat generated to keep the fuel burning without even an ignition device or source of heat.

So simple. What's the snag?

Well, of course, there is one, and it is rather obvious. **The athodyd will only work when it is going,** and moreover it will only work really well when it is going rather fast, 1,000 m.p.h. or so! **It gives no thrust at all at no forward speed,** so we cannot start. The only hope for the athodyd, therefore, is to use an auxiliary means of propulsion, possibly rockets, for starting and for low speeds, and to rely on the athodyd when high speed has been obtained—this means, of course, a sacrifice of its greatest virtue, simplicity.

Athodyds are not just an impossible ideal. They do work, they have been tested in practice, and no doubt we shall hear more of them. The "motor" of the German V1 or flying bomb, was almost an athodyd though complicated somewhat by the use of shutters which made the combustion intermittent instead of continuous. The real point of introducing the athodyd at this stage is to show the tendency, which is towards what might be called an aerodynamic engine, or an engine that

is part of the aircraft and part of the subject of Mechanics of Flight
with all the same problems as those of the aircraft.

Jet Propulsion

It is but a step backwards from the athodyd to what is commonly
called "jet propulsion." The athodyd, of course, relies on jet propulsion,
nothing more nor less, and perhaps in its purest form; but so does a
rocket and so does a propeller; they are all jet propulsion, they all

PLATE XVIII. JET PROPULSION
The Avro "Tudor VIII" with four gas turbine jet propulsion engines.
(*By courtesy of A. V. Roe & Co. Ltd.*)

provide thrust by the reaction of throwing a jet backwards. It has
become conventional, however, and we must accept convention up to a
point, to think of jet propulsion in terms of the gas-turbine-cum-jet, or
what might deservedly be called the Whittle type of engine. Fig. 79
illustrates this system by means of a diagrammatic sketch. **The air is
collected, largely by ram effect as in the athodyd, compressed by a compressor or supercharger exactly as in a piston engine, fired and burned as
in all types of heat engine, it gains energy and momentum and flows out
faster than it came in, as in the athodyd.** The jet velocity is of the order
2,000 ft./sec. or about 1,400 m.p.h. On its way out it loses some of its
energy and momentum in driving the turbine, which in turn drives the
compressor which, etc., etc. This engine is simply an athodyd provided
with a means of producing Thrust—by the turbine and compressor—
when there is little or no forward speed. The rotary parts have, of
course, introduced a complication, though nothing to compare with a
modern reciprocating engine, and the whole engine is but a fraction of
the weight of a reciprocating engine giving the same power.

While this system is a little more like an engine than the athodyd, and while many problems of thermodynamics are involved, the ordinary jet engine is essentially a part of the aircraft. The flow through and over the engine, the effects of the flow on the blades of the turbine and compressor, the design of the nozzle through which the gases are ejected

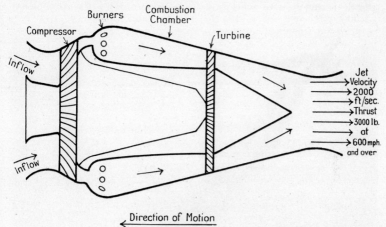

FIG. 79. PRINCIPLE OF JET PROPULSION

—all these are aerodynamic problems involving in particular a knowledge of high-speed flight, Mach Numbers, etc. (see Chapter X).

Rocket Propulsion

It is not easy to know where the rocket should come in this story. It differs from all the other forms of propulsion in that **it does not rely**

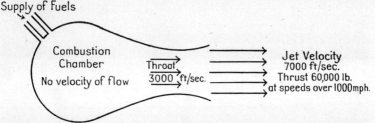

FIG. 80. PRINCIPLE OF ROCKET PROPULSION

on the air either to provide the oxygen for the combustion of the fuel, or to provide the mass which is thrown out backwards to produce the Thrust. For these reasons it is fundamentally uneconomical and, except for flights of very short duration, its most promising uses are as an auxiliary to other means of propulsion, as a means of testing research models at high speed, and for pilotless missiles such as the V2. It has, of course, the great advantage that **it needs no air in order to function, and so it can propel aircraft or missiles at great altitudes where the air is very thin and drag is very low, or even outside the atmosphere altogether** where there is no air and no drag—and no lift! It is the obvious means of propulsion for inter-planetary communication.

A machine gun, firing bullets backwards, is a form of rocket and an excellent illustration of the principle; but the usual method is to use the chemical reactions of two fuels, which may be solid or liquid, to create the heat, and to give energy to the gases formed by the combustion.

PLATE XIX. ROCKET PROPULSION

The Boeing B.47 Stratojet using some of its eighteen rockets which are
available for take-off or emergency power.
(*By courtesy of the Boeing Airplane Company and "The Aeroplane."*)

The gases are then ejected at high velocity through a duct again specially shaped rather like a venturi tube (Fig. 80).

In principle it is all very simple and the engine itself is light in weight, but it requires large quantities of fuel even for short durations and very high temperatures are involved in the combustion chambers. The external shape of the rocket type of "engine," and the internal flow, especially through the exit duct, are again aerodynamic problems, while the fuel combustion problem is largely chemical.

If and when the colossal energy of the atom is sufficiently tamed and harnessed to be put to practical use as a means of aircraft propulsion, it may well be that it will be used in the form of rockets. That, however far distant it may be, seems the only hope of reducing appreciably the weight of fuel required by rockets and so of increasing the duration of rocket flights.

Engine and Propeller Propulsion

Taking the final step backwards we come to the old and well-tried

PLATE XX. PROPELLER PROPULSION

The Avro "Lancastrian" with four Rolls Royce "Merlin" reciprocating engines driving Rotol propellers.
(*By courtesy of A. V. Roe & Co. Ltd.*)

system of a propeller driven by a heat engine (Fig. 81). Here there is the clear dividing line between the propeller and the engine. We shall consider the propeller in more detail later in this chapter. There are, of course, some problems of airflow even in a reciprocating engine, and we may often use **the ram effect of a forward-facing intake** as an aid to raising the pressure of the incoming air, just as we may use the **backward exhaust as a partial form of jet propulsion.** In the cooling system we may even emulate the athodyd by **collecting the air in ducts, using the otherwise wasted heat of the engine to give it energy, and ejecting it through a venturi tube**—another little bit of jet propulsion. Or, of course, the engine that drives the propeller may itself be a gas turbine, and in this case we can allot almost at will the proportion of the power that we take from the propeller and from the jet respectively; and we have all the advantages—and all the disadvantages—of the two systems.

The complications of the modern reciprocating engine, and of the modern propeller, are well known, nor is this the place to discuss them; what we ought to do at this stage is to try to form some idea of the relative merits of the various systems of providing thrust.

Thrust and Momentum

All these systems have the common feature that they provide Thrust by giving momentum to the air, or other gases. In accordance with the principles of mechanics (see Chapter I) the **amount of thrust provided will be equal to the rate at which momentum is given to the air.**

In symbols, **if m slugs is the mass of air affected per second,** and if it is given an extra velocity of v **feet per second** by the propulsion device, then the **momentum given to the air per second is mv,**

so $T = mv$.

Now clearly the same Thrust could be provided by a large M and a small v, or by a small m and a large V; in other words, by giving a

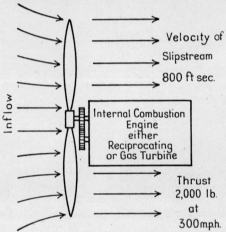

Velocity of Slipstream 800 ft sec.

Inflow

Internal Combustion Engine either Reciprocating or Gas Turbine

Thrust 2,000 lb. at 300 m.p.h.

FIG. 81. PRINCIPLE OF PROPELLER PROPULSION

large mass of air a small extra velocity or a small mass of air a large extra velocity. Which will work best in practice?

Well, let us work a step further in symbols and figures.

In speeding up the air to give it momentum, **we also give it energy** much of which is eventually wasted or dissipated into the surrounding air in the form of unnecessary and useless heat. **Whether we like it or not, we are bound to do the work to produce this wasted energy.** Now as we saw in Chapter I the **Kinetic energy of a mass of m slugs, moving at a velocity v ft./sec., is $\frac{1}{2}mv^2$ ft. lb.**

So while 1 slug given 10 ft./sec. has the same momentum, and therefore produces the same thrust, as 10 slugs given 1 ft./sec., the energy of the former is $\frac{1}{2} \times 1 \times 10^2 = 50$ ft. lb.

— and of the latter $\frac{1}{2} \times 10 \times 1^2 = 5$ ft. lb.

It is clear therefore that the latter will require less work and that there will be less waste of energy; **in other words, it will be more efficient than the former as a means of producing Thrust.**

From this point of view the propeller comes first because it throws back a large mass of air at comparatively low velocity, the jet engine comes next, and the rocket a bad third in that it throws back a very small mass at a very high velocity.

This, however, is not the whole story.

When the aeroplane is travelling through the air at a velocity of say V ft./sec. then, of course, the **propulsion device must add to this velocity** so as to give extra momentum to the air and so provide thrust. In other words, v ft./sec. will now be the **extra** velocity given to the air. Now it can be shown that the smaller the value of v/V, that is, the nearer the velocity of the backward stream to the velocity of the aircraft, the greater will be the efficiency.   On the other hand, for the system to

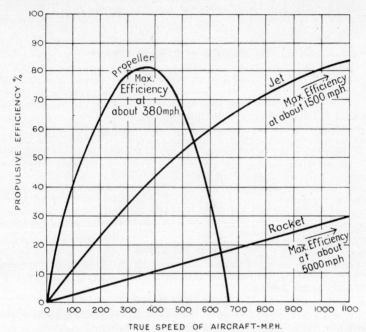

FIG. 82.   EFFICIENCY OF PROPULSION OF PROPELLER,
JET AND ROCKET

work at all, the velocity of the backward stream must be higher than that of the aircraft, so everything depends on the velocity at which we wish to fly and the velocity of the stream that is produced by the different means of propulsion.   **The jet system,** for instance, is inefficient at low speeds, particularly for take-off, etc., but **becomes more efficient as the speed of the aeroplane increases until it approaches the velocity of the jet.**   The same will apply to **rockets which become efficient at even higher speeds.**   The result is illustrated in Fig. 82.   It will be noticed that the jet system is as inefficient at 300 m.p.h. as the propeller is at 600 m.p.h.   It must not be forgotten, of course, that the 600 m.p.h. aeroplane must pass through the 300 m.p.h. stage—and even lower speeds for take-off and landing—while the 300 m.p.h. aeroplane will probably never approach 600 m.p.h.

A comparatively small point in regard to efficiency, but one perhaps worth mentioning, is that the ideal propulsive system should throw the air straight back without giving it any rotary or sideways motion.   In this respect the rocket comes first, with the jet a close second, and the propeller a bad third.

After so much talk of efficiency it is as well to remember that **efficiency is not everything!** We sometimes want value at all costs rather than value for money.

The Thrust given by a jet of constant velocity is almost independent of speed, while the Thrust of a propeller, especially if it is of fixed pitch, falls off badly both above and below a certain speed. It is Thrust that enables us to fly and gives us performance, and sometimes we may be more than willing to pay the price provided we get the Thrust.

The Propeller or Airscrew—Theory

Of the various systems of propulsion, the propeller or airscrew is still by far the most used and for many types of aircraft it is likely to be a long time in dying. We may see more and more gas turbines, rather than reciprocating engines, used for driving the propeller but that does not in any way affect the aerodynamic problems involved. It is right, therefore, that we should give brief consideration to those problems.

The subject will be treated from the practical viewpoint. The theory of airscrews is beyond the scope of this book, nor is it a necessary part of the training of pilots, ground engineers or even draughtsmen unless they are specially engaged on airscrew design work. The student who is particularly interested in the subject is advised to consult more advanced books. It will, however, help us if we understand the meaning of the terms that are used and some of the main considerations and problems in the design and practical use of airscrews. That is all we intend to give here.

Torque and Thrust

The object of the airscrew is to convert the **Torque,** or "turning effect," given by the power of the engine, into a straightforward pull, or push, called **Thrust.**

Tractor and Pusher

If the airscrew is in front of the engine it will cause tension in the airscrew shaft and will thus **pull** the aeroplane forward—such an airscrew is called a **Tractor.** If, on the other hand, it is behind the engine, it will **push** the aeroplane forward, and it is called a **Pusher,** or Propeller, It will be seen that, although the term "Propeller" is now used to apply to all kinds of airscrews, it should, strictly speaking, be applied only to those of the Pusher variety.

How it Works

Each part of a propeller blade has a cross-section similar to that of an aerofoil; in fact, in some cases exactly the same shape of section has been used for both purposes. The Thrust of the propeller is obtained by reason of the fact that the chord at each part of the blade is inclined at a small angle (similar to the Angle of Attack of an aerofoil) to its direction of motion. Since, however, the propeller is both rotating and going forward, the direction of the airflow against the blade will be at some such angle as is shown in Figs. 83 and 84. This will cause a Lift and Drag on the blade section, just as it does on an aerofoil, the Lift contributing towards the Thrust of the propeller and the Drag towards the Torque. Actually in a propeller we are not so much concerned with the forces perpendicular and parallel to the airflow, i.e.

PLATE XXI. PUSHER—OLD STYLE
Maurice Farman "Shorthorn," with pusher propeller.
(*By courtesy of " Flight."*)

PLATE XXII. PUSHER—NEW STYLE
The "Meteor IV."
(*By courtesy of the Gloster Aircraft Co. Ltd.*)

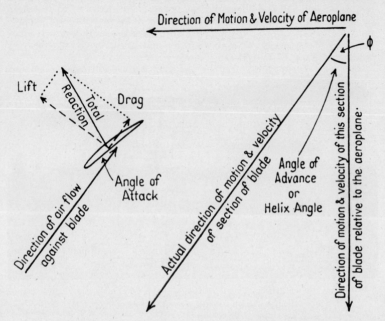

FIG. 83. MOTION OF A SECTION OF PROPELLER BLADE
Showing resolution of Total Reaction on Section into Lift and Drag.

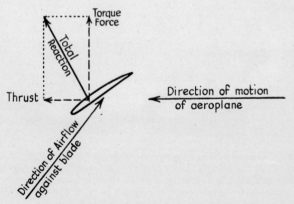

FIG. 84. MOTION OF A SECTION OF PROPELLER BLADE
Showing resolution of Total Reaction on Section into Thrust and
Torque Force.

Lift and Drag, as the forces acting along the axis of the aeroplane (which we will call the **Thrust Force**) and at right angles to the rotation (which we will call the **Torque Force**). So the total reaction on the blade must be resolved into Thrust and Torque Forces, as in Fig. 84. The difference between these and the Lift and Drag is clearly seen by comparing Figs. 83 and 84

The total Torque Force on the propeller blades will cause a turning

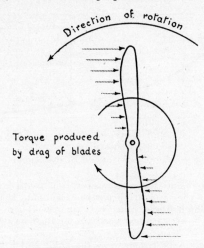

FIG. 85. PROPELLER TORQUE

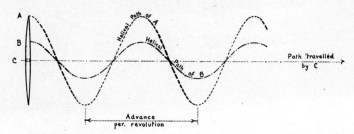

FIG. 86. HELICAL PATHS TRAVELLED BY VARIOUS SECTIONS
OF PROPELLER BLADE

moment or Torque which opposes the Engine Torque (Fig. 85), and also **tends to rotate the complete aeroplane in the opposite direction to that in which the propeller is revolving.** When the propeller is revolving at a steady number of revolutions per minute, then the **Propeller Torque and the Engine Torque will be exactly equal and opposite.**

Helix Angle and Blade Angle

Why is the theory of the propeller more involved than that of the aerofoil? Chiefly because the direction of motion is a helix instead of a straight line, and, what is more, every section of the propeller

blade travels on a different helix (Fig. 86). The angle (φ) between the
resultant direction of the airflow and the plane of rotation (Fig.
83) is called the **Angle of Advance** or **Helix Angle,** and it will, of course, be a
different angle for each section of the blade. The sections near the tip
will move on a helix of much greater diameter, and they will also move
at a much greater velocity than those near the boss.

Since all the sections must be set at a small **extra** angle to give the

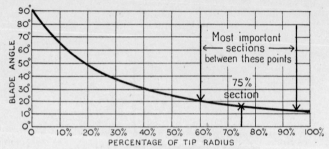

FIG. 87. VARIATION OF BLADE ANGLE

angle of attack, and since for maximum efficiency this extra angle should
be approximately the same at all parts of the blade, it is clear that the
Blade Angle, or **Pitch Angle,** must vary like the Helix Angle from boss
to tip. Fig. 87 shows a typical variation of Blade Angle for a modern
propeller.

The **Blade Angle** is best defined as **the angle which the chord of the**

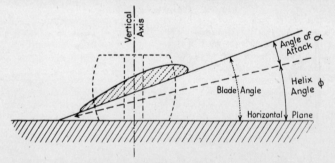

FIG. 88. BLADE ANGLE

propeller section at any particular place makes with the horizontal
plane when the propeller is laid flat on its boss on this horizontal plane,
its axis being vertical (Fig. 88). The under-surface of the section of
a propeller blade is very often flat, and this facilitates the placing of
a straightedge along the chord. The figure shows how the Blade Angle
is made up of the Helix Angle plus the Angle of Attack.

The Helix Angle may be likened to the slope of a hill. Suppose
there are several straight paths, each one of a different steepness, to
the top of a hill, and at a given moment a man starts from the bottom
of each and they all climb to the top in the same time (Fig. 89).

Obviously those who climb on the steeper paths will have a shorter distance to travel and therefore need not move so fast as those on the flatter paths. The steep paths correspond to the sections of the propeller blade which are near to the boss, and the flatter paths to those sections near the tips.

Imagine a section of the propeller blade which is at a distance r feet from the axis. If the propeller were to complete one revolution without travelling forward, then the distance moved by this section would be the circumference of a circle of radius r ft., i.e. $2\pi r$ ft. If, at the same time, the propeller were to move forward a distance of p ft.,

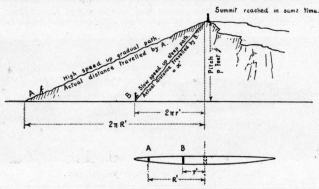

FIG. 89. ANALOGY BETWEEN THE PATHS TRAVELLED BY DIFFERENT SECTIONS OF A PROPELLER BLADE AND PATHS OF VARYING STEEPNESS TO THE SUMMIT OF A HILL

then the actual spiral distance moved by this particular section would correspond to the hypotenuse of a right-angled triangle of which the other sides were $2\pi r$ ft. and p ft.; in other words, it would be the actual length of path x ft. traversed by a man climbing a hill p ft. high, the horizontal base being $2\pi r$ ft. (see Fig. 89).

Now, in the case of an ordinary mechanical screw, the distance moved forward in one revolution is a fixed quantity, and is called the Pitch of the screw. In our analogy to the hill the Pitch corresponds to the height of the hill—i.e. p ft.—and if $\phi°$ is the slope or Helix Angle, $\tan \phi = p/2\pi r$. Therefore $p = 2\pi r \tan \phi$.

In this example we have worked in distances rather than velocities, but since the blade section moves forward (p ft.) and round ($2\pi r$ ft.) in exactly the same time, the corresponding velocities are V, the forward speed, and $2\pi r n$ the circumferential speed if n is the number of revolutions per second. So $p/2\pi r$ is the same value as $\dfrac{V}{2\pi r n}$ and we can therefore write $\tan \phi = \dfrac{V}{2\pi r n}$.

Advance per Revolution

But, in the case of a propeller, the Blade Angle at each section is greater than the Helix Angle and, what is more important, the distance moved forward in one revolution (called the **Advance per Revolution**) **is not by any means a fixed quantity,** as it depends entirely on the forward speed of the aeroplane.

For instance, if an aeroplane is moving forward at 100 ft. per sec. and the propeller is making 1,200 r.p.m.—i.e. 20 revs. per sec.—then the Advance per Revolution will be $\dfrac{100}{20} = 5$ ft. But the same aeroplane may move forward at 80 ft. per sec., and yet the revolutions per minute of the propeller may still remain at 1,200, the Advance per Revolution being only 4 ft.; while when the engine is run up on the ground and there is no forward motion, the Advance per Revolution will obviously be 0.

It would, therefore, be absurd to adopt the definition of pitch which is used for an ordinary screw, since the Advance per Revolution is a variable quantity and does not in any way represent the characteristic

PLATE XXIII. FIXED-PITCH PROPELLER
Two-blader, with very large pitch angle, as used in the Schneider Trophy
Contest, 1931.
(*By courtesy of The Fairey Aviation Co., Ltd.*)

of a particular propeller. Another difficulty is that nearly all modern propellers have variable blade angles, and therefore the pitch also is a variable quantity. But let us forget this problem of variable pitch for a moment and consider only the fixed pitch propeller. This will serve to give us a clearer understanding of the meaning of the various terms, and then it is comparatively simple to understand the advantages and problems of variable pitch propellers.

Now, if the angle of a blade section (of a fixed pitch propeller) at a radius of r ft. is $\theta°$, and if this particular blade section were to move parallel to its chord—i.e. so that its angle of attack was 0°, making the Helix Angle the same as the Blade Angle, i.e. $\theta°$—while at the same time it made one complete revolution, then the distance travelled forward, p ft., would be a definite quantity and would correspond to the pitch of the ordinary screw, the relation $p = 2\pi r \tan \theta$ being true. This is best seen graphically by setting off the blade angle θ from the distance $2\pi r$ drawn horizontally, p being the vertical height. If the same operation is carried out at different distances from the axis of the propeller (Fig. 90), it will be found that the value of p is practically the same for all sections of the blade, since as the radius r increases there is a corresponding decrease in the blade angle θ, and $2\pi r \tan \theta$ remains constant.

Geometric Pitch

This quantity p is called the **Geometric Pitch** of the Propeller, since it depends only on its geometric dimensions and not on its actual performance. The student who has access to either model or full-size propellers will find it an instructive exercise to carry out this operation for himself by measuring the pitch angle at two or three parts of the blade, and then either by calculation or drawing finding the value of $2\pi r \tan \theta$; this should come to the same value in each case. If a large variation is found in the value of p, then the blades have become twisted and the propeller is unfit for use. Propellers are sometimes designed so that the Geometric Pitch is not exactly constant throughout the blade, in which cases the pitch is taken at two-thirds, or three-quarters

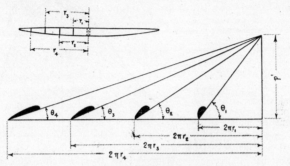

FIG. 90. GEOMETRIC PITCH

of the distance from boss to tip, and this value is used as the Geometric Pitch, and is sometimes called the Geometric Mean Pitch. The actual value of the Geometric Pitch of a fixed pitch propeller may vary from about 3 ft. for a slow type of aeroplane to the 16 or 20 ft. that was used on Schneider Trophy and other racing aircraft.

Experimental Mean Pitch

The designer of a propeller may find it convenient to consider the pitch from a totally different viewpoint. When the Advance per Revolution reaches a certain value, the Thrust will become zero, the reason being that the Angle of Attack of each part of the blade has become so small that the aerofoil section of the blade provides no Thrust. (Notice how this corresponds to the small negative angle at which an aerofoil ceases to give Lift.) The **Experimental Mean Pitch** is defined as **the distance the propeller will move forward in one revolution when it is giving no Thrust.**

Thus, in effect, when a propeller is advancing in each revolution a distance equal to the Experimental Pitch, the Angle of Attack of the blades on the air will be slightly negative; when, on the other hand, the distance advanced per revolution is equal to the Geometric Pitch, the Angle of Attack will be 0°. Therefore, as a general rule, **the Experimental Pitch will be slightly greater than the Geometric Pitch,** although there can be no direct relationship between the two values since the former depends entirely on the characteristics of the aerofoil sections of which the propeller is composed.

Variation of Thrust and Torque Along Blade

However much we try to get the best out of each part of the propeller blade it is evident that there will be losses both near the boss and near

the tip. At the boss the sections must be thick to provide strength, and
the flow of air through these sections will be seriously affected by the
engine behind—still more if the engine is in front as in a pusher. At the
tip there will be the vortices and induced drag as on a wing, and also
compressibility effects which will be explained later. The result of all
this is that only a small proportion of the propeller blade is really
effective and both Thrust and Torque vary along the blade, as illustrated
in Fig. 91. This figure shows clearly why it is that we consider the

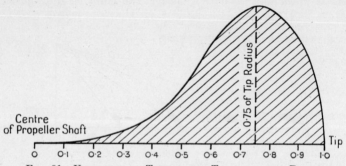

FIG. 91. VARIATION OF THRUST AND TORQUE ALONG BLADE

sections of the blade at between two-thirds and three-quarters of the
radius as the most important sections.

Efficiency

Now the **Efficiency** of a propeller, like the Efficiency of anything else,
is the ratio of the useful work given out by the propeller to the work
put into it by the engine. Mechanical work done is measured by the
Force multiplied by the Distance moved, and therefore when either the
Force or the Distance is zero, the useful work done will be zero and the
Efficiency will be nil. Thus when the propeller is moving forward in
each revolution a distance equal to the Experimental Pitch, the fact
that there is no Thrust will mean that there is no Efficiency. Further,
when there is no forward speed, there will be no distance moved, no
work done, and therefore no Efficiency. **Between these two extremes
will be the normal conditions of flight.**

The object of the propeller is to give the maximum Thrust (T) with
the minimum Torque (Q), in other words to give the maximum T/Q
ratio. An examination of Figs. 83 and 84 will make it clear that in
order to get a high value of T/Q two things are required—a high value
of L/D (this alone is not enough) and a small Helix Angle. The high
value of L/D is fairly easy, and is at least an old problem. What we
need is a good aerofoil section (old favourites like R.A.F.6 and Clark Y
have been used for years), set at the correct small angle, which means a
twisting of the blade as already explained. But when it comes to providing a small Helix Angle, the problem is very different—a small
Helix Angle implies a low forward speed of the aeroplane and a high
speed of the propeller tip. One might almost say "What a hope!"
Everything else is against the high tip speed, and certainly there is not
much future in trying to reduce the forward speeds of aeroplanes.

Under conditions of maximum efficiency the Advance per Revolution is usually considerably less than the Experimental Pitch; in fact, in some senses it may be said that the Experimental Pitch represents the "ideal" pitch, while the Advance per Revolution is the actual "practical" pitch. The difference between the two is called the Slip, and is usually expressed as a percentage. For instance, suppose the Experimental Pitch of a certain propeller is 10 ft. and the actual Advance per Revolution under certain conditions is 7 ft., then the Slip is 3 ft., or 30 per cent.

From the argument which has been followed it should be clear that the existence of Slip is necessary if there is to be any Thrust or Efficiency, since when the Slip is zero the advance per revolution is equal to the Experimental Pitch, and this is a condition of zero Thrust and Efficiency.

Slip and Efficiency

It is sometimes stated that when the Slip is 30 per cent the Efficiency must be 70 per cent. This, however, is not correct, since this 70 per cent is merely a ratio of Distances, whereas Efficiency is a ratio of Work done, i.e. it is concerned with Force as well as Distance.

If the total Drag of an aeroplane at 200 ft. per sec. is 1,000 lb., and the Power developed by the Engine when the aeroplane is flying at this speed is 450 Brake Horse Power—

Then Work given to propeller per minute $= 450 \times 33,000$ ft. lb.

and Work done by propeller per minute $= 1000 \times 200 \times 60$ ft. lb.

$$\therefore \text{ Efficiency of the propeller} = \frac{\text{Work got out}}{\text{Work put in}} \times 100 \text{ per cent}$$

$$= \frac{1000 \times 200 \times 60}{450 \times 33000} \times 100 \text{ per cent}$$

$$= 80 \cdot 8 \text{ per cent}$$

This represents the approximate value of the Efficiency obtainable from a good propeller, although in some instances it may rise as high as 85 or even 90 per cent. The best Efficiency is obtained when the slip is of the order of 30 per cent.

For those who prefer to examine this question in terms of mathematical symbols the Efficiency of a propeller can be deduced as follows—

Let $V =$ Forward velocity in ft. per sec.,

$\quad T =$ Thrust of propeller in lb.,

$\quad N =$ Revolutions per minute of Engine,

$\quad Q =$ Torque exerted by Engine in lb. ft.

Work done by Thrust T at V ft. per sec. $= TV$ ft. lb. per sec.

$$= 60 \ TV \text{ ft. lb. per min.}$$

Work given by Engine $= 2\pi Q$ ft. lb. per rev.

$$= 2\pi NQ \text{ ft. lb. per min.}$$

$$\therefore \text{ Efficiency of Propeller} = \frac{60TV}{2\pi NQ} \times 100 \text{ per cent}$$

If the Brake Horse Power of the Engine is given, then from the well-known formula

$$\text{B.H.P.} = \frac{2\pi N Q}{33000}$$

we can find the Engine Torque Q, or, instead of $2\pi N Q$ in the Efficiency formula, we can substitute the value $33{,}000 \times \text{B.H.P.}$

Efficiency at Different Forward Speeds

For low-speed aeroplanes the Thrust of a fixed pitch propeller is usually found to be greatest when there is no forward speed, i.e. when the aeroplane is stationary on the ground. The Thrust developed under these conditions is called the **Static Thrust,** and its large value is very useful since it serves to give the aeroplane a good acceleration when starting from rest and thus reduces the run required for taking off.

In modern high-speed machines, a fixed pitch propeller designed for maximum speed would have such a large pitch, and, therefore, such steep pitch angles, that some portions of the blades would strike the air at angles of as much as 70° or more when there is no forward speed. On such propellers the Efficiency and Static Thrust would be very poor, and great difficulty would be experienced in taking off. The only remedy is some kind of variable pitch propeller.

The speed reached when the Thrust eventually becomes zero at the high speed end of the range will be above the speeds of normal flight, and it is only likely to be reached when the aeroplane is diving with the engine on. If the aeroplane is dived at still higher speeds, the Thrust will become negative, i.e. the propeller will cause a Drag on the aeroplane in spite of the fact that the engine is running at its maximum revolutions per minute.

Between the two extremes of low and high forward speeds the efficiency of the propeller varies in accordance with Fig. 82. This shows how the propeller is only really efficient over a comparatively small range of speeds—what is perhaps rather surprising is how efficient it is over that range.

Tip Speed

The power developed by an engine depends upon the pressures attained during combustion in the cylinders and on the revolutions per minute. The greatest power in most engines is developed at a fairly high number of revolutions per minute; and if the propeller rotates at the same speed as the engine crankshaft, the **tip speed** of the propeller blades **is liable to approach or exceed the speed of sound** (about 1,100 ft. per second in air at ground level, and less at higher altitudes). This causes compressibility effects (see Chapter X), which, in turn, mean an increase in Torque and decrease in Thrust; in other words, a loss of efficiency. It is clearly of little purpose to design an engine to give high power, if at such power the propeller is to become less efficient and so transfer a lower proportion of the engine power to the aircraft. In the early stages of compressibility some improvement can be effected by changing the blade section near the tip to a thin laminar-flow type and by washing out the blade angle slightly; if this is done the loss is not serious so long as the actual speed of the tip does not exceed the speed of sound. As a further help a reduction gear is often introduced between the engine crankshaft and the propeller; the reduction is not usually very large, perhaps 0·7 or 0·8 to 1, but is just sufficient to reduce the tip speed to a reasonable margin below the speed of sound.

The tip speed, of course, depends not only on the revolutions per minute, but also on the forward speed of the aeroplane and the diameter of the propeller. The high forward speed of modern aeroplanes is such that it is becoming very difficult to keep the tip speed down below the speed of sound, and it would seem that at forward speeds of 400 m.p.h. or more, some loss in efficiency must be accepted. At 500 m.p.h. the loss in efficiency has become serious and has spread to a larger proportion of the propeller blades so that it affects not only the tips but what should be the most efficient sections. At this stage there is nothing for it but for the propeller to retire gracefully and hand over supremacy to jet propulsion.

A further objection to high tip speed is that the noise caused by the propeller (incidentally a large proportion of the total noise caused by the complete aircraft and engine) is much intensified, especially in the plane in which the propeller is rotating.

Variable Pitch

For some time the extra weight and complication of any type of variable pitch propeller was regarded with disfavour by most aircraft designers, and the relative merits of fixed pitch and variable pitch were much disputed. One aspect of the problem soon settled the matter and that was the Static Thrust mentioned above. What had been a doubtful luxury became a necessity for really high-speed aircraft. It will be noticed that what was required was a propeller that would be efficient at two extremes, at the maximum speed of flight and at the low forward speeds required for taking off. In other words, a **two-pitch propeller** was all that was really needed; it was hardly necessary to have one with pitch that was infinitely variable over a wide range. Thus the problem was simplified, and the two-pitch controllable airscrew came into its own. In this type the "fine-pitch" setting was used for taking off, and when in the air the pilot pushed a lever and the propeller automatically went into "coarse pitch." The more modern type is the **constant-speed propeller** in which the pitch is automatically adjusted so that the propeller revolves at a given rate decided by the pilot, and remains at that rate irrespective of throttle opening or the manoeuvres of the aeroplane. Thus engine and propeller can work at their best efficiency irrespective of conditions, such as take-off, climb, maximum speed, altitude, and so on.

An extension of the idea of variable pitch leads to a propeller with the pitch variable not only over the range of blade angles that will be required for normal conditions of flight but beyond these angles in both directions.

If the blade can be turned beyond the normal fully-coarse position until the chord lies along the direction of flight, thus offering the minimum resistance, the propeller is said to be **feathered.** This condition is very useful on a multi-engined aircraft for reducing the drag of the propeller on an engine that is out of action. It has another advantage too in that it is a convenient method of stopping the propeller and so preventing it from "windmilling"; this will reduce the risk of further damage to an engine that is already damaged.

The turning of the blade beyond the fully-fine position makes the propeller into an effective **air brake ;** it has exactly the opposite effect of feathering by causing the maximum drag, which occurs when the Blade Angle is approximately 2° or 3°. Fig. 92B shows what is happening when a propeller is windmilling. The Helix Angle is now greater than

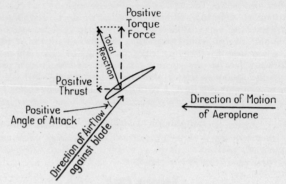

FIG. 92A. CONDITIONS OF NORMAL FLIGHT

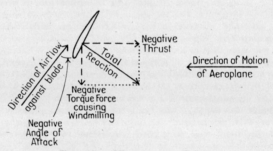

FIG. 92B. WINDMILLING BRAKE

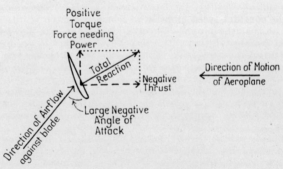

FIG. 92C. POWER-ON BRAKE

the Blade Angle, the Angle of Attack is negative and the airflow strikes the wrong side of the aerofoil section causing negative Thrust, i.e. Drag and negative Torque Force. The negative Torque Force is important in that it means that the propeller is driving the engine and at certain angles through which the blade must pass dangerously high r.p.m. may be reached. This prevents us from using the angles of maximum drag and the best we can do is to go beyond them to a setting of about 0°; if the pitch change is done sufficiently rapidly the inertia of the propeller will prevent overspeeding.

If the blade angle is still further reduced, i.e. to negative angles (Fig. 92c), the propeller can be used as a brake in another way. Notice that while the Thrust is still negative, the Torque Force is now in the same direction as usual, that is to say the propeller will no longer windmill of its own accord—if left to itself it would windmill backwards—and the engine must be used to drive it. This produces an **excellent brake for use in slowing up the aeroplane after landing** since it gives a high negative thrust at low forward speeds.

Diameter of Propeller

There are many factors which influence the choice of **Diameter** for a propeller, such as—

1. The necessary clearance above the ground or water to prevent accidental damage to the propeller tips, and clearance from the fuselage and other propellers in multi-engined aircraft.

2. The strength of the blades against bending and the centrifugal force.

3. The presence of a large fuselage or other bodies immediately behind the propeller.

4. The efficiency of the propeller itself.

Of these, the first two considerations definitely limit the diameter which can be employed, while the last two seem to demand as large a diameter as possible, except for the problem of tip speed, which has already been discussed.

When all four considerations are taken into account the question becomes very involved, and it must suffice to say that the first is usually the deciding factor, at any rate on small aircraft.

Number and Shape of Blades

The propeller must be able to absorb the power given to it by the engine; that is to say, it must have a resisting Torque to balance the engine Torque, otherwise it will race, and both propeller and engine will become inefficient.

The climbing conditions are particularly difficult to satisfy since high power is being used at low forward speeds; and if we do satisfy these conditions—by any of the methods suggested below—it will be difficult to get efficiency in high-speed flight. Thus the propeller becomes a compromise like so many things in an aeroplane.

The ability of the propeller to absorb power may be increased by—

1. Increasing the blade angle and thus the angle of attack of the blades.

2. Increasing the length of the blades, and thus the diameter of the propeller.

3. Increasing the revolutions per minute of the propeller.

4. Increasing the camber of the aerofoil section of which the blade is made.

5. Increasing the chord (or width) of the blades.

6. Increasing the number of the blades.

With so many possibilities one might think that this was an easy problem to solve, but in reality it is one that has caused considerable difficulty. Why this is so soon becomes clear if we consider the various possibilities in turn. First, the blade angle should be such that the angle of attack is that giving maximum efficiency; there is, therefore, little point in trying to absorb more power if, in so doing, we lose efficiency. The second possibility has already been covered; the propeller designer would like a large diameter, in other words, a large aspect ratio for the blades, but quite apart from the bogey of tip speed,

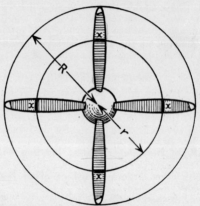

FIG. 93. SOLIDITY OF A PROPELLER

Solidity $= 4x/2\pi r$.

the aeroplane designer will probably not allow him to spread himself! The third, too, has been covered: it would mean high tip speed and consequent loss of efficiency. The fourth, as in the case of aerofoils, would simply mean a less efficient section; it would seem, too, that we must face even thinner aerofoil sections to avoid loss of efficiency at high speed. So we are left with the last two, and fortunately they provide some hope. Either will result in an increase in what is called the **solidity** of the propeller. This really means the ratio between that part of the propeller disc which, when viewed from the front, is solid and the part which is just air (Fig. 93). The ratio is measured by adding up the blade chords at a certain radius (say, three-quarters of the tip radius) and dividing the sum by the circumference at that radius. **The greater the solidity, the greater the power that can be absorbed.**

Of the two methods of increasing solidity, increase of chord and increase of number of blades, the **former** is the **easier,** the **latter** the **more efficient.** The so-called paddle blades which have been used on some types of American aircraft are examples of the former method. But there is a limit to this, first, because the poor aspect ratio makes the blades less efficient; and, secondly, because the greater the width of the blades, the greater is the tendency of the blades to turn to a fine pitch angle, and this effect may become so powerful that it puts severe stresses on the pitch-changing mechanism. This tendency is due to the **centrifugal turning moment** (Fig. 94). Consider the centrifugal force acting on a particle that is near the leading or trailing edge of the blade. The force will act outwards on a line from the centre of the propeller shaft to the particle, and this force can be divided into two components, one parallel to the axis on which the blade itself rotates, and the other at right angles to this, but also in the plane of rotation of the propeller. The former components, when all added up, produce tension in the blades; the latter tend to reduce the blade angle, i.e. to turn the blades towards fine pitch. **Both of these are forces to be reckoned with.** The centrifugal tension in the blades may be as much

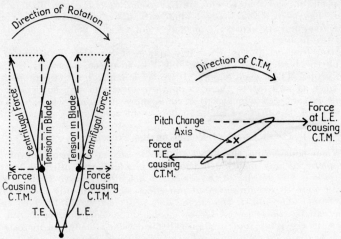

FIG. 94. CENTRIFUGAL TURNING MOMENT

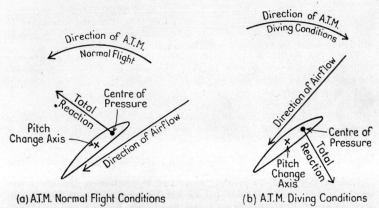

(a) A.T.M. Normal Flight Conditions   (b) A.T.M. Diving Conditions

FIG. 95. AERODYNAMIC TURNING MOMENT

as 80 to 100 tons, and the centrifugal turning moment can be as high as 10,000 lb. in. in the worst conditions.

There is sometimes a slight compensating effect so far as the centrifugal turning moment is concerned. The centre of pressure of the blade sections is usually forward of the pitch-changing axis, and this provides an **aerodynamic turning moment** (Fig. 95A) which is towards the coarse pitch position. Unfortunately, however, the effect is comparatively small. When the propeller is windmilling in a steep dive the

aerodynamic turning moment is reversed and acts in the same direction
as the centrifugal turning moment, i.e. towards fine pitch (Fig. 95B)—
the two together may provide a critical factor in the successful operation
of the pitch mechanism.

So, all in all, an increase in the number of blades is the most attractive
proposition, and that is why we have seen, first, the two-blader (yes,
there has been a one-blader!—but only one); then, in turn, three,
four, five, and six blades; and it may not be long before we see eight-
and ten-bladers.

After four or, at the most, five blades, it becomes inconvenient to
fit all the blades into one hub, and it is, in effect, necessary to have
two propellers for each engine. If we are going to have two propellers,
we may as well rotate them in opposite directions and so gain many
other advantages which will become more apparent when we have
considered the effects of the propeller on the aeroplane.

Effect of Height on the Propeller

When considering the effect of height on the performance of the
aeroplane, it was mentioned that the propeller was affected by the
decrease in the density of the air as the height increases. If the engine
power were to remain constant (an effect which can only be obtained
by "super-charging"), the engine and propeller would tend to race.
This can be compensated for in a constant-speed propeller by an increase in the pitch, but in a propeller with fixed blades an increase in
pitch or diameter will cause a loss of revolutions per minute at ground
level which may lead to difficulty in taking-off.

Therefore when a propeller is fitted to a supercharged engine it
should either be of variable pitch or, failing this, it must be designed to
give the best results at a certain definite height and a certain loss in
efficiency must be expected both above and below this height.

When the engine is not supercharged, there will be a progressive
falling off of the power with height; this may more than compensate
for the tendency of the propeller to race owing to the lack of air density,
and consequently the revolutions per minute may actually fall off.
In any case there will be a decrease in Thrust.

Another reason for loss of efficiency with height is the increase of
compressibility trouble at the tips owing to the decrease in the speed of
sound at low temperatures (see Chapter X).

The Slipstream

Just as the aerofoils provide their Lift by deflecting the air downwards, so the propeller produces Thrust by forcing the air backwards,
and the resultant stream of air which flows over fuselage, tail units, and
other parts of the aeroplane is called the **Slipstream.**

The extent of the Slipstream may be taken roughly as being that
of a cylinder of the same diameter as the propeller. (Actually there is
a slight contraction of the diameter a short distance behind the propeller.)

**The velocity of the Slipstream is greater than that at which the aero-
plane is travelling through the air:** the increase in velocity may be as
much as 100 per cent, or even more, at the stalling speed of the aeroplane. This would mean that the velocity of the air flowing over all
those parts in the Slipstream would be twice that of the airflow over

PLATE XXIV. A THREE-BLADED CONSTANT-SPEED PROPELLER

(*By courtesy of the De Havilland Aircraft Company, Ltd.*)

PLATE XXV. A SIX-BLADED CONTRA-ROTATING CONSTANT-SPEED
PROPELLER

By courtesy of the De Havilland Aircraft Company, Ltd.)

the other parts, and hence Drag would be four times as great as corre-sponding parts outside the Slipstream. At higher forward speeds of the aeroplane the difference is not so great, being only about 50 per cent at normal speeds, and as little as 10 per cent at high speeds. The extra velocity of the slipstream may be beneficial in providing more effective control for rudder and elevators, especially when the aeroplane is travelling slowly through the air, e.g. when taxying, or taking-off, or flying near the stalling speed.

In addition to this increased velocity, the propeller will impart a **rotary motion** to the Slipstream in the same direction as its own rota-tion. The result is that the Slipstream will strike one side only of such surfaces as the fin, and consequently it may have considerable effects on the directional and lateral balance of the aeroplane. If these effects are compensated for in normal flight—e.g. by "offsetting" the fin so that it does not lie directly fore and aft—then the balance will be upset when the engine stops and the Slipstream ceases to exert its influence.

When considering the balance of Flying Boats, we shall mention the use of the slipstream to provide a downward force on the Tail Plane. This is done by inclining the propeller shaft upwards. The result of this may be that only the upper portion of the rotating slipstream will strike the fin and rudder, so that the force on these surfaces will be all on one side, and this will tend to turn the machine. This is sometimes obviated by "offsetting" the engine or engines to one side as well as inclining them vertically. This method has the advantage that stoppage of the engines will remove both the cause of the trouble and the method of curing it, and thus the balance will still be maintained; if, on the other hand, the offsetting of the fin is the cure, then this will still remain after the engine has stopped and the cause of the trouble has been removed.

Effect of Propeller Torque

It has already been mentioned that **the Propeller Torque will tend to rotate the complete aeroplane in the opposite direction to the rotation of the propeller.** Where very high-powered engines are employed in comparatively small aeroplanes, this effect becomes very appreciable and must be counteracted in the design.

Many devices have been employed to counteract propeller torque. At one time the method nearly always used was to arrange for a "wash-out" towards the wing tip on the wing which tends to rise, thus de-creasing the angle of attack and lift on that wing during flight. This wash-out was often accompanied by a corresponding "wash-in" or increase of incidence, on the opposite wing. Another method was to have an unequal distribution of wing area or of weight on the two sides of the machine, e.g. on the Schneider Trophy seaplanes of 1929 and 1931 more fuel was carried in one float than the other. The action of the slipstream on a high fin and rudder may tend to roll the aeroplane in the opposite direction to the propeller torque; this method of com-pensation has the great advantage that when the trouble ceases, i.e. when the propeller stops, so does the cure. Where two or more engines are employed the propellers sometimes rotate in opposite directions. and thus the torque of one is counteracted by that of another. Finally, our old friends the trimming tabs on the ailerons may be used to counter-act the propeller torque.

Gyroscopic Effect

The rotating mass of the propeller may cause a slight **Gyroscopic effect.** A rotary body tends to resist any change in its plane of rotation, and if such change does take place there will be superimposed a tendency for the plane of rotation to change also in a direction at right angles to that in which it is forced. This can easily be illustrated with an ordinary bicycle wheel; if the wheel, while rapidly rotating, is held on a horizontal shaft and the holder attempts to keep the shaft horizontal while he turns, the shaft will either tilt upwards or downwards according as to whether he turns with the opposite or the same sense of rotation as that of the wheel. Thus if the propeller rotates clockwise when viewed from the pilot's cockpit (the usual method of denoting the rotation), the nose will tend to drop on a right-hand turn and the tail to drop on a left-hand turn. It is only in exceptional cases that this effect is really appreciable, although it used to be very marked in the days of rotary engines when the rotating mass was considerable.

Swing on Take-off

There is often a tendency for an aeroplane to swing to one side or another during the take-off run. This must be due to some asymmetric feature of the aircraft, and it is an interesting problem to try to track down the real villain that is causing the swing.

The pilot should be the first suspect. He himself is not symmetrical, he may be right-handed (or left-handed), he probably looks out on one side of the aeroplane and may even sit on one side. Certain it is that some aircraft which have swung violently when the pilot has tried to keep them straight have gone as straight as a die when left to themselves!

The second and main suspect is undoubtedly the propeller. But which of its asymmetric effects is the chief cause of swing in any particular aircraft is not so easy to determine. If the propeller rotates clockwise, the **torque reaction** will be anti-clockwise, the left-hand wheel will be pressed on the ground and the extra friction should **tend to yaw the aircraft to the left.** But let us not forget that the torque reaction may be compensated and, in that case, the behaviour of the aeroplane will depend on how it is compensated.

The slipstream—assuming the same clockwise propeller—will itself rotate clockwise and will probably strike the fin and rudder on the left-hand side, again **tending to yaw the aircraft to the left.** But the slipstream too may be compensated.

The **gyroscopic effect** will only come in **when the tail is being raised.** Again the tendency will be to **swing to the left** if the propeller rotates clockwise. Try it with the bicycle wheel.

There is yet another possible cause. When the tail is on the ground, and the propeller shaft is inclined upwards while the aircraft is travelling horizontally along the runway, the **down-going blade of the propeller will strike the air at a larger angle than the up-going blade** (the diagram illustrating this point is such a perfect exercise for the reader to sketch out for himself that it will be left to him). There is therefore more Thrust on the side of the down-going blade, i.e. with clockwise rotation, on the right-hand blade—again causing a **yaw to the left.**

The fact that all the tendencies are in the same direction makes it all the more difficult to find the real culprit; but all the more likely that the aeroplane will swing.

Apart from the compensating devices already mentioned the tendency to swing can be largely, if not entirely, eliminated by opposite rotating propellers on multi-engined aircraft, by counter-rotating propellers on single-engined aircraft and, of course, by jet propulsion or rocket propulsion instead of propellers.

The tricycle undercarriage is also a help in that it makes the aircraft more stable directionally on the ground, and makes it unnecessary to raise the tail at the beginning of the take-off run or to go along with the tail down, thus avoiding both the gyroscopic effect and the unequal thrust on the blades.

Contra-rotating Propellers

Contra-rotating propellers not only give the greater blade area, or solidity, that is required to absorb large power, but they eliminate or very nearly eliminate all the asymmetrical effects of slipstream, propeller torque, and gyroscopic action. It is curious that the average pilot hardly realizes the existence of these asymmetrical effects—until he loses them.· Test pilots who fly behind contra-rotating propellers for the first time report that the aircraft is easy to handle and nice to fly. This is hardly surprising; what perhaps is surprising is that the previous ill-effects of one-way rotation had been so little noticed. The second propeller straightens the slipstream created by the first and so causes a straight high-speed flow of air over wings and tail; this should improve the control and will certainly not give any ill-effects. There should be little or no resultant torque tending to roll the aircraft in one direction, and therefore no need to counteract such tendency; the gyroscopic effects should also be neutralized. As a result of all these effects there should be no tendency to swing to one side during take-off, no roll or yaw if the throttle is suddenly opened or closed, no difference in aileron or rudder trim, whether the engine is on or off—in short, as the test pilots report, the aircraft should be easy to handle and nice to fly.

Balance and Track

It is most important that a propeller should be properly **balanced**, otherwise unpleasant and dangerous vibrations will be set up. This means that the distribution of weight must be exactly similar throughout any two blades. **Static Balance,** which may be tested by balancing the propeller on a knife edge at the boss, is not sufficient; this ensures that the moments of the weight on each side of the boss are equal, but when a body is rotating it is not the moment, but what is called the **Moment of Inertia,** which matters. Whereas a moment depends on the weight of each part and its distance from the axis, the Moment of Inertia depends on the mass multiplied by the **Square** of the distance. To cut a long story short, if both **Static** and **Dynamic Balance** are to be obtained, it means practically that both blades must be identical in every respect.

There must also be **Aerodynamic Balance,** which, in the case of a propeller, means that the angle of each blade must be very accurately adjusted so that all blades give the same thrust. If one blade pulls more than another, vibrations will probably be set up, and these, too, may be serious, and may affect other parts of the aeroplane.

One very important, yet simple test which may be applied to a propeller, is to see that the blades **track** properly. This may be done by turning the propeller round slowly and seeing that the tip of each blade passes the same point. The position may be marked on a small trestle or other suitable object. If the blades do not "track" properly when tested in this way serious vibrations of the blades may be set up during flight.

_____

Some simple questions about Thrust and Propellers—

1. What are the various ways in which Thrust can be produced?
2. What is an athodyd?
3. Why is jet propulsion inefficient at low speeds?
4. Why is propeller propulsion inefficient at high speeds?
5. Distinguish between a "Tractor" and a "Pusher" propeller.
6. What is meant by the "Blade Angle" of a propeller, and why does this angle decrease from boss to tip?
7. What is the Helix Angle?
8. What factors make for the efficiency of a propeller?
9. Distinguish between the "Advance per Revolution," the "Geometric Pitch" and the "Experimental Pitch" of a propeller.
10. What is "Slip"?
11. What is the "Slipstream"?
12. What are the factors which decide the best diameter for a propeller?
13. Explain the effects of propeller torque and how it may be counteracted.
14. What are the advantages of a variable-pitch propeller?
15. Why is the tip speed an important factor in propeller design?
16. What is meant by the "Solidity" of a propeller?
17. Why is Solidity important, and how can it be increased?
18. What are the advantages of a contra-rotating propeller?
19. What are the possible causes of swing on take-off?

_____

Turn to page 350 for a few simple numerical examples on Propellers.

CHAPTER V

LEVEL FLIGHT

Introduction

IN an earlier chapter we discussed fairly fully the characteristics of aerofoils. If the reader has followed the conclusions which we have reached up to this stage, he should find little difficulty in the remainder of the subject; it is now merely a question of applying this knowledge, already gained, to the flight of the complete aeroplane.

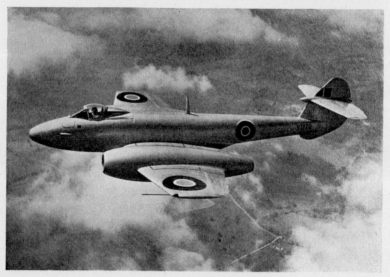

PLATE XXVI. LEVEL FLIGHT

The "Meteor IV," standard Air Force fighter and one time holder of the world air speed record.

(*By courtesy of the Gloster Aircraft Co., Ltd.*)

The flight of an aeroplane may be considered as consisting of various stages. First, the **take-off,** during which the aeroplane is transferred from one medium to another; then the **climb,** during which the pilot gains sufficient height to make sure that his flight will take place entirely in this new medium without any fear of accidental contact with the earth; then a period of **steady flight** at a constant height ("straight and level flight" is the pilot's term for this), interrupted in certain cases by periods of **manoeuvres,** or **aerobatics**; the **glide** back towards the earth; and finally the **landing** in which the aeroplane is restored to Mother Earth.

Straight and Level Flight

In many cases it is only during a very small portion of each such

142

flight that the aeroplane may be considered as travelling in straight
and level flight at uniform velocity. Yet this condition of affairs is of
importance, since it is considered as the standard condition when
designing the aeroplane, the other conditions being considered chiefly
in so far as they differ from those of Straight and Level Flight.

The Four Forces

Now, what are the forces which contrive to keep the aeroplane in

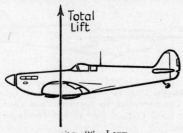

FIG. 96. LIFT

its state of steady flight? First and foremost, the **Lift** from our aerofoils, which will be vertically upwards since the direction of motion is
horizontal. This Lift, of course, we have created with the express
object of keeping the aeroplane in the air by opposing the force of
gravity, namely, the **Weight** of the aeroplane. But, as we have

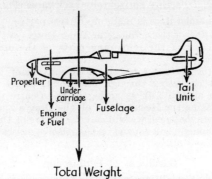

FIG. 97. WEIGHT

already discovered, we can only produce Lift if the aeroplane is moved
forward with a definite velocity, for which we need the forward **Thrust**
provided by the Propeller. We also know that the forward motion
will be opposed by the Resistance of both aerofoils and aeroplane,
which combine to form the total **Drag** of the aeroplane in opposition to
the Thrust.

The aeroplane, therefore, can be said to be under the influence of
four main forces—

1. **The Lift of the Main Planes,** L, **acting vertically upwards through
the Centre of Pressure (Fig. 96).**

2. The Weight of the aeroplane, W, acting vertically downwards through the Centre of Gravity (Fig. 97).

3. The Thrust of the propeller, T, pulling horizontally forwards along the propeller shaft (Fig. 98).

[NOTE. The Thrust is not always horizontal when the aeroplane is in the attitude of Normal Flight—i.e. when it is in "Rigging Position"—the propeller shaft sometimes being inclined upwards, thus giving the Thrust a vertical component. This may be done

FIG. 98. THRUST

for several reasons, but, since it introduces complications, it will be better for the moment to assume that the Thrust is parallel to the Longitudinal Datum line of the fuselage, as indeed it is in most aeroplanes.]

FIG. 99. DRAG

4. The Drag, D, acting horizontally backwards (Fig. 99).

The last-named item is made up of two parts—

(a) The Drag of the aerofoils or Wing Drag.

(b) The Drag of the remaining parts of the aeroplane, called Parasite Drag.

Just as for certain purposes it is convenient to consider all the Weight as acting through one point, called the Centre of Gravity, or all the Lift as acting at the Centre of Pressure, so we may imagine the Resultant of all the Drag acting at one point which, for convenience, we will call the Centre of Drag. Its actual position, of course, will depend on the relative resistance of different parts of the aeroplane.

Conditions of Equilibrium

Now, under what conditions will these four forces balance the aeroplane? That is to say, they must keep it travelling at a steady height at uniform velocity in a fixed direction, a state of affairs which, in the language of mechanics, is known as "equilibrium." It is sometimes hard to convince a traveller by air that he may travel at 200 miles per hour and yet be in a state of equilibrium, yet such is actually the case. Equilibrium simply means that the existing state of affairs is remaining unchanged; in other words, that the body concerned, in this case the aeroplane, is obeying Newton's First Law of Motion.

In order to do this the forces acting on it must be "balanced"—that is to say, **the Lift must be equal to the Weight** (this condition will keep the aeroplane at a constant height); and, secondly, the **Thrust must be equal to the Drag** (this condition will keep the aeroplane moving at the same steady velocity). These two statements, simple and straightforward though they are, always seem to cause difficulty to students who, though able to say Newton's Laws off by heart, have not tumbled to the fact that these laws are true in real practical life. Therefore the idea is often prevalent among students that the Lift must be greater than the Weight, or, as it is often expressed, the Lift must "overcome" the Weight; and when it comes to the question of Thrust and Drag the author has known students dismiss the idea that the Thrust need only be equal to the Drag as "contrary to common sense," "ridiculous," and it often needs an hour or more of interesting discussion to convince them of the truth of the statement. The mechanical aspects of this problem have been dealt with in Chapter I.

Prevention of Rotation

There still remains a third condition for equilibrium. In order to maintain straight and level flight, we must prevent the aeroplane from rotating, and this depends not only on the magnitudes of the four forces, but also on the positions at which they act. If the Centre of Pressure through which the Lift acts is behind the Centre of Gravity, then the nose of the aeroplane will tend to drop and the tail to rise, and vice versa if the Centre of Pressure is in front of the Centre of Gravity. But we are also concerned with the lines of action of the Thrust and Drag, for obviously if the line of Thrust is high and the line of Drag is low, these two forces also will tend to make the nose drop. Such tendencies of the aeroplane to rotate could probably be prevented by the pilot using his controls, but it is the aim of the designer to make an aeroplane which will "fly by itself," or, in the words of the pilot, will fly "hands off." Therefore he must see that the forces act in the right places. But this is by no means an easy task. Let us consider what it means.

Difficulties in Balancing the Four Forces

First, the Lift. The Lift will act through the Centre of Pressure, which will depend on the position of the aerofoil. Therefore the designer must be careful to place the planes in the correct position along the fuselage; they must be neither too far forward nor too far back. But the problem is further complicated by the fact that if the Angle of Attack is slightly altered, the Lift will move, and, to make matters worse, it will move in the unstable direction.

Secondly, the Weight. This will act through the Centre of Gravity, which in turn will depend on the weight and position of every individual part of the aeroplane and the load that it carries. Here alone is sufficient problem, but again, as in the case of Lift, there is a possibility of a movement of the Centre of Gravity during flight, caused, for instance, by consumption of petrol or dropping of bombs.

Thirdly, the Thrust. Here the problem is easier. The line of Thrust is, of course, settled by the position of the propeller shaft or the centre line of the jet, which in turn depend on the position of the engine or engines. In this matter the designer has very little choice, although he must seriously consider such important problems as keeping the propeller clear of the ground and giving the pilot a good field of view in a forward direction.

Lastly, the Drag. This is, perhaps, the most difficult problem of all. The Drag of the aeroplane is, of course, composed of the Drag of all the separate parts, and the designer must either estimate the Drag of each part separately, and so find the Total Drag and its line of action, or he must rely on wind-tunnel experiments on a model of his aeroplane. And, in any case, when he has found the position of his Drag, it, too, will be liable to alter its position at different Angles of Attack.

The Problem

What, then, can he do with these four unruly forces? He might try to concentrate them all at one point, but he could never be certain that their positions would not alter and upset the balance. Also there is an advantage to be gained by having the Lift slightly behind the Weight (Fig. 100); this will give these two forces a tendency

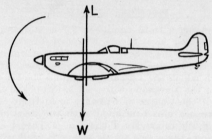

FIG. 100. LIFT BEHIND WEIGHT, CAUSING NOSE-HEAVY MOMENT

to turn the aeroplane nose downwards, which, in the case of engine failure, will automatically put it in a position ready for a glide, whereas if the Lift were in front of the Weight there would be a tendency to stall. If, then, he places the aerofoils so that the Lift will be behind the Weight, he must at the same time counteract this "nose downwards" tendency while the engine is running and the aeroplane is in normal horizontal flight. The obvious way in which to do this is to arrange that the line of Drag shall be above the line of Thrust so that these two forces will cause a "tail downwards" tendency, as in Fig. 101. In order to do this the Thrust must be low, and this always causes difficulty because it means either making the propeller of very small diameter or bringing it very close to the ground, both of which are bad features in design. This problem is rather easier in aircraft driven by jets or rockets in which it is possible to obtain a lower Thrust line. Even so, it is hardly ever possible to keep the line of Drag high, especially as the lowest portion of the aeroplane, the undercarriage, often causes a very large proportion of the Drag. Retractable under-carriages, which are almost universal in modern high-performance machines, are a help in this direction. But in the case of the Flying Boat, or even of the Floatplane, where the line of Drag will be ex-ceptionally low and where the Thrust must be even higher than in the landplane so that the propeller may clear the waves and spray, our proposition of putting the Drag above the Thrust does, in fact, become virtually impossible. But if we reverse matters and put the Thrust higher than the Drag, this will cause a "nose downward" tendency which must be counteracted for normal flight. To do this we can, of course, reverse the positions of Lift and Weight, putting the Lift in front of the Weight; then if the engine stops, the Thrust will cease to exist, the "tail downwards" tendency of Lift and Weight will take charge, and the machine will tend to stall, which, in the hands of an unskilled pilot, may lead to disaster.

The Solution

So much for the problem. What solution can be found? In the first place, where circumstances permit, the forces will be arranged as in Fig. 102, which we may call the ideal disposition. Where this is impossible, as in the case of a Flying Boat, they have sometimes been

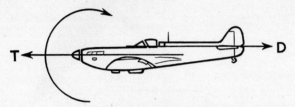

FIG. 101. DRAG ABOVE THRUST, CAUSING TAIL-HEAVY MOMENT

arranged as in Fig. 103; this, however, cannot be considered satisfactory, and we need to look for help from some new quarter altogether. **We find it eventually in the Tail Plane.**

The Tail Plane

At a considerable distance behind the main planes, as the chief lifting aerofoils are usually called, we fit a small plane whose duty

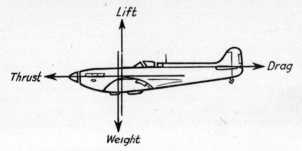

FIG. 102. FORCES ON AN AEROPLANE IN NORMAL FLIGHT

it is to provide the upward or downward force necessary to counteract the unruly behaviour of the four main forces. The force on the tail plane need only be a small one, because, owing to its long leverage, even a small force will produce a large correcting moment, or turning effect, on the aeroplane (Fig. 104).

The " Tail-less " Aeroplane

The reader will probably have realized by now that the existence of this auxiliary plane—the "stabilizer," as the Americans rather appropriately call it—is a necessity rather than a luxury, because even if the four main forces can be balanced for one particular condition of flight, they are not likely to remain so for long. Therefore it may

PLATE XXVII. TAIL-LESS—OLD TYPE
Westland (Hill) "Pterodactyl."
(By courtesy of "Flight.")

PLATE XXVIII. TAIL-LESS—NEW TYPE
The DH. 108 jet-propelled aircraft with heavily swept-back wings and no
tail-plane
(By courtesy of the De Havilland Aircraft Co., Ltd.)

be as well to mention that in certain rather freak types of aeroplane
its presence may be disguised to such an extent that in one particular
instance we sometimes hear the phrase "tail-less machine" applied

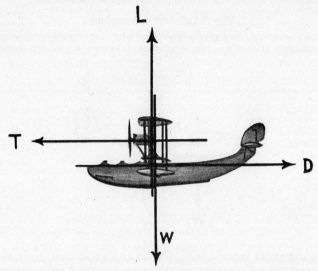

FIG. 103. UNSATISFACTORY ARRANGEMENT OF THE FORCES
ON A FLYING BOAT

to the Pterodactyl type! But if this type appears to have no tail,
the exact equivalent is immediately found at its wing tips, the wings
being, in fact, swept back so that the tip portion can fulfil the functions

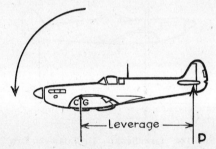

FIG. 104. UPWARD FORCE ON THE TAIL PLANE

of the tail plane in the orthodox aeroplane. In fact, it is true to say
that the "tail-less" type of aeroplane has two tails instead of one!
(Plates XXVII and XXVIII.)

Perhaps we ought to apologize for the use of the term "freak" in
connection with the tail-less type of aeroplane. Some designers have
for many years claimed advantages for these types, particularly in
regard to their stability and control, but, what is more important,
there is a definite revival in favour of the tail-less type with heavily

swept-back wings—and for two very good reasons. First, the absence of a tail to get in the way has obvious points in aircraft driven by jets or rockets; and, secondly, there are definite advantages to be gained from swept-back wings at very high speeds (see Chapter X).

The "Tail-first" Aeroplane

Much more of a freak type is the "tail-first" or canard aeroplane. A good example of this was the original Wright machine which made the

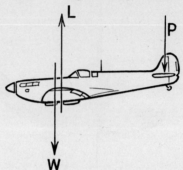

FIG. 105. HIGH SPEED—DOWN LOAD ON TAIL

first power-driven flight. Although at various times certain advantages have been claimed for this type, it has never proved really successful, and there can be little doubt that the serious drawbacks inherent in such a design far outweigh any small advantages. In this case the

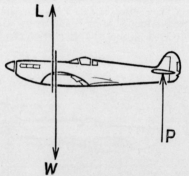

FIG. 106. LOW SPEED: UP LOAD ON TAIL

small auxiliary surface in front of the main planes (which we can hardly call a tail!) fulfils the duties of the normal tail plane.

Loads on Tail Plane

To return, then, to our normal aeroplane. Where the four main forces can be satisfactorily balanced in themselves, the duty of the tail plane will be merely to act as a "stand-by." Therefore it will be set at such an angle of attack that it carries no load in normal flight; at high speeds it must carry a down load (Fig. 105), because for high

speed the main aerofoils will be at a small Angle of Attack, the Centre
of Pressure will move backwards, tending to make the nose drop, so
that the tail must be held down to counteract this tendency; correspondingly, **at low speeds**—i.e. at large **Angles of Attack of the main
planes**—the tail plane must carry an upward load (Fig. 106).

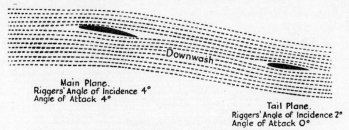

Main Plane.
Riggers' Angle of Incidence 4°
Angle of Attack 4°

Tail Plane.
Riggers' Angle of Incidence 2°
Angle of Attack 0°

Fig. 107. Effect of Downwash on the Tail Plane

" Non-lifting " Tail Planes

Since in this case the tail plane is equally likely to have to carry an
upward or a downward load, it is usually of symmetrical camber, and
therefore provides no lift when the angle at which it strikes the airflow
is 0°. For this reason such tail planes are sometimes given the rather

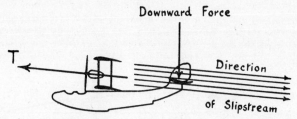

Fig. 108. Force on Tail of Flying Boat: Engine Running

misleading adjective of "non-lifting," which simply means that they
provide no lift when the Angle of Attack is 0°.

Effect of Downwash

There is one very important point to be remembered in connection
with the angles at which tail planes are set: **the air which strikes the
tail plane has already passed over the main planes, which**, as we have
already seen, **will cause a downwash on to the tail plane** (Fig. 107).
The angle of this downwash may be at least half the Angle of Attack
on the main planes, so that if the main planes strike the airflow at
4°, the air which strikes the tail plane will be descending at an angle
of 2°, so that if the tail plane were given a Riggers' Angle of Incidence
of 2°, it would strike the airflow head-on and, if symmetrical, would
provide no force upwards or downwards. Again, the angle of downwash
will, of course, change with the Angle of Attack of the main planes,
and it is for this reason that the angle at which the tail plane should
be set is one of the most difficult problems confronting the designer.

Further difficulties arise from the fact that in a propeller-driven aircraft the tail plane is usually in the "slipstream," or back-wash from the propeller, which is a rotating mass of air and will therefore strike the two sides of the tail plane at different angles. Yet again, the fuselage and other parts of the aeroplane may deflect the air which strikes the tail plane.

" Lifting " Tails

Now, where the four main forces **cannot** be satisfactorily balanced in themselves, the tail plane may be called upon to provide a more or

FIG. 109. FORCE ON TAIL OF FLYING BOAT: ENGINE STOPPED

less permanent balancing force either upwards or downwards. For this purpose it may be cambered in the same way as an ordinary aerofoil, or, as the force required is often a downward one, it may even be shaped like an inverted aerofoil. Interesting cases of this sort

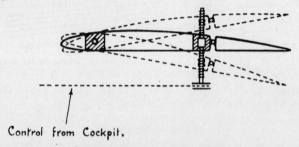

FIG. 110 ADJUSTABLE TAIL PLANE

may often be found in Flying Boats; here we have the difficulty of high Thrust line and low Drag turning the boat nose downwards. If we counteract this by arranging that the Lift shall be in front of the Weight, we are confronted with the stalling problem, already mentioned, and much ingenuity has been used in Flying Boat design in the attempt to find a satisfactory solution. One method is to arrange for a large downward force upon the tail plane in normal flight; this may be done by having an inverted camber on the tail plane and also by inclining the engines and therefore the propeller shafts with their nose upwards, so that the slipstream flows downwards on to the tail. By this means the inverted tail plane may be given a positive Riggers' Angle of Incidence and yet still cause a downward force while the engines are running (Fig. 108). If, however, the engines stop, whether voluntarily or involuntarily, the downward slipstream will automatically cease to exist, and the tail, by virtue of its positive Angle of Incidence, which will now give it a positive Angle of Attack, will receive an upward lift which will help to put the Flying Boat into a position for a glide (Fig.

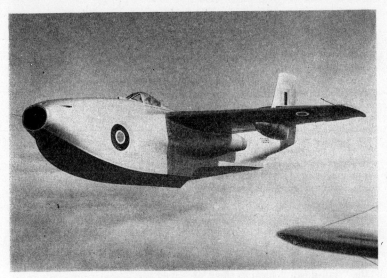

PLATE XXIX. SAUNDERS-ROE FLYING BOAT SR.A1
(*By courtesy of Messrs. Saunders-Roe Ltd.*)

109). *Voilà!* Everything which we required. What is the "snag" in this delightful solution? Simply that it means that in normal flight we have to carry a perpetual downward force on the tail, which is just the same as carrying so much extra weight, and this extra force has to be compensated for by just so much extra lift from the main planes or by so much reduction in the weight-carrying capacity of the machine.

The Adjustable Tail Plane

Even in the normal type of aeroplane the problem of balance is not yet completely solved, because, once the designer has settled the size and angle of the tail plane, the forces which it will experience will be outside the control of the pilot, and although they may automatically compensate for such things as changes in the position of the Lift on the main planes, they cannot possibly deal with changes of weight such as are caused by the dropping of bombs and consumption of fuel. For this reason the **Adjustable Tail Plane** was introduced, this being operated by an actuating gear and controlled by a wheel or lever in the pilot's cockpit. This enabled the pilot to **alter the angle of setting of the tail planes during flight** (Fig. 110), and so cause downward or upward forces upon it at will, thus balancing the aeroplane under all conditions. Although this device was originally intended to cure such vices as "nose-" or "tail-heaviness" caused by the dropping of bombs or changes in the distribution of weight, it was found so useful in compensating for slight changes of balance due to flying or climbing at different Angles of Attack, gliding with the engine "off," and so on, that it was soon employed on nearly all aeroplanes. It was, in fact, one of those many simple devices which made one wonder why "someone didn't think of it before."

Trimming Tabs

But it was not long before someone thought of something even better; a device which does the same job just as effectively, and is even lighter and simpler than the adjustable tail plane—this is the "trimming tab" which will be considered under the heading of "Control."

Since they also come under the heading of "Control," we have not yet mentioned the **Elevators,** the hinged flaps behind the tail plane which provide the pilot with the means of momentarily adjusting his balance or altering his position, as distinct from the more permanent effect of the tail plane itself.

Conditions of Balance considered Numerically

We have so far avoided any numerical consideration of the forces which balance the aeroplane in Straight and Level Flight; in simple cases, however, these present no especial difficulty.

When there is no load on the tail plane our conditions of balance are these—

1. **Lift = Weight,** i.e. $L = W$.
2. **Thrust = Drag,** i.e. $T = D$.
3. The "nose-down" turning effect of L and W must balance the "tail-down" turning effect of T and D.

The two forces, L and W, are two equal and opposite parallel forces, which in Mechanics is called a "couple." Their moment, or turning effect, is measured by "one of the forces multiplied by the perpendicular distance between them." Therefore, if the distance between L and W is x ft., the Moment is Lx or Wx lb. ft.

Similarly, T and D form a couple, and if the distance between them is y ft., their Moment is Ty or Dy lb. ft.

Therefore our third condition is that Lx (or Wx) $= Ty$ (or Dy).

To take a numerical example—

Suppose the weight of an aeroplane (W) is 2,000 lb.

$$L = W \quad \therefore L = 2,000 \text{ lb.}$$

Now, what will be the value of the Thrust and Drag? The reader must beware of falling into the ridiculous idea, which is so common among students, that the Thrust will be equal to the Weight! The statement is sometimes made that the "Four forces acting on the aeroplane are equal," but nothing could be farther from the truth. $L = W$ and $T = D$, but these equations certainly do not make $T = W$. This point is emphasized here for the very simple reason that out of over a thousand students to whom the author has put the question, "How do you think the Thrust required to pull the aeroplane along in normal flight compares with the Weight?" more than 50 per cent have suggested that the Thrust must obviously equal the Weight and over half the remainder have insisted that, on the other hand, the Thrust must be many times greater than the Weight! Such answers, of course, show that the student has not really grasped the fundamental principles of flight, for is not our object to obtain the maximum of Lift with the minimum of Drag, or, what amounts to much the same thing, to Lift as much Weight as possible with the least possible engine power? Have we not seen that our wings can produce, at their most

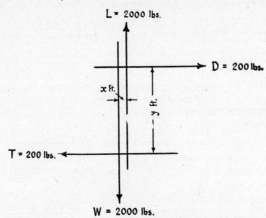

L = 2000 lbs.

D = 200 lbs.

x ft.

y ft.

T = 200 lbs.

W = 2000 lbs.

FIG. 111. BALANCE OF THE FOUR FORCES: NO LOAD ON TAIL

efficient angle, a Lift of 12, 16, or even 20 times as great as their Drag?

But there is a great deal of difference between an aeroplane and a wing; for whereas a wing provides us with a large amount of Lift and a very much smaller amount of Drag, all the other parts which go to make up the aeroplane help to increase the Drag and provide no Lift in return. Actually it is not quite true to say that the wings provide all the Lift of an aeroplane, for by clever design even such parts as the fuselage, the floats of a float plane or the hull of a flying boat, may be persuaded to lend a hand in lifting the aeroplane. Such efforts to increase the Lift may be very well worth while, but it must be admitted that even the total increase in Lift from these sources will be small, whereas the addition of all the Parasite Drag of the fuselage, tail, and undercarriage will form a large item; in old designs it used to total as much as, or even more than, the Drag of the wings, but in modern monoplanes with retractable undercarriages and "clean" design, the proportion of Parasite Drag is being much reduced. None the less it may result in the reduction of the Lift/Drag ratio of the **Aeroplane,** as distinct from the Aerofoil, down to, say, 8, 10, or 12.

From these remarks it will be obvious that our **ideal aeroplane** must always be one in which there is no Parasite Drag, i.e. it must be in the nature of a " **Flying Wing.**" In this case we would hope to obtain a Lift some twenty times greater than the Drag. At present we seem to be a long way off the ideal, and indeed there seems to be some doubt as to whether such an ideal is capable of practical attainment. On the other hand, there is no reason to doubt that we shall approach much nearer to our ideal than we are at present, and the jet-propelled aeroplane and high-speed types are tending to revive interest in the flying wing.

For the sake of our numerical example, let us assume that the Lift is ten times the Total Drag, this being a reasonable figure for an average aeroplane. Then the Drag will be 200 lb. Therefore Thrust = 200 lb. So we see that an aeroplane of weight 2,000 lb. can be lifted by a Thrust of 200 lb., but the Lift is not direct; the work is all being done in a forward direction, not upwards. The aeroplane is, in fact,

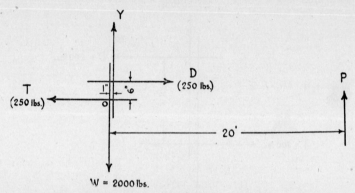

FIG. 112. THE FOUR FORCES AND THE TAIL LOAD

in no sense a **Helicopter,** which is a type of machine in which the Thrust is vertical and in which the Thrust must be at least equal to the Weight.

To return to our problem—

$L = W = 2000$ lb.

$T = D = 200$ lb.   (This is merely an approximation for a good type of aeroplane.)

$Lx = Ty.$

∴ $2000x = 200\ y.$

∴ $x = \dfrac{1}{10} \cdot y.$

So that if T and D are 1 ft. apart, L and W must be $\dfrac{1}{10}$ ft. apart.

In other words, the lines of Thrust and Drag must be farther apart than the lines of Lift and Weight in the same proportion as the Lift is greater than the Drag (Fig. 111).

Finding the Tail Load

This conclusion only applies to cases where there is no force on the tail plane. When there is such a force the problem is slightly more complicated, but can still be solved by the principle of moments. Consider a further example—

An aeroplane weighs 2,000 lb. The Drag in normal horizontal flight is 250 lb. The Centre of Pressure is 1 in. behind the Centre of Gravity, and the line of Drag is 6 in. above the line of Thrust. Find what load on the tail plane, which is 20 ft. behind the Centre of Gravity, will be required to maintain balance in normal horizontal flight.

Let the Lift force on main planes $= Y$ lb.

Let force on tail plane $\qquad = P$ lb. (assumed to be upwards).

Then total Lift $= L = Y + P$ (Fig. 112)

But $L = W = 2000$ lb.

$\therefore Y + P = 2000$. $\qquad$. $\qquad$. (1)

also $T = D = 250$. $\qquad$. $\qquad$. (2)

Take Moments about any convenient point: in this case perhaps the most suitable point is O, the intersection of the Weight and Thrust lines.

Nose-down Moments about O are caused by Y and P.

(W and T will, of course, have no Moments about O.)

$\therefore$ Total Nose-down Moments $\quad = \dfrac{1}{12} Y + 20P \quad$ (all distances being expressed in feet).

Tail-down Moments about O are caused by D only.

$\therefore$ Total Tail-down Moment $= \frac{1}{2} D$.

$\therefore \dfrac{1}{12} Y + 20P = \frac{1}{2}D$.

$\qquad$ i.e. $Y + 240P = 6D$. $\qquad$. $\qquad$. (3)

But from (1) $Y + P = 2000$

$\therefore 239P = 6D - 2000$

But $D = 250$. $\qquad$. $\qquad$. $\qquad$. (2)

$\therefore 239P = 6 \times 250 - 2000$.

$\qquad = 1500 - 2000$

$\qquad = - 500$.

$\therefore P = - \dfrac{500}{239} = - 2 \cdot 1$ lb. (Approx).

Therefore a small **downward** force of $2 \cdot 1$ lb. is required on the tail plane, the negative sign in the answer simply indicating that the force which we assumed to be upwards should have been downwards.

The student is advised to work out similar examples which will be found at the end of this book (p. 352).

Inclined Thrust Line

In cases where the Thrust is inclined when the aeroplane is in the attitude of Normal Horizontal Flight, the problem will be complicated in two ways—

1. The Thrust must be split up into its vertical and horizontal components, $T \sin \theta$ and $T \cos \theta$ (Fig. 113). In equating the forces $T \sin \theta$ must be added to the Lift and $T \cos \theta$ will equal the Drag.

2. In taking moments it is advisable to choose a point on the Thrust line so that the Thrust will have no moment about that point; if this is not done, care must be taken, when estimating the moment of T, to use the perpendicular distance from the chosen point to the line of action of T, as this will no longer be the vertical distance.

If these two points are borne in mind, no difficulty will be experienced in working out examples when the Thrust is inclined.

A small inclination of the line of Thrust may be very useful in counter-acting the nose-down moment caused by a high Thrust line, because it will not only minimize the actual moment by reducing the perpendicular distance from the Centre of Gravity to the Thrust line, but it will also tend to give a downward force on the tail plane. It is for such reasons that an inclined Thrust line is used rather than in an attempt to obtain any vertical Lift force from the propeller in the manner of a **Helicopter.**

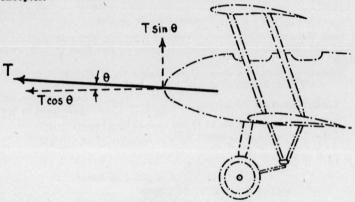

FIG. 113. INCLINED THRUST LINE

Helicopters

A Helicopter is an aircraft in which the whole of the Lift is provided by the Thrust of a propeller which revolves in a horizontal plane. In such a case it becomes true to say that, in normal flight, Thrust = Weight. Forward motion must be produced by an auxiliary engine and propeller, or by inclining the shaft of the lifting propeller. Owing to the reaction of the torque of the lifting propeller the whole aircraft will tend to rotate in the opposite direction, causing a tendency to yaw which corresponds to the rolling tendency produced by the propeller in the conventional aircraft. The yawing tendency can be counteracted either by an auxiliary propeller or by a jet reaction system at the tail; the auxiliary propeller or jet can also be used to provide directional control and so save the necessity of having a rudder.

The Helicopter has had a varied history and it was a long time before a successful type was built. Modern types can certainly do extraordinary things, they can hover at will, land in confined spaces, drop and pick up mails without even landing, fly sideways or backwards or forwards at will. All these things they can do better than the conventional aircraft, but there is one thing they cannot do—fly at high speeds. The reason for this limitation is quite simple. Since the blades rotate in the horizontal plane, there will always be one blade moving in the same direction as the aircraft, and its speed relative to the air will be the combined speeds due to the rotation and forward motion. This means that the tip of the rotating blade will meet compressibility troubles (see Chapter X) long before the aircraft itself is travelling anywhere near the speed of sound—so the limiting speed of such aircraft is about 200 m.p.h. Of course speed is not everything, and there is no doubt whatever that the Helicopter has its uses both now and in the future, and especially for short-range work, communication with the hearts of cities and so on.

It is a type that has always had its advocates—and its opponents. The former must surely admit that however ingenious a contraption it may be, it still is a contraption—the latter, on the other hand, must admit that it can do things that conventional aircraft cannot do.

Level Flight at Different Air Speeds

So far we may seem to have assumed that there is only one condition of level flight; but this is not so. Level flight is possible over the

PLATE XXX. HELICOPTER

The Bristol Type 171 Helicopter with tail rotor to give directional control and to prevent the aircraft from rotating in the opposite direction to the main propeller.

(*By courtesy of the Bristol Aeroplane Co. Ltd.*)

whole speed range of the aeroplane, from the maximum air speed that can be attained down to the minimum air speed at which the aeroplane can be kept in the air, both without losing height. This speed range is often very wide on modern aircraft; the maximum speed may be in the region of 300 to 600 m.p.h. or even more, and the minimum speed (with flaps lowered) less than 100 m.p.h. Mind you, though level flight is **possible** at any speed within this range, it may be very **inadvisable** to fly unduly fast when considerations of fuel economy are involved, or to fly unduly slowly if an enemy is on your tail! There is nearly always a correct speed to fly according to the circumstances, and war experience has proved that the maintenance of the correct speed may well be a matter of life or death.

Relation between Air Speed and Angle of Attack

An aeroplane flying in level flight at different air speeds will be flying at different angles of attack, i.e. at different attitudes to the air. Since the flight is **level,** this means different attitudes to the ground, and so the pilot will be able to notice these attitudes by reference to the horizon (or to the "artificial horizon" on his instrument panel).

For every air speed—as indicated on the Air Speed Indicator—there is a corresponding angle of attack at which level flight can be maintained (provided the weight of the aeroplane does not change).

Let us examine this important relationship more closely. It all depends on our old friend the lift formula, $L = C_L . \frac{1}{2}\rho V^2.S.$ To maintain level flight, the Lift must be equal to the Weight. Assuming for the moment that the Weight remains constant, then the Lift must also remain constant and equal to the Weight. The wing area, S, is unalterable. Now, if we look back, or think back, to Chapter II we will realize that $\frac{1}{2}\rho V^2$ represents the difference between the pressure on the pitot tube and on the static tube (or static vent), and that this difference represents what is read as air speed on the Air Speed Indicator; in other words, the **Indicated Air Speed.** There is only one other item in the formula, i.e. C_L (the lift coefficient). Therefore if $\frac{1}{2}\rho V^2$, or the Indicated Air Speed, goes up, C_L must be reduced, or the Lift will become greater than the Weight. Similarly, if $\frac{1}{2}\rho V^2$ goes down, C_L must go up or the Lift will become less than the Weight. Now C_L depends on the angle of attack of the wings (see Chapter III); the greater the angle of attack (up to the stalling angle), the greater the value of C_L. Therefore for every Angle of Attack there is a corresponding Indicated Air Speed.

This is a most fortunate fact, since the pilot has no instrument on which he can read the Angle of Attack, whereas the Air Speed Indicator gives him an easy reading of his Air Speed. That is why a pilot always talks and thinks in terms of **speed,** landing **speed,** stalling **speed,** best gliding **speed,** climbing **speed,** range or endurance **speed,** and so on. The experimenter on the ground, on the other hand, especially if he does wind tunnel work, is inclined to talk and think in terms of **angle,** stalling **angle, angle** of attack for flattest glide, longest range, and so on. This difference of approach is very natural. The pilot, after all, has little choice; he does not know the angle of attack and he does know the speed. To the experimenter on the ground, speed is rather meaningless; he can alter the angle of attack and still keep the speed constant —something that the pilot **cannot** do. But, however natural the difference of outlook, it is unfortunate; and it is undoubtedly one of the causes of the gap between the two essential partners to progress, the practical man and the theoretical man.

Let us examine our general statement more critically by working out some figures. Suppose an aeroplane weighs 10,000 lb. and that its wing area is 250 sq. ft. (i.e. a wing loading of 40 lb. per sq. ft.). Assume that the aerofoil section has the lift characteristics shown in the lift curve on page 82 (Fig. 57). Consider, first, the ground level condition, the density being 0·0024 slugs per cu. ft.

Whatever the speed, the Lift must be equal to the Weight, 10,000 lb.; but the Lift must also be equal to $C_L . \frac{1}{2}\rho V^2.S.$

$$\therefore \ 10{,}000 \text{ lb.} = C_L . \tfrac{1}{2} \times 0{\cdot}0024 \times V^2 \times 250,$$

from which $$C_L = \frac{33{,}333}{V^2}$$

Now insert values of V of 60, 80, 100 m.p.h. and other values up to 300 **m.p.h.,** converting them, of course, to ft./sec., and work out the

Air Speed	Lift Coefficient	Angle of Attack
60	4·3	—
80	3·2	—
100	1·54	—
120	1·37	—
140	0·97	11°
160	0·61	6°
180	0·48	4°
200	0·39	3°
220	0·32	$2\frac{1}{2}$°
240	0·27	$1\frac{3}{4}$°
260	0·23	1°
280	0·20	$\frac{1}{2}$°
300	0·17	0°

corresponding values of C_L, and then by referring to Fig. 38A read off the angle of attack for each speed.

The result will be something like that shown in the table above.

Now let us see what this table means, and we will find it very interesting. In the first place at speeds below about 130 m.p.h., the lift coefficient needed for level flight is greater than the maximum lift coefficient (1·12) provided by our aerofoil, therefore level flight is not possible below this speed. Secondly, as the speed increases to 140, 150, 160 m.p.h., etc., the angle of attack decreases to 11°, 6°, 4°, etc.; and for each speed there is a corresponding angle of attack. We should notice, in passing, that at comparatively low speeds there is a much greater change in angle of attack for each 20 m.p.h. increase in air speed than there is at the higher speeds, e.g. the angle of attack at 160 m.p.h. is 5° less then at 140 m.p.h., whereas the angle of attack at 300 m.p.h. is only $\frac{1}{2}$° less than at 280 m.p.h. This change in proportion is interesting, and is one of the arguments for an **Angle of Attack Indicator,** which would be sensitive at low speeds, which is just where the Air Speed Indicator is most unsatisfactory.

We could, of course, continue our table to speeds higher than 300 m.p.h. and we should find that we needed even smaller lift coefficients, and negative angles of attack (though never less than $-3°$, since at this angle there would be no lift, whatever the speed). But at this stage we must begin to consider another factor affecting speed range, namely, the power of the engine. What we have worked out so far is accurate enough, provided we can be sure of obtaining sufficient thrust from the propeller. It may be that at speeds above 300 m.p.h., or even at 300 m.p.h., or, for that matter, even at 140 m.p.h., we shall not be able to maintain level flight for the simple reason that we have not sufficient engine power to overcome the drag. Thus the engine power will also determine the speed range, not only the top speed, but also, to some extent, the minimum speed.

In case the reader should be feeling somewhat alarmed by the high minimum speed of this aeroplane, we should perhaps point out, first, that we have not used flaps; secondly, that our aerofoil gives rather a poor value of maximum lift coefficient; and, thirdly, that it has a fairly high wing loading, or ratio of weight to wing area, which, as we shall see later, has an important influence on minimum speed. All we wish to establish at the moment is the relationship between air speed in level flight and angle of attack, and this is clearly shown by the table.

Effect of Height

Our table was worked out for ground level conditions. What will be the effect of height on the relationship between air speed and angle of attack? The answer, once it is understood, is simple—but very important. Whatever the height, the Air Speed Indicator reading is determined by the pressure $\frac{1}{2}\rho V^2$. In this expression, V is the **true** air speed. As has already been explained in Chapter II, when the Air Speed Indicator reads 200 m.p.h. at 10,000 ft., it simply means that the difference in pressure between pitot and static tubes (i.e. $\frac{1}{2}\rho V^2$) is the same as when the air speed was 200 m.p.h. at ground level. Now, it is not only the pitot pressure that depends on $\frac{1}{2}\rho V^2$; so do the Lift and the Drag. Therefore, at the same value of $\frac{1}{2}\rho V^2$, i.e. **at the same indicated speed,** the Lift and Drag will be the same as at ground level, other things (such as C_L) being equal. Therefore our table remains equally true **at all heights,** provided the air speed referred to is the **indicated speed,** and not the true speed. Thus the **angle of attack, or the attitude of the aeroplane to the air, is the same in level flight at all heights, provided the indicated air speed remains the same.**

Effect of Weight

Our table was worked out for a constant weight of 10,000 lb. What will be the effect of changes of weight such as must occur in practical flight owing to fuel consumption, dropping of bombs, etc.? The answer to this is not quite so simple. Suppose the weight is reduced from 10,000 lb. to 8,000 lb. At the same indicated air speed, the angle of attack would be the same, and the Lift would be the same as previously, i.e. 10,000 lb. This would be too great. Therefore, in order to reduce the Lift, we must adjust the attitude, so that the wings strike the air at a smaller angle of attack, or we must reduce the speed, or both. Whatever we do, we shall get a slightly different relationship between air speed and angle of attack: the reader is advised to work out the figures for a weight of 8,000 lb. Although the relationship will be slightly different from that for 10,000 lb. weight, it will again remain constant at all heights for the same indicated speeds. To sum up the effect of weight, we can say that **the less the total weight of the aircraft, the less will be the indicated air speed corresponding to a given angle of attack.** A little calculation will show that the indicated air speed for the same angle of attack will be in proportion to the square root of the total weight.

Flying for Maximum Range

Whether in war or peace, we shall often wish to use our aircraft to best advantage for some particular purpose—it may be to fly as fast as possible, or as slowly as possible, or to climb at maximum rate, or to stay in the air as long as possible, or, perhaps, most important of all, to achieve the maximum distance on a given quantity of fuel. Flying for maximum range is one of the outstanding problems of practical flight, but it is also one of the best illustrations of the principles involved. To exploit his engine and aircraft to the utmost in this respect, a pilot must be not only a good flier, but also an intelligent one.

The problem concerns engine, propeller, and aircraft; it also concerns the wind. In this book we are concerned chiefly with the aircraft, but we cannot solve this problem, and indeed we can solve few, if any, of the problems of flight, without at least some consideration of the engine and the propeller, or jet, or rocket, or whatever it may be, and how the pilot should use them to get the best out of his aircraft. As for the wind, we shall, as usual in this subject, first consider a condition of still air.

The engine is some type of **heat engine.** This applies whether it be air-cooled or water-cooled, radial or in-line, sleeve valve or poppet valve; whether it is a reciprocating engine driving a propeller, or a turbine working on the jet-propulsion system, or for that matter, an athodyd or a rocket. The object in a heat engine is to burn fuel so as to get heat energy and then to convert this heat energy into mechanical work. In order to get the greatest amount of work from a given quantity of fuel, we must, first of all, get the maximum amount of heat out of it, and then we must change the heat energy to mechanical energy in the most efficient way. Our success or otherwise will clearly depend to some extent on the use of the best fuel for the purpose, and on the skill of the engine designer. But the pilot, too, must play his part. To get the most heat from the fuel, it must be properly burned; this means that the mixture of air to fuel must be correct. What is usually called "weak mixture" is, in fact, not so very weak, but approximately the correct mixture to burn the fuel properly. If we use a richer mixture, some of the fuel will not be properly burned, and we shall get less heat from the same amount of fuel: we may get other advantages, but we shall not get economy. Both the manifold pressure and the revolutions per minute will affect the efficiency of the engine in its capacity of converting heat to work. The problem of the best combination of boost and r.p.m., though interesting, is outside the scope of this book and at this stage, too, the principles of the reciprocating and turbine engine begin to differ, while the rocket or athodyd has not got any r.p.m.! For the reciprocating engine we can sum up the engine and propeller problem by saying that, generally speaking, the pilot will be using them to best advantage if he uses weak mixture, the highest boost permissible in weak mixture, and the lowest r.p.m. consistent with the charging of the electrical generator and the avoidance of detonation. All this has assumed that he has control over such factors, and that the engine is supercharged and that the propeller has controllable pitch. Without such complications, the pilot's job will, of course, be easier; but the chances are that, whereas a poor pilot may get better results, the good pilot will get worse—far, far worse.

Before leaving the consideration of the engine and propeller, let us examine a few figures—they will help us to understand the principles. One gallon of aviation fuel weighs about 7 lb. Each pound, if properly burned, will produce about 19,000 B.Th.U. A British Thermal Unit, as the name implies, is a heat unit, and is the heat required to raise 1 lb. of water through 1° F. change of temperature. Thus 1 lb. of fuel should be able to raise 19,000 lb. of water 1° F. It sounds a lot, but it is approximately true. The next step in the argument is not quite so true. If, with suitable apparatus, we do 778 ft.lb. of mechanical work, e.g. by rubbing two discs together under water, we can produce 1 B.Th.U., i.e. we can raise 1 lb. of water 1° F. This is fairly true, though the experiment is not easy to perform accurately—what is **not** true is the converse, that from 1 B.Th.U. we can produce 778 ft.lb. of mechanical work. Although it has never been done, and although we even know the reasons why we cannot do it, we are in a sense always trying to do it in a heat engine, and then we call the engine inefficient because we do not succeed! All we get, even in the best engines and in the hands of the best pilots, is something like 30 per cent of this figure. Even so, if the argument has been followed, it will be seen that from each gallon of fuel we should get about—

30% of 7 × 19,000 × 778 ft.lb., or about 31,000,000 ft.lb.

This is what the engine gives to the propeller. We may lose 20 per cent of this due to the inefficiency of the propeller, and so the aircraft will only get about 80 per cent of 31,000,000, i.e. about 25,000,000 ft.lb.

It still seems a large figure—it is a large figure—but, as we shall see later, it will not take our aircraft very far. However, we have done this little calculation, not so much to get the numerical value, as to get the **unit**, the **ft.-lb.** We have found that a gallon of fuel, if used in the best possible way (notice, by the way, that we have said nothing about how quickly or slowly we use it), will give to the aircraft so many foot-pounds. Suppose, then, that we want **to move the aircraft the maximum number of feet, we must pull it with the minimum number of pounds.** That simple principle is the essence of flying for range.

Let us examine it more closely. It means that we must fly so that the propeller gives the least Thrust with which level flight is possible. Least Thrust means least Drag, because Drag and Thrust will be equal.

Flying with Minimum Drag

Now, on first thoughts, we might think that flying with minimum drag meant presenting the aeroplane to the air in such an attitude that it would be most streamlined; in other words, in the attitude that would give least drag if a model of the aircraft were tested in a wind tunnel. But if we think again, we will soon realize that such an idea is erroneous. This "streamlined attitude" would mean high speed, and the high speed would more than make up for the effects of presenting the aeroplane to the air at a good attitude; in a sense, of course, it is the streamlined attitude that enables us to get the high speed and the high speed, in turn, causes drag. We are spending too much effort in trying to go fast.

On the other hand, we must not imagine, as we well might, that we will be flying with least drag if we fly at the minimum speed of level flight. This would mean a large angle of attack, 15° or more, and the induced drag particularly would be very high—we would be spending too much effort in keeping up in the air.

There must be some compromise between these two extremes—it would not be an aeroplane if there was not a compromise in it somewhere. Perhaps, too, it would not be an aeroplane if the solution were not rather obvious—**once it has been pointed out to us! Since the Lift must always equal the Weight,** which we have assumed to be constant at 10,000 lb., **the Drag will be least when the Lift/Drag ratio is greatest.** Now, the curve of Lift/Drag ratio given on page 84 (Fig. 59) refers to the aerofoil only. The values of this ratio will be less when applied to the whole aeroplane, since the Lift will be little, if any greater, than that of the wing alone, whereas the Drag will be considerably more, perhaps twice as much. Furthermore, the change of the ratio at different angles of attack, in other words, the shape of the curve, will not be quite the same for the whole aeroplane. None the less, there will be a maximum value of, say, 8 to 1 at about the same angle of attack that gave the best value for the wing, i.e. at 4°, and the curve will fall off on each side of the maximum, so that the Lift/Drag ratio will be less, i.e. the Drag will be greater, whether we fly at a smaller or a greater angle of attack than 4°; in other words, at a greater or less speed than that corresponding to 4°, which our table showed to be 180 m.p.h.

These are typical of the sort of figures we shall get—

Air Speed	Angle of Attack	L/D Ratio	Total Drag
130	15°	4·2	2,380 lb.
140	11°	6	1,670 lb.
160	6°	7·5	1,330 lb.
180	4°	8	1,250 lb.
200	3°	7·5	1,330 lb.
220	$2\frac{1}{2}$°	7	1,430 lb.
240	$1\frac{3}{4}$°	6	1,670 lb.

This table is very instructive, and shows quite clearly the effect of different air speeds in level flight on the total Drag that will be experienced. It shows, too, that the least total Drag is at the best Lift/Drag ratio, which in this case is at 4° angle of attack, which, in turn, is at 180 m.p.h. air speed.

The angle of attack that gives the best Lift/Drag ratio will be the same whatever the height and whatever the weight; it is simply a question of presenting the aeroplane to the air at the best attitude, and has nothing to do with the density of the air, or the loads that are carried inside the aeroplane, or even the method of propulsion.

As has already been explained, this means that the corresponding air speed, which is what the pilot must go by, will be the same, whatever the height, but will increase slightly for increased loads. The same indicated air speed means the same Drag at any height, and therefore the same range.

On the other hand, the higher speed which must be used for increased weights means greater Drag, because, looking at it very simply, even the same Lift/Drag ratio means a greater Drag if the Lift is greater. So added Weight means added Drag—in proportion—and therefore less range—also in proportion.

Let us go back for a moment to our **foot-pounds,** the 25,000,000 ft.lb. that we hope to get from 1 gall. of fuel. Let us see how far we can fly at the various air speeds. At 130 m.p.h. we shall get 25,000,000 divided by 2,380, i.e. about 10,500 ft. or 1·99 miles; at 140 m.p.h., 2·84 miles; at 160 m.p.h., 3·57 miles; at 180 m.p.h., 3·79 miles; at 200 m.p.h., 3·57 miles; at 220 m.p.h., 3·32 miles; and at 240 m.p.h., 2·84 miles. These will apply at all heights. If the load is 12,000 lb. instead of 10,000 lb., each distance must be divided by 1·2; if the load is less than 10,000 lb., each distance will be correspondingly greater.

Let us sum up this interesting argument: **in order to obtain the maximum range, we must fly at a given angle of attack, i.e. at a given air speed, we may fly at any height, and we should carry the minimum load; but if we must carry extra load, we must increase the air speed.**

That is the whole thing in a nutshell **from the aeroplane's point of**

view. Unfortunately, there are considerations of engine and propeller efficiency, and of wind, which may make it advisable to depart to some extent from these simple rules, and there are essential differences between jet and propeller propulsion in these respects. We cannot enter into these problems in detail, but a brief survey of the practical effects is given in the next paragraphs.

Another way of thinking of the significance of flying with minimum Drag is to divide the Total Drag into Induced Drag—which decreases in proportion to the square of the speed—and All-the-remainder of the Drag—which increases in proportion to the square of the speed. This idea is well illustrated in the numerical examples (page 353).

Effects of Height—Propeller Propulsion

So far as the aeroplane is concerned, we will get the same range and we should fly at the same indicated speed, whatever the height. Now, **although the Drag is the same** at the same indicated speed at all heights —the **power is not.** This may sound strange, but it is true and a very important fact. If it were not so, if we needed the same power to fly at the same indicated speed at all heights, then the advantage would always be to fly high, the higher the better, because for the same power the higher we went, the greater would be our true speed. However, it can hardly be considered a proof that an idea is incorrect simply because it would be very nice if it were correct. The real explanation is quite simple. Power is the **rate of doing work.** Our fuel gives us so many foot-pounds, **however long we take to use it**; it will do a certain amount of work irrespective of time. But if we want the work done quickly, if we want to pull with a certain **Thrust** through a certain **distance** in a certain **time,** then the power will depend on the Thrust **and** the distance **and** the time, in other words, on the **Thrust** and the **Velocity.** But which velocity, indicated or true? Perhaps it is easier to answer that if we put the question as, which **distance?** Well, there is only one distance, the actual distance moved, the **true** distance. So it is the **true air speed that settles the power. The higher we go, the greater is the true air speed for the same indicated speed and therefore the greater the power required,** although the Thrust and the Drag remain the same.

Now the modern supercharged reciprocating engine, unlike the old normally aspirated type, is designed to work most efficiently at some considerable height above sea-level. If we use it at sea-level, and if we fly at the best speed for range, the thrust will be a minimum, that is what we want, but, **owing to the low speed, little power will be required from the engine.** That may sound satisfactory, but actually it is not economical; the engine must be throttled, the venturi tube in its carburettor is partially closed, the engine is held in check and does not run at its designed power, and, what is more important, does not give of its best efficiency; we can say almost literally that it does not give best value for money. In some cases this effect is so marked that it actually pays us, if we **must** fly at sea-level, to fly considerably faster than our best speed and use more power, thereby using the aeroplane less efficiently but the engine more efficiently. But to obtain maximum range, both aircraft and engine should be used to best advantage, and this can easily be done if we choose a greater height such that when we fly at the correct indicated speed from the point of view of the aeroplane, the engine is also working most efficiently, that is to say, the throttle valve is fully open, but we can still fly with weak mixture. At this height, which may be, say, 10,000 ft., or 15,000 ft., we shall get the best out of both, and so will obtain the maximum range.

What happens at greater heights? At the same indicated speed we shall need more and more power; but if the throttle is fully open, we cannot get more power without using a richer mixture. Therefore we must either reduce speed and use the aircraft uneconomically, or we must enrich the mixture and use the engine uneconomically.

Thus there is a best height at which to fly, but the height is determined by engine efficiency (and to some extent by propeller efficiency) and not by the aircraft, which would be equally good at all heights. The best height is not usually very critical, nor is there generally any great loss in range by flying below that height. It may well be that considerations of wind, such as are explained in the next paragraph, make it advisable to do so.

Range Flying—Effects of Wind

If the flight is to be made from A towards B and back to A, then wind of any strength from any direction will adversely affect the radius of action. This fact, which at first sounds rather strange, but which is well known to all students of navigation, can easily be verified by working out a few simple examples, taking at first a head and tail wind, and then various cross-winds. But the wind usually changes in direction and increases in velocity with height, and so a skilful pilot can sometimes pick his height to best advantage and so gain more by getting the best, or the least bad, effect from the wind than he may lose by flying at a height that is slightly uneconomical from other points of view. It may pay him, too, to modify his air speed slightly according to the strength of the wind, but these are really problems of navigation rather than of the mechanics of flight.

Flying for Endurance—Propeller Propulsion

We may sometimes want to stay in the air for the longest possible time on a given quantity of fuel. This is **not** the same consideration as flying for maximum range. **To get maximum endurance, we must use the least possible fuel in a given time, that is to say, we must use minimum power.** But, as already explained, power means Drag × Velocity, the Velocity being true air speed. Let us look back to the table on page 165 showing total drag against air speed; multiply the Drag by the Air Speed and see what happens.

At 130 m.p.h.   Drag = 2,380 lb.   130 × 2380 = 309,400 (826 h.p.)
„ 140 m.p.h.   Drag = 1,670 lb.   140 × 1670 = 233,800 (623 h.p.)
„ 160 m.p.h.   Drag = 1,330 lb.   160 × 1330 = 212,800 (568 h.p.)
„ 180 m.p.h.   Drag = 1,250 lb.   180 × 1250 = 225,000 (600 h.p.)
„ 200 m.p.h.   Drag = 1,330 lb.   200 × 1330 = 266,000 (710 h.p.)
„ 220 m.p.h   Drag = 1,430 lb.   220 × 1430 = 314,600 (840 h.p.)
„ 240 m.p.h.   Drag = 1,670 lb.   240 × 1670 = 400,800 (1,070 h.p.)

[The figures have been multiplied direct to make the point clearer, and then converted into units of horse power by changing the m.p.h. to ft./sec. and dividing by 550.]

This table shows that, although the Drag is least at about 180 m.p.h., the Power is least at about 160 m.p.h. The explanation is quite simple; by flying slightly slower, we gain more (from the power point of view) by the reduced speed than we lose by the increased drag.

Therefore the speed for best endurance is less than the speed for best range and, since we are now concerned with **true** speed, the **lower the height, the better.**

The endurance speed is apt to be uncomfortably low for accurate flying; even the best range speed is not always too easy and, as neither is very critical, the pilot is often recommended to fly at a somewhat higher speed.

The reader who would like to consider endurance flying a little further should look back to page 86. Here he will find some of the desirable qualities of a good aerofoil. No. 3 was a good Lift/Drag ratio —the quality required to obtain maximum range. No. 4 was a high maximum value of $C_L^{\frac{3}{2}}/C_D$—the quality which means minimum power, i.e. maximum endurance. There we were considering only the aerofoil, and the aeroplane is not quite the same thing as regards values, but the idea is the same. So for endurance flying we must present the aeroplane to the air at the angle of attack that gives the best value of $C_L^{\frac{3}{2}}/C_D$ (for the aeroplane), and this will be a greater angle of attack and so a slower speed, than for range.

Flying for Range—Jet Propulsion

In trying to get maximum range or endurance out of any aircraft we are, in effect, simply trying to get maximum value for money, the value being the range or endurance and the money being the fuel used. We shall only get the maximum overall efficiency if in turn we get the maximum efficiency **at each stage** of the conversion of the fuel into useful work done. The three main stages are **the engine,** the **system of propulsion,** and the **aeroplane.**

This applies to **every type of aircraft**—it is necessary to emphasize this point because there seems to be a growing tendency to think that jet or rocket propulsion involves completely new principles. This is not so—the principles are exactly the same, the only difference lies in the degree of importance of the various efficiencies.

From the point of view of an aeroplane, as an aeroplane, flying for maximum Range means flying with minimum Drag. It is in that condition that the aeroplane is most efficient no matter by what means it is driven. But if, when we fly with minimum Drag, either the propulsive system, or the engine, or both, are hopelessly inefficient—then, rather obviously, it will pay us to make some compromise, probably by flying rather faster than the minimum Drag speed.

From the point of view of an aeroplane, as an aeroplane, we shall obtain the same Range at whatever height we fly, provided we fly in the attitude of minimum Drag. But if at some heights the propulsive system, or the engine, or both, are more efficient than at other heights—then, rather obviously, it will pay us to fly at those heights so as to get the maximum overall value out of the engine-propulsion-aeroplane system.

Now an aeroplane is an aeroplane whether it is driven by propeller or jet and, as an aeroplane, the same rules for Range flying will apply. But when the efficiencies of the propulsive system and the engine are included the overall effects are rather different. In the propeller-driven aeroplane we do not go far wrong if we obey the aeroplane rules although, even so, it usually pays us to fly rather faster than the minimum Drag speed because, by so doing, engine and propeller efficiency is improved—and flying is more comfortable. It also definitely pays us to fly at a certain height because at that height the engine-propeller combination is more efficient. But in the **main it is the aeroplane efficiency that decides the issue. Not so with the jet aircraft.**

There are two important reasons for the difference—

1. **Whereas the Thrust of a propeller falls off as forward speed increases, the Thrust of a jet is nearly constant at all speeds (at the same r.p.m.).**

2. **Whereas the fuel consumption in a reciprocating engine is approximately proportional to the power developed, the fuel consumption in jet propulsion is approximately proportional to the Thrust.**

Both of these are really connected with the fact that the efficiency of the jet propulsion system increases with speed, and this increase in

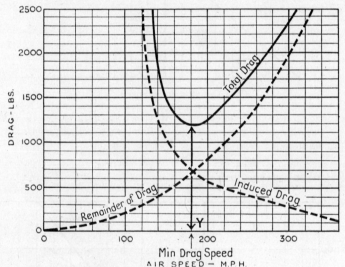

FIG. 114. FLYING FOR MAXIMUM RANGE: HOW THE TOTAL
DRAG IS MADE UP

Induced Drag decreases with square of speed. Remainder of Drag increases with square of speed. Total Drag is the sum of the two. Air speed of Minimum Drag 180 m.p.h. (*Y*).

efficiency is so important that it is absolutely necessary to take it into account, as well as the efficiency of the aeroplane. When we do so we find that **we shall get greater Range if we fly a great deal faster than the minimum Drag speed.** The Drag will be slightly greater—not much, because we are on the low portion of the curve (Fig. 114)—the Thrust, being equal to the Drag, will also of course be slightly greater, and so will the fuel consumption in gallons per hour. The speed, on the other hand, will be considerably greater and so we shall get more miles per hour. Everything, in fact, depends on getting the **maximum of speed compared with Thrust,** or speed compared with Drag. In short, we **must fly at minimum Drag/Speed** which as the figure shows, **will always occur at a higher speed than that giving minimum Drag. So to get maximum Range jet aircraft must fly faster than propeller-driven**

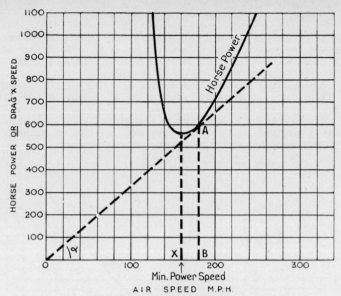

FIG. 115. FLYING FOR MAXIMUM ENDURANCE

Showing Minimum Power Speed of 160 m.p.h. (X). When OA is a tangent to the Horse Power curve the value of $\frac{AB}{OB}$ will be least. But

$$\frac{AB}{OB} = \frac{\text{Power}}{\text{Speed}} = \frac{\text{Drag} \times \text{Speed}}{\text{Speed}} = \text{Drag}.$$

Therefore Minimum Drag is at air speed of point B, i.e. at 180 m.p.h. (see Fig. 114)

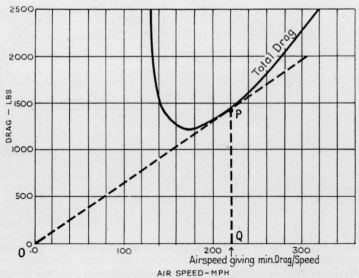

FIG. 116. FLYING FOR RANGE—JET PROPULSION

Showing how the tangent OP to the curve of Total Drag gives the air speed (220 m.p.h.) of minimum Drag/Speed.

aircraft—the difference being due to the different relationship between propulsive efficiency and speed in the two systems.

As a matter of interest let us go back to our table of figures and work out for each speed the value of Drag/Speed—

At 130 m.p.h. . . . . Drag/Speed = 2380/130 = 18·3
„ 140 m.p.h. . . . . Drag/Speed = 1670/140 = 11·9
„ 160 m.p.h. . . . . Drag/Speed = 1330/160 = 8·3
„ 180 m.p.h. . . . . Drag/Speed = 1250/180 = 6·9
„ 200 m.p.h. . . . . Drag/Speed = 1330/200 = 6·6
„ 220 m.p.h. . . . . Drag/Speed = 1430/220 = 6·5
„ 240 m.p.h. . . . . Drag/Speed = 1670/240 = 7·0

Note that the minimum value for Drag/Speed is at 220 m.p.h., so the range speed for this aircraft, if driven by jets, is 220 m.p.h. instead of 180 m.p.h.

At what height shall we fly? That is an easy one to answer. We know that it makes no difference as far as the efficiency of the aeroplane

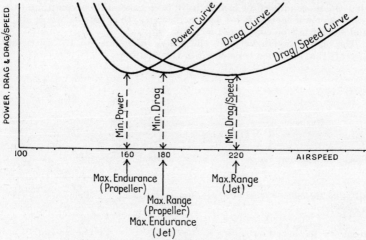

FIG. 117. POWER, DRAG AND DRAG/SPEED CURVES
Showing minimum points of each.

is concerned—but it makes all the difference to the efficiency of jet propulsion. The aircraft will be in the same attitude, and we shall get the same Drag and the same Thrust, if we fly at the same indicated speed at altitude—**but the true speed will be greater.** Now it is the true speed that settles the propulsive efficiency (it is just a question of momentum) so at **40,000 ft.,** where the true speed is doubled, **the efficiency will be doubled,** and, provided the fuel consumption remains proportional to Thrust, **the range will be doubled. So to get Range on jet aircraft—fly high.**

Flying for Endurance—Jet Propulsion

If the argument has been followed so far, there will be no difficulty in understanding the problem of maximum Endurance for jet-driven aircraft. Since fuel consumption is proportional to Thrust, we shall get **maximum Endurance by flying with minimum Thrust,** i.e. **with minimum**

Drag. So the endurance speed of a jet aircraft corresponds to the Range speed of a propeller-driven aircraft (180 m.p.h. in our example) and, from the comfort point of view, this makes the jet aircraft easier to fly in the condition of maximum Endurance.

Since the Thrust, and hence the consumption, should be the same at the same indicated speed at any height, it should not matter at what height we fly for Endurance. Actually, when engine efficiency is taken into account, there are advantages in flying high.

Summary

The table below summarizes the difference between jet and propeller-driven aircraft so far as Range and Endurance are concerned. It must be considered as a first approximation only—it takes into account the aeroplane efficiency for the propeller-driven type (neglecting propeller and engine efficiency), and both aeroplane and propulsive efficiency for the jet-driven type (neglecting engine efficiency). All this means is that the more important factors have been taken into account, and the less important factors have been neglected. It is **not** the whole story, and should not be considered as such.

The figures in brackets are the speeds in m.p.h. for the particular aircraft that has been considered in this chapter.

	Propeller	Jet
Speed for Maximum Range . .	Minimum Drag (180)	Minimum Drag/Speed (220)
Height for Maximum Range . .	Unimportant	High
Speed for Maximum Endurance .	Minimum Power (160)	Minimum Drag (180)
Height for Maximum Endurance .	Low	Unimportant

Now try these—

1. What are the four most important forces which act upon an aeroplane during flight?

2. What are the conditions of equilibrium of these four forces?

3. Are these forces likely to alter in value, and to move their line of action during flight?

4. What are the functions of the tail plane in an aeroplane?

5. What is meant by a "non-lifting" tail plane?

6. What are the advantages of an adjustable tail plane?

7. What are the special problems connected with a flying boat in so far as the balance of the four main forces is concerned?

8. Explain how it is that an aeroplane can fly level at a wide range of air speeds.

9. Is the relationship between air speed and angle of attack the same at height as at sea-level?

10. What is the effect of weight on the relationship between air speed and angle of attack?

11. From the point of view of aeroplane efficiency—
    (a) At what angle of attack will we get maximum range?
    (b) Will this angle be the same at all heights and at all loads?

12. On a propeller-driven aircraft—
    (a) Why will we get less range if we fly too high?
    (b) At what height should we fly for best endurance?
    (c) Why is the air speed for best endurance different from the air speed for best range?

13. Why are these problems different on jet-driven aircraft?

14. On a jet-driven aircraft—
    (a) Under what conditions should we fly for maximum range?
    (b) At what height should we fly for maximum range?
    (c) At what speed and height should we fly for maximum endurance?

On page 351 you will find some simple numerical examples on the problems of Level Flight.

CHAPTER VI

GLIDING AND LANDING

Gliding

LET us next consider the flight of an aeroplane while **gliding** under the influence of the force of gravity and without the use of the engine.

Of the four forces, Lift, Weight, Thrust, and Drag, we are now deprived of the Thrust, and therefore when the aeroplane is travelling in a steady glide it must be kept in a state of equilibrium by the Lift, Drag, and Weight only. This means that the total reaction—that is to say, the resultant of the Lift and Drag—must be exactly equal and opposite to the Weight (see Fig. 118). If the reader remembers our original

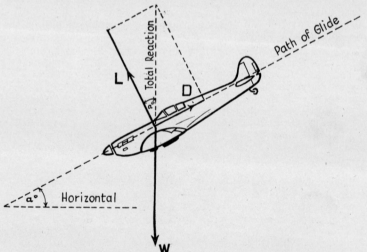

FIG. 118. FORCES ACTING ON AN AEROPLANE DURING A GLIDE

definition of Lift and Drag, he will realize that the Lift is now not vertical, but at right angles to the path of the glide, while the **Drag** acts directly backwards parallel to the gliding path.

Gliding Angle

By a process of simple geometry, it is easy to see that the angle formed between the Lift and the Total Reaction is the same as the angle a between the path of the glide and the horizontal, which is called the **Gliding Angle.**

Therefore (by Trigonometry) $D/L = \tan a$.

This means that the less the value of D/L—i.e. **the greater the value of L/D—the flatter will be the gliding angle.**

From this simple fact we can very easily come to some important conclusions; for instance—

1. The Gliding Angle is directly dependent on the L/D, which is

really the "efficiency" of the design of the aeroplane, and therefore the more "efficient" the aeroplane, the further it will glide, or, expressing it the other way round, the **measurement of the angle of glide will give a simple estimate of the " efficiency " of the aeroplane.**

The word "efficiency" is apt to have a rather vague meaning, and the reader must understand that we are using it here in a particular sense only—we are not concerned with its efficiency as regards engine power, nor with the merits of its internal structure from the standpoint of weight for strength. We are concerned only with the success or otherwise of the designer in obtaining the maximum amount of Lift with the minimum of Drag, or what is sometimes called the "aerodynamic" merit of the aeroplane. For instance, our conclusion shows that any improvement in streamlining which reduces the Drag will result in a flatter gliding angle.

It will be noticed that this is the same criterion as for maximum range, so that an aeroplane that has a flat gliding angle should also be efficient at flying for range. This is undoubtedly true; but, owing to the effects of slipstream and so on, there are slight differences between the values of Lift/Drag when the engine is on and when it is off.

2. **If an aeroplane is to glide as far as possible, the Angle of Attack during the glide must be such that the Lift/Drag is a maximum.**

The aeroplane is so constructed that the Riggers' Angle of Incidence is a small angle of, say, 2° or 3°. This particular angle is chosen because it is the most suitable for level flight. As was explained when considering the characteristics of aerofoils, the modern tendency is to make this angle rather less than the angle of maximum L/D (because we are out for speed rather than economy), but, even so, it will be within a degree or so of that angle, so it is true to say that the Angle of Attack during a flat glide will be very nearly the same as the Angle of Attack during straight and level flight, and almost exactly the same as when flying for maximum range.

The pilot finds it fairly easy to maintain ordinary horizontal flight at the most efficient angle because his fuselage is then in a more or less horizontal position and the horizon is a considerable help to him. When gliding, however, his task is by no means so easy. It would be very little use to tell a pilot that, if he wishes to glide a certain aeroplane the greatest distance, he must keep his wings at an angle of 3°, for he has no instrument nor any other means of knowing the Angle of Attack. Fortunately, as in level flight, there is a direct connection between the air speed and the Angle of Attack for any given aeroplane, and therefore the air speed can be found which gives the best gliding angle, and this acts as a guide to the pilot. The fact remains, however, that it requires considerable skill, instinct, or whatever one likes to call it, on the part of a pilot to glide at the flattest possible angle. This is the type of skill which is especially needed by the pilot of a motorless glider or sail-plane.

It should be noted that, although there is a relationship between air speed and angle of attack on the glide just as there is in level flight, the relationship is not exactly the same, and the speed that gives the flattest gliding angle is usually rather less than the speed that gives maximum range. The difference, however, is small and the principle is the same.

3. **If the pilot attempts to glide at an Angle of Attack either greater or less than that which gives the best L/D, then in each case the path of descent will be steeper.**

Perhaps this conclusion may be considered redundant because it is simply another way of expressing the preceding one. It is purposely repeated in this form because there seems to be such a strong natural instinct on the part of pilots learning to fly and of students of the subject to think that if the aeroplane is put in a more horizontal attitude it will glide farther. Even if one has never flown it is not difficult to imagine the feelings of a pilot whose engine has failed, and who is trying to reach a certain field in which to make a forced landing.

PLATE XXXI. GLIDING

The " Gull IV " high performance sailplane with good L/D ratio owing to the clean design and the high aspect ratio of the wings.
(*By courtesy of Slingsby Sailplanes Ltd.*)

It gradually dawns on him that in the way in which he is gliding he will not reach that field. What, then, could be more natural than that he should pull up the nose of his aeroplane in his efforts to reach it? What happens? In answer to this question the student often says that he will stall the aeroplane. Not necessarily. He should in the first place have been gliding nowhere near the stalling angle, but at an Angle of Attack of only about 3° or 4°, so that he has many degrees through which to increase the angle before stalling. But what will most certainly happen is that the increase in angle will decrease the value of L/D and so increase the gliding angle, and although the aeroplane will lie flatter to the horizontal, it will glide towards the earth at a steeper angle, and will not reach even so far as it would otherwise have done. The air speed during such a glide will be less than that which gives the best gliding angle.

Suppose, on the other hand, that, when a pilot is gliding at the Angle of Attack which gives him his greatest value of L/D, he puts the nose of the aeroplane down, this will decrease the Angle of Attack, which will, as before, decrease the value of L/D and therefore increase the

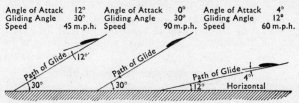

Angle of Attack	12°	Angle of Attack	0°	Angle of Attack	4°
Gliding Angle	30°	Gliding Angle	30°	Gliding Angle	12°
Speed	45 m.p.h.	Speed	90 m.p.h.	Speed	60 m.p.h.

FIG. 119. HOW THE ANGLE OF ATTACK AFFECTS THE GLIDING ANGLE

steepness of the gliding path, the air speed this time being greater than that which gives the best gliding angle.

There is a certain amount of difficulty in visualizing the Angle of

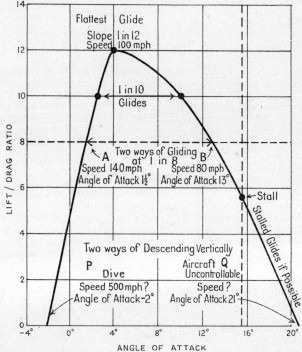

FIG. 120. LIFT/DRAG CURVE AND GLIDING ANGLES

Attack during a glide; it is, of course, the angle between the chord of the wings and the actual path followed by the aeroplane during the glide. The reader must be careful not to be confused between the direction in which the aeroplane is pointing and the direction in which it is actually travelling. It is hoped that the figures may help to make this important point clear (Fig. 119).

In the previous chapter we discovered that the ratio of Lift to Drag of complete aeroplanes may be in the neighbourhood of 8, 10, or 12 to 1. These values will correspond to Gliding Angles of which the Tangents are $\frac{1}{8}$, $\frac{1}{10}$ and $\frac{1}{12}$, i.e. approximately angles of 7°, 6° and 5° respectively. Thus, neglecting the effect of wind, a pilot will usually be in error on the right side if he assumes that he can glide one mile for every 1,000 ft. of height, i.e. if he reckons on a Gliding Angle of which the Tangent is 1/5·28.

Real and Apparent Angles of Glide

Perhaps it may be as well to remind the reader once again that all we have said with reference to gliding must be considered **as relative to the air.** To an observer on the ground an aeroplane gliding into the

FIG. 121. EFFECT OF WIND ON ANGLE OF
GLIDE RELATIVE TO THE EARTH

wind may appear to remain still or, in some cases, even to ascend. In such instances there must be a wind blowing which has both a horizontal and an upward velocity, and to an observer travelling on this wind in a balloon the aeroplane would appear to be both travelling forwards and descending. When viewed from the ground an aeroplane gliding against the wind will appear to glide more steeply, and when gliding with the wind will appear to glide less steeply than the real angle measured relative to the air (Fig. 121).

Effect of Weight on Gliding

It is commonly thought that heavy aeroplanes should glide more steeply than light aeroplanes, but a moment's reflection will make one realize that the principle that has already been explained, namely, that the gliding angle depends on the ratio of Lift to Drag, is quite independent of the weight. Probably another moment's reflection will reveal the simple fact that modern aeroplanes, which are heavier in every respect than old types, have a much flatter gliding angle. No, neither in principle nor in fact does weight have an appreciable influence on the gliding angle, **but what it does affect is the air speed during the glide.**

Look back for a moment at Fig. 118. Imagine an increase in the line representing the Weight; there will need to be a corresponding increase in the Total Reaction, and a greater Lift and a greater Drag. But the proportions will all remain exactly the same, the same Lift/Drag ratio, the same gliding angle. But the greater Lift, and greater Drag, can only be got by greater speed. If we now think back to flying for range, it will be remembered that the condition was the same: greater weight meant greater speed. But there is an interesting and important difference in this case. In flying for range, greater speed meant greater Drag, greater Thrust, and so less range. In gliding without engine power, greater speed means greater Drag, but now the "thrust" is provided by the component of the Weight which acts along the gliding path and this, of course, is automatically greater because the Weight is greater. **So greater Weight does not affect the gliding angle and does not affect the range,** on a pure glide—**but it does affect the speed.**

Endurance on the Glide

The conclusion of the previous paragraph might perhaps lead one to ask whether, in that case, there is any need for a sail-plane to be built

PLATE XXXII. EFFECT OF SPOILERS ON GLIDING

The "Gull IV" with spoilers, or air brakes, in action to spoil the L/D ratio and thus to steepen the gliding angle and take off surplus speed before landing.

(*By courtesy of Slingsby Sailplanes Ltd.*)

of light construction. The answer is definitely—Yes. A sailplane must have a flat gliding angle if it is to get any distance, any range from its starting point; but, even more important, it must have a **low rate of vertical descent or sinking speed ;** it must be able to stay a long time in the air and be able to take advantage of every breath of rising air, however slight. It is easy to see that **the rate of vertical descent** depends **both** on the **angle of glide** and on the **air speed during the glide.** Therefore to get a low rate of descent we need a good Lift/Drag ratio, i.e. good aerodynamic design, and a low air speed, i.e. low weight.

Actually we shall get a lower rate of descent by reducing speed below that which gives the flattest glide; this is because we gain more by the lower air speed than we lose by the steeper glide. Thus there is an "endurance" speed for gliding just as for level flight and, as before, it is lower than the range speed.

Disadvantages of Flat Gliding Angle

It should not be thought, from what has been said about gliding, **that a flat gliding angle is always an advantage;** when approaching a small aerodrome near the edge of which are high obstacles, such as trees or hangars, it is very necessary to reach the ground as soon as possible after passing over such obstacles. In these circumstances a flat gliding angle will be a definite disadvantage, and even if the aeroplane is dived steeply it will pick up such speed that it will still tend to "float" across the aerodrome before touching the ground.

The gliding angle can be steepened by reducing the ratio of Lift to Drag; this can be done by decreasing the angle of attack (resulting in

PLATE XXXIII. GLIDING IN TO LAND

The Airspeed "Oxford" (famous twin-engined trainer of the Second World War) gliding in to land, with flaps and undercarriage lowered.
(*By courtesy of "The Aeroplane."*)

too high a speed as already mentioned), or by increasing the angle of attack (resulting in an air speed which may be too low for safety), or by using an "air brake." The last is by far the most satisfactory means of steepening the gliding angle as required, and the air brake usually takes the form of some kind of flap, such as was described in the chapter on Aerofoils. The effect of flaps on the approach and landing will be considered in the following paragraphs.

Landing

The art of landing an aeroplane consists of bringing it in contact with the ground at the lowest possible vertical velocity and, at the same time, the lowest possible horizontal velocity relative to the ground. It is true that under certain circumstances a "fast landing" may be permissible, but the above rule applies to the majority of landings, and especially to "forced landings," in which everything usually depends on the minimum horizontal velocity obtainable. The act of landing is in many ways similar to stalling. The chief difference is that in landing the aeroplane must be in a definite attitude relative to the ground, whereas when stalling it may be in almost any attitude such as gliding, climbing or turning.

The reader will have noticed that it is the horizontal velocity **relative to the ground** which must be as low as possible. Now, the first step in this direction is to land against the wind and so reduce the **ground speed.** This, however, is entirely up to the pilot; in our present problem

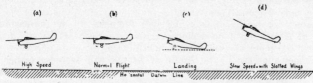

Fig. 122. Attitudes for Level Flight

we are only concerned with obtaining the least possible **air speed.** When this has been obtained, the pilot can combine the two and so obtain a low ground speed. In the case of landing on the decks of ships, if the ship herself steams into the wind, the ground speed will be still further reduced. Supposing, for instance, the minimum air speed of an aeroplane is 80 m.p.h., the wind speed is 20 m.p.h., and the ship is steaming at 30 m.p.h. into the wind, then the "ground" speed" of the aeroplane when landing will be only 30 m.p.h.; while if the wind speed had been 50 m.p.h., the "ground speed" would have been reduced to nil—a perfectly possible state of affairs.

In an early chapter it was mentioned that the wind speed is apt to be irregular near the ground, and it is when landing that such irregularity may be very important. If the wind speed suddenly decreases, the aircraft, owing to its inertia, will tend to continue at the same ground speed and will therefore lose air speed, and, if already flying near the critical speed, may stall. Similarly, if the wind speed suddenly increases, the aircraft will temporarily gain air speed and will "balloon" upwards, making it difficult to make contact with the ground at the right moment. Such instances may occur in changeable and gusty winds, in up-currents caused by heating of parts of the earth's surface, in cases of turbulence caused by the wind flowing over obstructions such as hills and hangars, and due to wind gradient. Of these, wind gradient is probably the most important, and the most easily allowed for. An aeroplane, when landing against a high wind, will encounter a decreasing wind speed as it descends through the last few feet and will be in danger of stalling unless it has speed in hand to compensate for the air speed lost. If landing up a slope or towards a hangar, one may suddenly run into air which is blanketed by the obstruction, or a head wind may even become a following wind blowing up the hill or towards the hangar. In a really high wind these conditions may be dangerous, and the obvious moral is to allow for them by approaching to land at a higher speed than usual.

The vertical velocity of landing can be reduced to practically nothing provided the forward velocity is sufficient to keep the aeroplane temporarily in horizontal flight—that is to say, provided the Lift of the wings is sufficient to balance the Weight of the aeroplane.

We have already seen that there is a definite relationship between the indicated air speed and the angle of attack. Fig. 122 illustrates the attitudes of a certain aeroplane at various speeds and the corresponding angles of attack required to maintain level flight: (a) shows the attitude of maximum velocity; (b) that of normal cruising flight; (c) that for an ordinary landing; and (d) the attitude when fitted with slotted wings and flying as slowly as possible.

Now, since Lift must equal Weight, and must also equal $C_L \cdot \frac{1}{2}\rho V^2$. S, it is **quite obvious that if** V **is to be as small as possible,** C_L **must be as large as possible.** The pilot may never have heard of a Lift coefficient, and he may be none the worse a pilot for that; but none the less, consciously or unconsciously, he **will increase** C_L **by increasing the Angle of Attack until he decides** (it matters not whether his decision is based on scientific knowledge, instinct or bitter experience!) **that any further increase in the Angle of Attack will decrease rather than increase his Lift**; in other words, until he has reached that **Stalling Angle** which we considered so fully when dealing with aerofoils. At this angle (about 15° to 20° in the case of an ordinary aerofoil), C_L is at its maximum, and therefore V is a minimum.

If the pilot, through lack of any of the three qualities mentioned above, exceeds this angle, then both C_L and V will decrease; therefore $C_L \cdot \frac{1}{2}\rho V^2$. S can no longer equal the weight and the aeroplane will commence to drop vertically! For 50 ft., 100 ft., or more, this vertical velocity will increase and the nose of the aeroplane will drop, therefore the pilot must beware that, when he does this experiment of flying as slowly as possible, he is either very near the ground or at a considerable height above it. In fact, landings should not be practised between 1 ft. and 2,000 ft. from the earth's surface, and the whole skill of the pilot is exercised in approaching the ground in such a manner that he has reached the above-mentioned condition of affairs just as he skims over the blades of grass on the aerodrome, provided, of course, that he has sufficient clear run in front in which to pull up after landing.

Stalling Speed

All that has been said above applies not only to level flight, but to stalls when gliding, climbing or even when turning; for instance, the pilot will find that when banking on a turn the Lift on the wings must be greater than the Weight, and therefore the stalling speed is higher than when landing. Also at height the air density ρ will be less, and this means that in order to keep $C_L \cdot \frac{1}{2}\rho V^2$. S equal to the Weight, the stalling speed V will be greater than at ground level. This fact is not, however, of great importance, for two reasons—first because where the pilot is at a considerable height, an accidental stall does not matter, as there is plenty of time to recover; and, secondly, because, although the stalling speed is in reality greater, the **air speed indicator,** which is in itself worked by the effect of the air density, **will record the same speed when the aeroplane stalls** as it did at ground level; in other words, the **indicated stalling speeds** will remain the same at all heights.

This consideration of the air density shows us that on high aerodromes, such as are found in mountainous countries, the true landing speed of an aeroplane will be appreciably higher than on sea-level aerodromes. Also in tropical countries the high temperature decreases the air density and thus increases the landing speed. The taking-out speed, and the run required, are also increased in both these cases, and this is perhaps an even more important consideration.

When stalling intentionally—for amusement or for training purposes —the aeroplane is pulled into a steeply climbing attitude and the air speed allowed to drop to practically nil until the nose suddenly drops or, as frequently happens, one wing drops and the aeroplane commences to dive or spin. It is simply a case of "the same, only more so."

Before leaving the subject of stalling it might be as well to mention that there has always been difficulty in deciding upon an exact definition of stalling or stalling speed. The stall occurs because the smooth airflow over the wing becomes turbulent—**but this is a gradual process.** At quite small angles of attack there is some turbulence near the trailing edge ; as the angle increases, the turbulence spreads forward. What is even more important is that it also spreads fanwise, usually from tip to root on highly-tapered wings, and from root to tip on rectangular wings. **If we define the stall as being the break up of the airflow, when did it occur? and how do we know that it has occurred?** There may be buffeting of the tail plane or main planes, but this too may be slight and unimportant, or it may be violent. As a result of the change from smooth to turbulent air flow the curve of Lift Coefficient reaches a maximum and then starts to fall. We defined the stalling angle in Chapter III as the **angle at which the Lift Coefficient is a maximum. But how does the pilot know that it is at its maximum value? In any case, how does he know at what angle of attack he is flying? All the pilot knows is that if he tries to fly below a certain speed he gets into difficulties.** How great the difficulties depends on the type of aircraft, and the extent to which the pilot can overcome them depends on a lot of things but particularly on his own skill. **Some pilots can fly at lower speeds than others—so which is the stalling speed?**

In fact, there are different definitions of stalling according to the point of view of the person who wishes to define it—the pilot looks at it one way, the aerodynamicist another, and so on. What is important is that each should realize that it is his own definition, and that all these things do not necessarily occur at the same time.

Possibilities of Lower Landing Speeds

Before leaving the subject of landing and stalling, we must consider the **possibilities of reducing this minimum velocity of flight.**

In all forms of transport, with the exception of flying, the maximum velocity attainable is the chief consideration ; in fact. it is really the only consideration, because the minimum velocity may usually be reduced to nothing and in many cases reversed. But in the exceptional case of flight it is equally important to obtain a low minimum velocity as it is to obtain a high maximum velocity. This low velocity of landing is of such importance that it is apt to be exaggerated at the expense of the maximum velocity. Whatever we say about obtaining a low landing velocity, **we must never forget that the chief advantage of flight over other means of transport depends entirely on the high velocity obtainable.** But provided we bear this in mind, everything must be done to reduce the landing speed, because only in this way can flying be made a popular and safe means of transport. The landing speed of most ordinary aeroplanes is as much as 60 or 70 m.p.h. and of some aeroplanes more than 100 m.p.h. ; imagine a motor-car which could not travel at less than 100 m.p.h. when under power. That is all very well, the reader will say, but aeroplanes are intended to land on a special aerodrome with plenty of room in which to pull up. Yes, that is just the point; and while aeroplanes can only land on large aerodromes, they can never become either popular or safe. They cannot be popular because everyone does not live even within easy reach of such an aerodrome, and they cannot be safe because, in the event of a "forced landing," the aerodrome is not likely to be available.

High Lift Aerofoils

What, then, has been done, and what can yet be done to decrease landing speed? If V is to be small, C_L must be as large as possible.

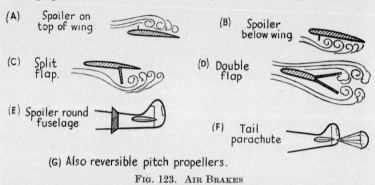

(A) Spoiler on top of wing.

(B) Spoiler below wing

(C) Split flap.

(D) Double flap

(E) Spoiler round fuselage

(F) Tail parachute

(G) Also reversible pitch propellers.

FIG. 123. AIR BRAKES

In other words, we must have a larger Lift coefficient. So the aerofoils which give the largest maximum Lift coefficient will give the lowest landing speeds. Unfortunately, however, these aerofoils are usually those with a large Drag, and so they seriously affect the high speed end of the range. Therefore we must turn to some device by which the shape of the aerofoil can be altered during flight, and so we naturally think of flaps and slots.

In an earlier chapter (Fig. 73) we noticed the effect of various kinds of flaps and slots on maximum Lift and speed range. The idea of variable camber is an old one, but it is only in recent years, when maximum speeds have increased so much, that the problem has become really urgent and these devices have come into their own. In this respect necessity has proved to be the mother of invention, and many and varied have been the devices which have been tried. It is not easy to compare the respective merits of all these types of slots and flaps, or combinations of slot and flap, because so many conflicting qualities are required. If a low landing speed was our **only** aim, the problem would be comparatively simple, the device giving the highest maximum Lift coefficient being the most suitable. But what we really need is a **low landing speed and a high maximum speed, i.e. a good speed range.** This condition means that the device must be such that it can be altered, or will alter automatically, from the position giving maximum Lift (e.g. slot open or flap down), to the position of minimum Drag (e.g. slot closed or flap neutral). Even that is not the end of our requirements for, having landed as slowly as possible, we must pull up quickly after landing. The former (slow landing) needs high Lift, the latter (quick pull-up) needs much Drag, Lift being of no consequence at all. For a quick pull-up we really need a definite "air brake" which will assist the wheel brakes. Notice, however, that an air brake cannot reduce actual landing speed, it can only improve the pull-up **after** landing.

Yet another aspect of the problem is the question of **attitude** of landing, and in this respect slotted wings seem to be at a disadvantage in comparison with most types of flap, for they attain their maximum Lift coefficient at a greater Angle of Attack than is the case with the ordinary aerofoil; this means that in order to make full use of the slots the Angle of Attack when landing may need to be 25°, or even more. Now, when an ordinary aeroplane rests with its wheels and tail skid on the ground, the angle of

(a)   (b)   Horizontal Datum Line (c)   (d)

Taif Skid First   High Undercarriage   Variable Incidence   Large Riggers'
Angle of Incidence

FIG. 124. DIFFICULTIES OF LANDING AT LARGE ANGLES OF ATTACK
WITH SLOTTED WINGS

inclination of the wings is only in the neighbourhood of 15°. (The reader who is interested should check this angle on several types of aeroplane, not those with tricycle undercarriages because their attitude on the ground is approximately that of normal flight and not of landing.) So that, in order to land at an angle of 25°, we are faced with four possibilities (Fig. 124), all of which have serious drawbacks—

1. To allow the tail to touch the ground before the wheels (Fig. 124, a). This is obviously not a practical solution.

2. To have a much higher undercarriage (Fig. 124, b). This will cause extra drag and probably do more harm than good.

3. To provide the main planes with a variable incidence gear similar to that which was used for tail planes (Fig. 124, c). This idea was often suggested before the introduction of slots, when it could have been of no real use. However, with the modern possibility of using very large Angles of Attack, it might be well worth while reconsidering the question, although there are obviously considerable mechanical difficulties barring the way.

4. To set the wings at a much greater angle to the fuselage (Fig. 124, d). This will mean that in normal flight the rear portion of the fuselage will stick up into the air at an angle which not only looks ridiculous, but which is an inefficient angle from the point of view of reducing drag.

The last-named method gives the fuselage the appearance of a "broken back," and it has sometimes been employed not only for the purpose of providing a large Angle of Attack for slow landing, but also so that **after landing the Drag on the wings will help to pull the aeroplane up in a short distance**; it is therefore obviously suitable for deck-landing aeroplanes.

Slotted wings do definitely provide us with a real, and by no means negligible, reduction in landing speed, provided they extend the full length of the wings. The reader may have noticed that in many cases slots are only fitted near the wing tips, but the full explanation of this fact will land us in a discussion on control and stability, which we must leave to a later chapter, although it might be as well to mention, even at this stage, that, assuming we can solve the problem of flying more slowly, we immediately find ourselves up against an even greater problem—namely, that of controlling the movements of the aeroplane at these low velocities.

On biplanes with forward stagger, slots are usually fitted to the top plane only; this is because experiments show that the airflow over the top plane of a biplane becomes turbulent at a smaller angle than that flowing over the bottom plane; in other words, the top plane of a biplane is the first to stall. With backward stagger, however, the position is reversed—the bottom plane stalls first, and therefore slots are fitted to the bottom plane.

PLATE XXXIV. ABOUT TO LAND

The "Sea Vampire" about to land on the deck of a carrier—with undercarriage, flaps and arrester hook all lowered and ready to check the landing run.

(*By courtesy of the De Havilland Aircraft Co. Ltd.*)

Variable Wing Area

We assumed, at an earlier stage, that the Area of the Wings was bound to remain constant, but we ought to mention that inventors have from time to time investigated the problem of providing wings of variable area.

$$\text{Since } W = C_{\mathrm{L}} \cdot \tfrac{1}{2}\rho V^2 \cdot S$$
$$W/S = C_{\mathrm{L}} \cdot \tfrac{1}{2}\rho V^2$$

The fraction W/S, Weight divided by Wing Area, is called the " Wing Loading " of the aeroplane. An increase in the Wing Area will reduce the value of W/S and therefore reduce the landing velocity.

The objections to variable area are chiefly mechanical; the operating gear will mean extra weight, and therefore, since W will increase, it by no means follows that the value of W/S will actually be decreased. Also let it be remembered that neither the aeroplane designer nor the pilot is particularly anxious for more "gadgets" of this kind: for the designer they spell more Drag and more Weight; for the pilot more levers to fiddle with, more chances of something going wrong. So the inventor must beware that in his attempts to solve these problems he does not incur the wrath of these important people; he may rest assured that without their co-operation his invention will not go very far.

Wing Loading

Apart from the question of altering the Wing Area during flight, the equation $W/S = C_{\mathrm{L}} \cdot \frac{1}{2}\rho V^2$ shows us that, **other things being equal, the aeroplane with a small Wing Loading will have a lower landing speed than the one with a high Wing Loading.** The so-called "light aeroplane" may, of course, have a high Wing Loading and therefore a high landing speed; in other words, it is not a question of weight, but of weight compared with wing area, that settles the landing speed. The Wing Loading of a sail-plane may be less than 2 lb. per sq. ft. of wing area, of a training aeroplane 7 to 20 lb. per sq. ft., of a fighter or bomber anything from 30 up to 40, 50, or more lb. per sq. ft. The modern tendency is to increase Wing Loading by reducing Wing Area and thus raising the maximum speed, and then using flaps to keep down the landing speed. One already hears rumours of loadings of up to 100 lb. per sq. ft. The student is advised to work out the Wing Loading of existing aeroplanes and to compare the figures obtained with their landing speeds; in making this comparison, however, he must be careful to notice the above phrase, "other things being equal," because the maximum lift coefficient of the aerofoil used also affects the result. An old example of very high Wing Loading was the 41·3 lb. per sq. ft. of the S.6b Schneider Trophy racing seaplane; the corresponding figure for fighters like the "Spitfire" and "Hurricane" at the beginning of the war was 24·8 lb. per sq. ft. and for the German fighter, Messerschmitt 109, 31·8 lb. per sq. ft. Modern figures for both fighters and bombers are considerably higher than these.

Method of Finding Landing Speed

It is easy to work out simple problems on landing speed by using the now familiar formula—

$$\text{Weight} = \text{Lift} = C_{\mathrm{L}} \cdot \tfrac{1}{2}\rho V^2 \cdot S$$

If we denote the maximum value of the Lift Coefficient by C_{L} max. and the landing speed by V_{L}. then our formula becomes

$$W = C_{\mathrm{L}}\text{max.} \cdot \tfrac{1}{2}\rho V_{\mathrm{L}}^2 \cdot S$$

Consider this problem—Find the Wing Area required for an aeroplane of weight 3,000 lb. if the landing speed is to be 40 m.p.h. and the max. value of the lift coefficient for the aerofoil used is 1·2. (Assume the air density to be 0·08 lb. per cu. ft., i.e. 0·00248 slugs per cu. ft.)

DATA—
$$W = 3000 \text{ lb.}$$
$$\rho = 0\cdot00248 \text{ slugs/cu. ft.}$$
$$V_{\mathrm{L}} = 40 \text{ m.p.h.} = 58\cdot7 \text{ ft./sec.}$$
$$C_{\mathrm{L}} \text{ max.} = 1\cdot2$$
$$S = ?$$
$$\therefore 3000 = 1\cdot2 \times \tfrac{1}{2} \times 0\cdot00248 \times 58\cdot7 \times 58\cdot7 \times S$$
$$\therefore S = 585 \text{ sq. ft. approx.}$$

This is rather a large wing area for an aeroplane of this weight, and it is doubtful whether the structure involved would not make the total weight greater than 3,000 lb., in which case, of course, our landing speed would be raised above 40 m.p.h.

Suppose we could use a flapped wing with a maximum lift coefficient of 1·8 instead of 1·2, neglecting any small increase in weight, the necessary wing area to produce the same landing speed would be

$$\frac{1\cdot2}{1\cdot8} \times 585 = \frac{2}{3} \times 585 = 390 \text{ sq. ft. approx.}$$

It would certainly be much easier to design a wing structure of this size so as to conform to a total weight of 3,000 lb., and, further, the reduced wing area would enable a much greater maximum speed to be obtained.

Again, let us take a problem of this kind: compare the minimum landing speeds of the following—

    (a) A sailplane of Wing Loading 2 lb. per sq. ft.
    (b) A training machine of Wing Loading 7 lb. per sq. ft.
    (c) A fighter of Wing Loading 30 lb. per sq. ft.
    (d) The S.6b of Wing Loading 41·3 lb. per sq. ft.

Supposing other things to be equal—e.g. taking the value of ρ given above, and assuming that each machine is fitted with the same aerofoil section having a maximum lift coefficient of 1·12, then—

$$(a) \text{ Wing Loading} = W/S = 2 = C_L \cdot \tfrac{1}{2}\rho V^2$$
$$= 1\cdot12 \times \tfrac{1}{2} \times 0\cdot00248 \times V^2$$
$$\therefore V^2 = \frac{2 \times 2}{1\cdot12 \times 0\cdot00248} = 1438$$
$$\therefore V = \sqrt{1438} = 37\cdot8 \text{ ft./sec.} = 25\cdot8 \text{ m.p.h.}$$
$$= 26 \text{ m.p.h. approx.}$$

Similarly for (b) Landing Speed = 48 m.p.h.
    (c) Landing Speed = 100 m.p.h.
    (d) Landing Speed = 117 m.p.h.

Such is the type of problem which confronts the designer of an aeroplane in the very early stages, when, by a process of intelligent guessing and simple calculations, he has to decide such important items as the wing area, the type of aerofoil, and the landing speed of his aeroplane. It will now be obvious that in order to settle these he must know the weight—the weight of an aeroplane which he has not yet commenced to design! Here comes the first great guess; but it is a guess based on experience, and often proves remarkably accurate. A decision as to landing speed and as to the type of aerofoil will then decide the wing area, on which the whole lay-out of the aeroplane depends, so it will be seen how important is this question of landing speed and its influence on the whole design of the finished aeroplane.

The Autogiro

Perhaps the most successful attempt at making a real reduction in the landing speeds of aeroplanes was the invention and development of the Cierva Autogiro. It was mentioned in the last chapter that very few really successful Helicopters had ever been built; but, although often given that name, the **Autogiro is not a Helicopter.** It differs from the latter in one vital particular, namely, that whereas in the Helicopter the wings or blades are rotated by the power of the main engine, which is thus directly responsible for the Lift, in the Autogiro the rotating wings are not driven except by the action of the air upon them, and this in turn is caused by the forward or downward air speed of the machine. Thus forward speed is necessary in the Autogiro just as it is in a conventional aeroplane, and, as in the latter, it is provided by the Thrust of an ordinary engine and airscrew. Thus it is true to

PLATE XXXV. AUTOGIRO
"Cierva" Autogiro cabin type C24.
(By courtesy of "Flight.")

say that, in principle, the Autogiro has a closer resemblance to the normal aeroplane than to the Helicopter. What, then, is the secret of its success in obtaining such remarkably low landing speeds?

Space does not permit a full consideration of the principles underlying this remarkably interesting flying machine, and it must suffice to say that the secret lies in the fact that even when the forward speed of the complete machine is far lower than the stalling speed of a conventional aeroplane, the rotating wings are still striking the air at a considerable velocity, and thus they can still provide sufficient Lift to keep the machine in the air. In this way the forward air speed can be reduced to 5 m.p.h. or 10 m.p.h., which, if there is a slight head wind, will mean a ground speed of practically nil. Of course, all kinds of problems are involved and many people maintain that an aeroplane " was never meant to look like that " ; but in spite of all its problems—and its looks ! —the Autogiro succeeded in achieving, in one fell swoop, a landing speed such as the experimenters of all nations had considered to be a dream of the distant future.

Landing Speeds and the Future

So far as landing speed is concerned, we are reaching an interesting stage in the history of aviation. As has already been stated, Wing Loadings are going up; they have gone up slowly but surely for the past thirty years, and rather less slowly but more surely during the years of the second World War, and since. There is at the moment no sign of any halt in this progress—for progress it certainly is. **We must assume, therefore, that Wing Loadings will go still farther.**

During this time, slots and flaps, and then better flaps, have been invented, and the maximum value of C_L has gone up from just over 1 (R.A.F. 15 was 1·22) to an absolute maximum of about 3 (good modern aerofoil section with Fowler flaps and Handley Page slots extending along 60 per cent of the wing span). Now, when the maximum C_L was 1·22, a Wing Loading of 10 lb. per sq. ft. was considered high; now with a maximum C_L of 3, even 50 lb. per sq. ft. has already been exceeded. Now, C_L max. of 1·22 and W/S of 10 gives a landing speed of about 56 m.p.h., whereas C_L max. of 3 and W/S of 50 gives a landing speed of about 80 m.p.h.

Thus we have accepted a considerably higher landing speed—but **how long can this go on?** The increase in wing loading has already had a greater effect than the increase in C_L max., but up to now we have discovered better and better flaps. Now, however, there is no sign of any great improvement in flaps—so what of the future? The first thing we must do is clear enough—**flaps must extend along the whole span of the wing,** perhaps also under the fuselage. This has already been done in some types of aircraft by arranging that the ailerons act also as flaps (actually it was tried in the very early days of flaps), but it is not altogether successful, and a more promising idea would seem to be that the ailerons should be dispensed with and that some alternative form of lateral control should be found. This is not at all beyond the bounds of possibility; it has already been done in experimental form, and the idea will be mentioned again in connection with control.

This would give us perhaps another 40 per cent increase in C_L max. and a landing speed of about 68 m.p.h. for a Wing Loading of 50 lb. per sq. ft. But it is only a temporary reprieve. What next? Are we to accept higher and higher landing speeds?—surely there must be a limit somewhere! Are we to call a halt to increase in Wing Loading?—we may try, but it is doubtful whether we will succeed. Or are we to discover some new device for increasing C_L max.? Who knows?

The Complete Approach and Landing

Having considered fairly fully the problems of gliding and of landing, let us now see how they are applied to the complete approach and landing.

During the few years preceding the second Great War, a new technique in flying was developed. In this book we are not concerned with the art of flying as such, but we are very much concerned with the alteration of technique **because it was brought about by progress in the science of flight accompanied by the corresponding changes in aeroplane design.** To the outward eye the main change was that the monoplane, rather suddenly, took precedence over the biplane. Less obvious, perhaps, but far more important, was the **increase in wing loadings**—which incidentally was itself the reason behind the ascendancy of the monoplane. With increase in wing loading came higher landing speed (already explained), higher landing speed meant that flaps—once a luxury—became a necessity, and flaps, in their turn, were largely responsible for the new technique, especially in so far as it affects the approach and landing.

A pilot, when approaching a landing ground, may find that he is either undershooting or overshooting. If he is undershooting there is little than he can do (assuming, of course, that he is already gliding at the best angle) except use his engine power to flatten his glide. In the old days such a method was considered bad flying; if the engine was functioning satisfactorily, it showed lack of judgment; if the engine was out of action—that is to say in the case of a forced landing—it could not be done. **Nowadays the " engine-assisted approach,"** as it is called, **is a standard method of approaching to land.** It might almost be said that on the most modern machines the "glide approach" is only used as practice for a forced landing.

In the anxiety to avoid undershooting there is a natural tendency to overshoot, especially since, even without engine power, it would seem to be an easy matter to lose any unnecessary height. In practice this is not quite such an easy matter. In the older types of aircraft the following methods were available as means of losing height in the event of overshooting—

   (*a*) **Sideslipping.**
   (*b*) **Prolonging the glide by S-turns.**
   (*c*) **Putting the nose down and gliding fast.**
   (*d*) **Holding the nose up and gliding slowly.**

The last two were unsatisfactory, (*c*) because it had very little effect, since the extra speed gained had to be lost by "floating" before the actual landing could take place, (*d*) because it was dangerous, being critically near the stalling speed, which might easily be reached during an attempt to turn or due to wind gradient or other air disturbances near the ground. **The first two methods, on the other hand, were successfully employed for very many years.**

Then came the modern type of aircraft—its **superior streamlining gave it a very flat gliding angle,** so flat that even a slight degree of overshooting caused it to float much too far before landing. But that was not all—**it did not like sideslipping** (reasons for this will be given later), and with its very flat angle of glide the **S-turn did not result in sufficient loss of height.**

Necessity may be the mother of invention, but in this little bit of aviation history the invention existed before the necessity arose. Nevertheless, although flaps had been in use for many years, they had not really been fully applied to their modern purposes. These purposes can best be described by considering the whole process of approaching and landing as consisting of five separate phases (Fig. 125)—**the glide, the flattening-out, the float or hold-off, the landing,** and **the pull-up.** In each and all of these flaps have their part to play. Let us consider them in turn.

First, then, let it be understood that the modern idea is that **the last 500 ft. or so of the glide should be straight, without any slipping or turning to one side or the other.** This can only be put into practice if the pilot has means of controlling the gliding angle relative to the earth without unduly raising or lowering his air speed. Flaps can give him the means to do this, at any rate over a limited range of gliding angles. As the flaps are lowered both Lift and Drag are increased. The **increase in Lift** tends to **flatten the gliding angle** and to make it possible to **glide at a slower air speed** without approaching dangerously near to the stall. The **increase in Drag** tends to **steepen the gliding angle,** and gliding attitude, of the aeroplane **for the same air speed.**

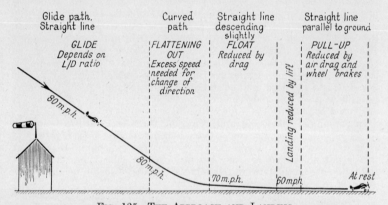

Glide path.   Curved   Straight line   Straight line
Straight line   path   descending   parallel to ground
     slightly

GLIDE   FLATTENING   FLOAT   PULL-UP
Depends on   OUT   Reduced by   Reduced by
L/D ratio   Excess speed   drag   air drag and
     needed for   wheel brakes
     change of
     direction

80 m.p.h.

80 m.p.h.

Landing reduced by lift

70 m.p.h.   60 m.p.h.   At rest

FIG. 125. THE APPROACH AND LANDING

(*Note.* The air speeds shown on the diagram are approximate only, but indicate at what parts of the approach and landing air speed is lost.)

What, then, will be the net effect? That all depends on whether Lift or Drag has the greater proportional increase, i.e. on whether the L/D ratio is raised or lowered, and that in turn depends on how much the flaps are lowered and on the type of flap. This aspect of flaps has already been discussed on page 110. All that need be added is that the split flap is the type most used, and that it is generally lowered to 50° or 60°—sometimes to 90°—and that there is then no doubt that the L/D ratio is reduced and so the gliding path is steeper. So much, then, for the actual glide—we can sum it up by saying that **flaps give us at least some control over the gliding angle.**

Next comes the process of **flattening out,** i.e. the change from the downward gliding path to a path very nearly parallel to the ground. This involves a change of direction, which means that there must be an acceleration, and therefore a force, towards the centre of the curved path. This force must be provided by the wings, which must therefore have more speed and more angle. In effect, we can say that the stalling speed is higher. Now **the steeper the original glide, the greater the change of flight path to the horizontal,** and therefore **the more speed must there be in hand for flattening out.** All this is very annoying —it means that the more steeply we glide, the faster must we glide, and this was the very thing we were trying to avoid. The solution of this part of the problem is to use engine power, and we will consider that method later.

After flattening out, we have got to lose any excess speed before we can actually land—this may be called the **float** or hold-off. In this the **Drag of the flaps plays a great part.** At the same time the attitude of the aeroplane is being altered so as to present the wings at the stalling angle for the actual landing, and thus the Drag of the wings themselves will help to reduce the speed.

After the float comes the **landing.** This, in a sense, is momentary only, and thus it might not seem to be a very vital factor in the sequence of events, but, in practice, the landing speed is of the utmost importance, because it settles both the gliding speed and the distance needed to pull up after landing. The problem of landing speed has already been

PLATE XXXVI. TOUCHING DOWN

The Avro "Tudor II" at the moment of touch down with flaps fully lowered
and engines throttled back.

(*By courtesy of A. V. Roe & Co. Ltd.*)

fully discussed, but it must be emphasized, because it is so often misunderstood, that **Drag,** whether caused by flaps or anything else, **cannot reduce landing speed**—it is entirely a question of **Lift.**

After the landing, the **pull-up.** This at any rate is easy to understand; **what we need for a quick pull-up is Drag;** wheel brakes and air brakes. The more the better, provided the aircraft can stand it and does not tip on its nose. The Drag of the flaps, especially if lowered to the 90° angle, gives us a most efficient air brake, and the wings themselves, at their angle of 16° or so, help considerably. **The air-braking effect is greatest at the beginning of the landing run,** the wheel braking towards the end, when it can be more safely used. The problem of brakes is a straightforward one of mechanics, though possibly it can hardly be called "mechanics of flight." Apart, however, from the ordinary problems of coefficient of friction between wheels and ground, there are some aspects of brakes which are peculiar to aircraft. When on the ground the centre of gravity of the aeroplane is, of necessity, high above the wheels. It is also only a short distance behind the wheels, and thus if the brakes are applied violently there is an immediate tendency to go over on to the nose. Another difficulty is that if the aeroplane starts to swing, the centre of gravity, being behind the wheels, will cause the swing to increase. This can be checked by the differential action of the brakes, which can be applied more to one

PLATE XXXVII. TRICYCLE UNDERCARRIAGE

The "Meteor III." Notice how the tricycle undercarriage enables the aircraft to stand in the flying attitude on the ground.

(*By courtesy of the Gloster Aircraft Co. Ltd.*)

wheel than another, but it is interesting to note that the **tricycle undercarriage** can remove the cause of this and other troubles. When this type of undercarriage is used, the centre of gravity is in front of the main wheels and there is no tendency to swing, and at the same time the aircraft is prevented from going on to its nose by the front wheel. The effect on braking, and consequent shorter pull-up, has to be seen —or, better still, tried—to be believed. And there are other advantages too.

So much for the glide approach and landing; for forced landings it is the only way. For approaching over high obstacles at the edge of an aerodrome it may also come in useful. **In all other circumstances, with modern types of aircraft,** the engine-assisted approach **is better.** We have already been into all the principles involved, so it will probably be sufficient if we simply sum up the reasons as to why it is preferred—

1. By slight adjustments of the throttle the path of glide can be flattened or steepened at will. (The reader will realize that in such an approach only a small proportion of power is used, not by any means full power.)

2. The gliding path is flatter, so there is less change of path in flattening out, less acceleration, less extra Lift required, less increase in stalling speed, and thus less excess speed is needed, and the glide can safely be made more slowly.

3. The extra speed of the slipstream over elevators and rudder makes these controls more effective—their effectiveness reduces the need of extra speed which may be needed in the glide approach to give good control—their effectiveness enables us to counteract wind gradient and turbulence effects near the ground.

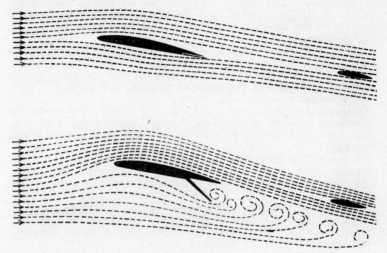

FIG. 126. FLOW OVER WING AND TAIL—FLAPS UP AND FLAPS DOWN

4. Since there is less excess speed to be lost—due to (2) and (3) above—the float is reduced.

5. An engine, already running, will respond more readily to the throttle if it is found necessary to make another circuit before landing.

6. For all the reasons already given less judgment is required—the whole process is easier.

Well, all that sounds pretty convincing, and not only is it perfectly sound reasoning but it is amply confirmed by experience.

In all of this, too, flaps have played their part because they have enabled us to alter the characteristics of an aerofoil during flight, if not at will, at any rate more so than we once could. Some day we shall have flaps which will enable us to increase the Lift or the Drag independently of each other, just as much as we wish of each; when we can do that we shall be much more the master of the aeroplane, flying will be easier—and safer.

Effect of Flaps on Trim

Before leaving the subject of flaps and their influence on flight, some mention should be made of their effect on the balance or trim of the aeroplane.

The lowering or raising of flaps affects the airflow not only over the lower surface of the wing, but also over the upper surface—probably the more important effect—and in front of the wing and behind the wing (Fig. 126). The airflow in turn affects the pressure distribution. and the forces acting on the wing and on the tail plane. It is hardly surprising, therefore, that the trim may be affected, but it may seem curious that the lowering of the flap sometimes tends towards nose-heaviness, sometimes tail-heaviness. A little thought will soon offer an explanation.

Consider the top surface of the wing. When the flap is lowered, the air flows faster over the top, especially near the leading edge. There will be greater suction here and the chances are that **the centre of pressure on the top surface will move forward,** thus tending towards tail-heaviness.

Consider the lower surface. The lowering of the flap retards the airflow particularly over the flap itself, and there will be greater pressure on the under-surface and on the flap, the result probably being a **backward movement of the centre of pressure,** thus tending towards nose-heaviness.

The downwash behind the wing will be increased; and if the tail plane is so situated as to receive the full benefit of this downwash, there will be **a downward force on the tail plane,** tending towards **tail-heaviness.**

In a low-wing monoplane the **low position of the drag** on the flap, especially when fully lowered, will tend towards **nose-heaviness.** On a high wing monoplane the drag, being high, may tend towards **tail-heaviness.**

On top of all this, presumably with the object of counteracting such tendencies, the flaps have sometimes been interconnected with the tail-trimming tab, on some German aircraft with the adjustable tail plane, and then goodness knows what may happen!

Enough has been said to show that it is a little tricky to decide what will be the final result of lowering the flaps, and the different behaviour of different aircraft is a good illustration of the difficulty. Sometimes the change of trim is in one direction for the first part of the lowering of the flap, usually tail-heavy; and in the other direction, nose-heavy, when full flap is lowered. In some aircraft the effects, whether by design or good luck it is often hard to say, so cancel each other that there is little or no change of trim, and no one is more pleased than the pilot.

See if you can answer these questions about gliding and landing—

1. What is the connection between the gliding angle and the efficiency of an aeroplane?

2. If, when an aeroplane is gliding at its minimum angle of glide, the pilot attempts to glide further by holding the nose of the aeroplane up, what will be the result, and why?

3. Discuss the effect of flaps on the gliding angle.

4. How does the load carried in an aeroplane affect the gliding angle and gliding speed?

5. How does wind affect the glide?

6. Does the flattest glide give the longest time in the air? If not, why not?

7. What do you understand by the "stalling" of an aeroplane?

8. Does (*a*) the stalling speed, (*b*) the stalling angle, change with height?

9. What attempts have been made to reduce the landing speed of aeroplanes?

10. What is the effect of "wing loading" on the landing speed of an aeroplane?

11. What is an autogiro?   How does it differ from a helicopter?

12. What are the advantages of the engine-assisted approach?

13. How would a pure air brake (increasing the Drag but not the Lift) affect the various parts of an approach and landing?

14. Why may the lowering of flaps affect the trim of an aeroplane?

Numerical examples on Gliding and Landing will be found on page 354.

CHAPTER VII

PERFORMANCE

IT may seem rather illogical that we should first consider level flight, then gliding and landing, and now the take-off, climb and general performance of the aeroplane. But there is method in our madness. Level flight is, as it were, the standard condition of flight with which all other manoeuvres are compared; whether we are learning to fly, or merely learning to understand the principles of flight, it is right and proper that we should first learn the problems of level flight. Gliding, too, involves simple fundamental principles, in some ways more elementary than those of level flight, but not so closely linked with the principles of other conditions of flight. Landing we have used to illustrate the principles of flight at low speeds. All these have followed quite naturally one on the other, but the take-off is a problem on its own, having little connection with anything else, and the climb involves very little in the way of new principles.

Taking-off

The pilot needs skill and practice before he can be sure of making a good take-off, one of the main problems being to keep the aircraft on a straight and narrow path. This difficulty is mainly the result of the propeller, and has already been touched on in Chapter IV. In general, it may be said that the object during the take-off is to obtain sufficient Lift to support the Weight with the least possible run along the ground. In order to obtain this result, it is usual to keep the tail up at the commencement of the run so as to reduce the Drag; then, when the speed has reached the minimum speed of flight, if the tail is lowered and the wings brought to about 15° Angle of Attack, the aeroplane will be capable of flight. Although by this method the aeroplane probably leaves the ground with the least possible run, it is apt to be dangerous because, once having left the ground, any attempt to climb by further increase of angle will result in stalling and dropping back on to the ground. Therefore it is advisable to allow the speed to increase beyond the stalling speed before "pulling-off," and sometimes the aeroplane is allowed to continue to run in the tail-up position until it takes off of its own accord.

The process of taking-off is largely influenced by such things as the aerodrome surface, or the state of the water when seaplanes are concerned, and although of extreme interest, the subject is too practical (if considered from the practical point of view) and too highbrow (if considered from the theoretical point of view) to be within the scope of this book. In order to reduce the length of run, and increase the angle of climb after leaving the ground—so as to clear obstacles on the outskirts of the aerodrome—the take-off will, when possible, be made against the wind. Other aids to taking-off are slots, flaps or any other devices which increase the Lift without unduly increasing the Drag, and, essential in propeller-driven high-speed aircraft, the variable-pitch propeller.

The question as to whether or not flaps should be used for taking-off purposes has been much disputed. The answer really depends upon whether the increased Lift of the flap, with the resulting decrease in taking-off speed, makes up for the slower acceleration caused by the increased Drag of the flap. Some people say that it depends on whether or not the lowering of the flap increases or decreases the L/D ratio, but that is not strictly true. If it were, the answer would almost certainly be that no flap should be used, because the L/D ratio is probably

PLATE XXXVIII. TAKING OFF

The "Meteor IV" about to climb away just after take-off, with undercarriage already retracted.
(*By courtesy of the Gloster Aircraft Co. Ltd.*)

greatest without any flap angle—or at any rate with only a very small angle. But the problem is a little more complicated than that, because while we wish to avoid Drag throughout all the take-off run, we only really need the extra Lift at the end, when we are ready to take off. No doubt we could get off most quickly by a sudden application of flap at this stage, but such a method is apt to be dangerous. Taken all round, it can be said that it is one of the problems of flight to which a proper solution has not yet been found. The Lift type of flap helps the take-off considerably, the split flap may have some beneficial effect if used at a moderate angle. Once again it is clear that we still need a flap that will provide us with Lift or Drag at will.

Some interesting new problems are arising in connection with the take-off. Modern undercarriages may tuck away nicely during flight, but when lowered they are less streamlined than the older types and their Drag may hamper the take-off quite considerably. It is already becoming evident that steps will have to be taken to reduce such Drag. Again, just as landing speeds go up with high wing loading, so do take-off speeds, and the length of run needed to attain such speeds is liable to become excessive. The idea of catapulting is an old one; it has been used with some success, but its application has never been very wide, and it raises many new problems of its own. The assistance of rockets gives much the same effect as catapulting and has great advantages in that it does not require bulky apparatus on the airfield

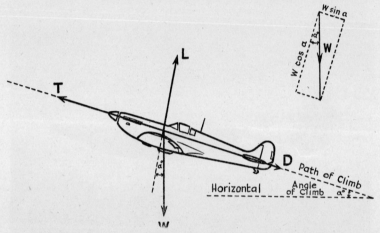

FIG. 127. FORCES ACTING ON AN AEROPLANE DURING A CLIMB

and so it can be used away from the main base; another point in favour of rockets is that they may have alternative uses, as for instance, for special accelerations when required during flight. Refuelling in the air does not sound like a form of assisted take-off, but it does present possibilities in that an aircraft can be taken off lightly loaded as regards fuel. Perhaps the most interesting experiment in this direction was the pick-a-back method in which a small very highly loaded aircraft was released from its large mother craft during flight. It is feared that the war hindered progress in experiments such as these.

Climbing

During level flight the power of the engine must produce, via the propeller, jet or rocket, a Thrust equal to the Drag of the aeroplane at that particular speed of flight. If now the engine has some reserve of power in hand, and if the throttle is further opened, **either—**

(a) The pilot can put the nose down slightly, and **maintain level flight at an increased speed and decreased Angle of Attack,** or

(b) **The aeroplane will commence to climb.**

A consideration of the forces which act upon an aeroplane during a climb is interesting, but slightly more complicated than the other cases which we have considered.

Assuming that the path actually travelled by the aeroplane is in the same direction as the thrust, then the forces will be as shown in Fig. 127. If α is the angle of climb, and if we resolve the forces parallel and at right angles to the direction of flight, we obtain two equations—

(1) $T = D + W \sin a$.

(2) $L = W \cos a$.

Translated into non-mathematical language, the first of these equations tells us that during a climb the Thrust needed is greater than the Drag and increases with the steepness of the climb. This is what we would expect. If a vertical climb were possible, a would be 90°

PLATE XXXIX. CLIMBING

The Avro "Athena I," an advanced type of training aircraft with side-by-side seating and driven by a propeller—gas turbine combination.
(*By courtesy of A. V. Roe & Co. Ltd.*)

and therefore sin a would be 1, so the first equation would become $T = D + W$, which is obviously true because in such an extreme case the Thrust would have the opposition of both the Weight and the Drag. Similarly if $a = 0°$ (i.e. if there is no climb), sin $a = 0$. Therefore $W \sin a = 0$. Therefore $T = D$, the condition which we have already established for Straight and Level Flight.

The second equation tells us that the Lift is less than the Weight, which is rather interesting because one often hears it said that an aeroplane climbs when the Lift is greater than the Weight! One must admit, however, that the misunderstanding is largely due to the rather curious definition which we have assigned to the word "Lift." Let us consider the second equation under extreme conditions. If the climb were vertical, cos 90° = 0. Therefore $L = 0$. So that in a vertical climb we have no Lift. This simply means that all the real lift is provided by the Thrust, the Wings doing nothing to help. If, on the other hand, $a = 0°$, cos $a = 1$, and therefore $L = W$, which we already know to be the condition of Straight and Level Flight.

The assumption mentioned above—namely, that the aeroplane travels in the direction of the Thrust—would mean that the Angle of Attack during the climb was the same as that during horizontal flight. This, however, is not always the case even in order to obtain the best rate of climb, and the problem becomes complicated and is hardly worth considering further from this point of view.

Horse Power Curves

A more interesting and more practical way of approaching the climbing problem is by means of what are called " **Performance Curves.**"

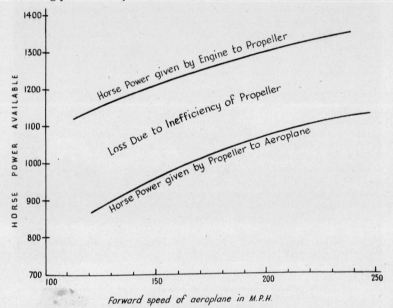

FIG. 128. HORSE POWER AVAILABLE

By estimating the **Horse Power which will be available** from the engine and also the **Horse Power which is required** for level flight at various speeds, we can arrive at many interesting deductions. It is largely by this method that forecasts are made of the probable performance of an aeroplane, and it is remarkable how accurate these forecasts usually prove to be.

The procedure for jet and rocket systems of propulsion is rather different because, as explained in Chapter IV, it is more convenient in these systems to think in terms of Thrust rather than Horse Power. They will therefore be dealt with separately.

Horse Power Available—Propeller Propulsion

The deduction of the curve which gives the Horse Power output of the engine is outside the scope of this book, as it depends on a knowledge of the characteristics of the Internal Combustion Engine. From this curve must be subtracted the Horse Power which is lost through the inefficiency of the propeller (the efficiency of a good propeller is about 80 per cent). The resulting curve (Fig. 128) shows the Horse Power which we will have available at various forward speeds of the aeroplane.

Horse Power Required

The Horse Power which will be required is found by estimating the Drag. For this purpose the Wing Drag and the Parasite Drag are usually found separately, the former from the characteristics of the aerofoils and the latter by estimating the Drag of all the various parts and summing them up. Another method of finding the total Drag is by measuring the Drag of a complete model in a Wind Tunnel and scaling up to full size. After the total Drag has been found at any speed, the Horse Power is obtained by multiplying the Drag by the speed and reducing to units of Horse Power, e.g. if the total Drag is 1,250 lb. at 180 m.p.h. (264 ft./sec.)—

Power required $= 1250 \times 264$ ft. lb. per sec.

$$\therefore \ \text{H.P.} = \frac{1250 \times 264 \times 60}{33000} = 600 \ \text{H.P. at } 180 \ \text{m.p.h.}$$

And in a similar way the Horse Power required is found at other speeds, the lower curve in Fig. 129 illustrating a typical result. The reader may be puzzled as to why the Horse Power required increases so rapidly at low speeds; the explanation is that in order to maintain level flights at these low speeds, a very large Angle of Attack is required, and this results in an increase of Drag in spite of the reduction in speed. If this argument sounds familiar, it is simply because we are returning to the same arguments as when discussing range and endurance in Chapter V. The figures we have just quoted are taken from that argument, and the curve of Horse Power Required in Fig. 129 is based on the aeroplane of Chapter V. This follow-up of the same aeroplane will make the Horse Power curves even more interesting and instructive.

It should be noted that there will be no fundamental difference in the shape of the horse power required curve for jet and propeller-driven aircraft. It is in the horse power available that the difference lies.

Maximum and Minimum Speeds of Horizontal Flight

From the combination of the two curves (Fig. 129) some most interesting deductions can be made. Wherever the Horse Power Available Curve is above the Horse Power Required Curve, it means that level flight is possible, whereas both to the left and right of the two intersections level flight becomes impossible for the obvious reason that we would need more Horse Power than we have available! Therefore the intersection A shows the least possible speed (127 m.p.h.) and the intersection B the greatest possible speed (245 m.p.h.), at which level flight can be maintained. Between the points A and B the difference between the Horse Power available and the Horse Power required at any particular speed—i.e. the distance between the two curves—shows the amount of *extra* Horse Power which can be used for climbing purposes at that speed; and where the distance between the two curves is greatest—i.e. at CD—the rate of climb will be a maximum, while the corresponding point E shows that the best speed for climbing is 170 m.p.h. If we know the weight of the aeroplane (10,000 lb.) and the extra Horse Power CD $(1020 - 570 = 450)$ available for climbing, we can deduce the vertical rate of climb.

If the rate of climb is x ft. per min., then the work done per minute in lifting our 10,000 lb. aeroplane is 10,000 x ft. lb. per min.

$$\therefore\ 10000\ x = 450 \times 33000$$

$$x = \frac{450 \times 33000}{10000} = 1485 \text{ ft. per min.}$$

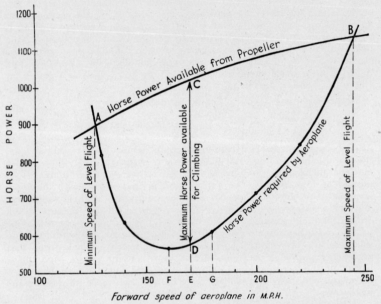

FIG. 129.　HORSE POWER AVAILABLE AND HORSE POWER REQUIRED

This represents the best rate of climb for this particular aeroplane, but it will only be attained if the pilot keeps his aeroplane at the right speed of 170 m.p.h. As in gliding, there is a natural tendency to try to hold the nose up higher, but, as will be seen from the curves, if the speed is reduced to 140 m.p.h. only about 330 H.P. will be available for climbing, and this will reduce the rate of climb to $\dfrac{330 \times 33000}{10000} = 1089$ ft. per min. Similarly, at speeds above 170 m.p.h. the rate of climb will be decreased, although it will be noticed that between certain speeds the curves run roughly parallel to each other and there is very little change in the rate of climb between 150 m.p.h. and 190 m.p.h.; obviously at 127 m.p.h. and 245 m.p.h. the rate of climb is reduced to nil, while below 127 m.p.h. and above 245 m.p.h. the aeroplane will lose height.

As a matter of interest, the speeds for maximum endurance (F), 160 m.p.h., and maximum range (G), 180 m.p.h., have also been marked. As was explained in Chapter V, these are the best speeds from the point of view of the aeroplane, but they may have to be modified to suit the best engine conditions. It will be noticed that the speed for maximum endurance (F) could be deduced from the curve, since it is the lowest point on the curve, i.e. at the point of minimum Horse Power required for level flight. The speed for maximum range (G),

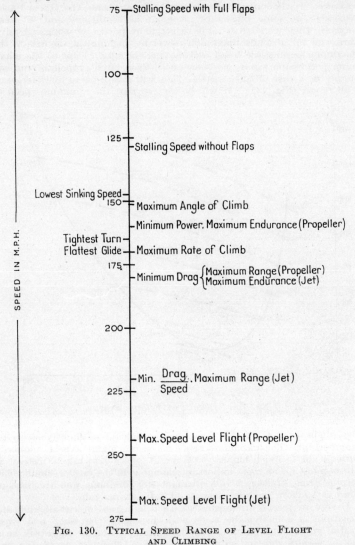

FIG. 130. TYPICAL SPEED RANGE OF LEVEL FLIGHT AND CLIMBING

however, must be obtained from the table on page 165, which showed the Drag at various speeds.

Effect of Changes of Engine Power

We have so far assumed that for a certain forward speed of the aeroplane the Horse Power Available is a fixed quantity. This, of course, is not so, since the Horse Power of the engine can be varied considerably by manipulating the engine controls of boost, r.p.m., and mixture. If the curve shown in Fig. 129 represents the Horse Power Available at some reasonably economical conditions and in weak mixture, then we shall be able to get more power by using rich mixture, and the absolute maximum power by opening the throttle to the maximum permissible boost and moving the r.p.m. lever to the maximum permissible r.p.m. position—with fixed pitch propellers this will simply be a case of full throttle. This will give a curve of Emergency Full Power (Fig. 131). It will be noticed that the minimum speed of

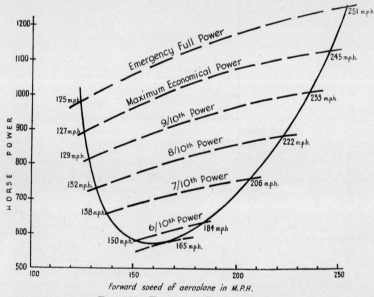

FIG. 131. EFFECT OF ENGINE POWER

level flight is now slightly lower—very slightly, so slightly as to be unimportant. The maximum speed is, as we might expect, higher—perhaps not so much higher as we might expect (251 m.p.h. instead of 245 m.p.h.). The most important change is in the rate of climb: 550 surplus Horse Power is now available for climbing, and the rate of climb is 1,815 ft. per min. instead of 1,485 ft. per min.

Except in special circumstances, such as a race or certain military situations, it is inadvisable to fly with the engine "flat out," and, even so, full power must be used only for a limited time or there will be a risk of serious damage to the engine. The effects of decreasing the power are also shown in Fig. 131. From the point of view of the aeroplane, it makes no difference whether the power is decreased by reducing boost, or lowering the r.p.m., or both; but for fuel economy it is generally advisable to lower the r.p.m. It will be noticed that as the power is reduced, the minimum speed of level flight becomes slightly greater, the maximum speed becomes considerably less, and the possible rate of climb decreases at all speeds.

All this is what we might expect, with the possible exception of the fact, which pilots often do not realize, that **the lowest speeds can be obtained with the engine running at full throttle.** This, however, is a condition of flight which is very unfavourable to the engine as it entails the expenditure of full power without sufficient air speed for cooling purposes; in fact, it is in some ways similar to the ascent of a steep hill in a motor-car which is not provided with a fan for cooling purposes.

Eventually, as the engine is throttled down, we reach a state of affairs at which there is only one possible speed of flight. This is the speed at which least engine power will be used, and at which we shall therefore obtain maximum endurance. It is rather puzzling to find that this speed (165 m.p.h.) is slightly different from the speed (160 m.p.h.) at the lowest point of the Horse Power Required curve. This is because the engine and propeller efficiency is slightly better at 165 m.p.h. than at 160 m.p.h.

Effect of Altitude on Horse Power Curves

We have not yet exhausted the information which can be obtained from these magic performance curves, for if we can estimate the corresponding curves for various heights above sea-level we shall be able to see how our performance is affected at different altitudes. There is much to be said, and much has been said, on the subject of whether it is preferable to fly high or to fly low when travelling from one place to another. It is one of those many interesting problems about flight to which no direct answer can be given, chiefly because there are so many conflicting considerations which have to be taken into account. Some of them, such as the question of temperature, wind and the quantity of oxygen in the air, have already been mentioned when dealing with the Atmosphere, but the most important problem of all is that of Performance.

How will the Performance be affected as the altitude of flight is increased? At first one is tempted to think that since the density of the air is decreased, resistances will be less and therefore speeds will be higher. Unfortunately, however, the decrease in the air density has more far-reaching effects which may be summarized as follows—

1. Decrease in Lift.
2. Decrease in Drag.
3. Decrease in Propeller Thrust.
4. Decrease in the weight of air supplied to the engine, and hence a falling-off in the power of the engine.
5. Decrease in the air supply, and therefore in the amount of oxygen, to the pilot.

Some of these can to a certain extent be compensated for, and others inter-act on each other to such an extent that the problem becomes very complicated. For instance, in the case of Lift and Drag, since the Lift must be kept equal to the weight, any loss in Lift due to decrease in air density must be made up for by an increase in the Angle of Attack or increase in Air Speed, or both; and these, in turn, will increase the Drag and thus balance, or probably overbalance, the decrease in Drag, which is directly due to the change in the air density. The loss in the Propeller Thrust can to some extent be compensated for by the use of a propeller having variable pitch, the air supply to the engine can be augmented by supercharging, and the pilot can be supplied with oxygen from cylinders.

Whatever attempts are made to mitigate the difficulties of flight at high altitudes, in propeller-driven aircraft the general tendency remains for the **Power Available to decrease** and the **Power Required to increase with the altitude** (Fig. 132). This will cause the curves to close in towards each other, resulting in a gradual **increase in the minimum speed** and a **decrease in the maximum speed,** while the distance between the curves, and therefore the **rate of climb, will also become less.** Any

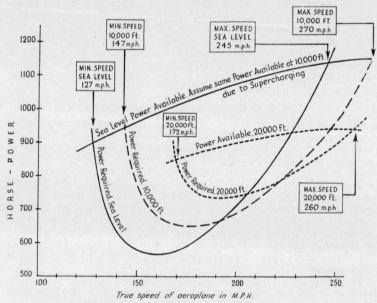

FIG. 132. EFFECT OF ALTITUDE

pilot will confirm that this is what actually happens in practice, although, as previously mentioned, he may be somewhat deceived by the fact that the air speed indicator is also affected by the change in density and consequently reads lower than the true air speed. This is really what accounts for the curve of Horse Power Required moving over to the right as the altitude increases (see Fig. 132); if the curves were plotted against "indicated speed," the curves for 10,000 ft. and 20,000 ft. would simply be displaced upwards, compared with that for sea-level. The difference between true and indicated speed also accounts for another apparent discrepancy in that the curves as plotted (against **true** speed) suggest that the air speed to give the best rate of climb **increases with height.** This is so, but the **indicated** speed for best rate of climb **falls with height.**

For military purposes **good performance at high altitudes may be of such importance that it becomes worth while to design the engine, propeller and aeroplane to give their best efficiencies at some specified height,** such as 15,000 ft. For instance, we can supercharge the engine to give full power at 15,000 ft. (this is then called the "Rated Altitude"), but we may have to forbid the use of the supercharger at sea-level because it would cause stresses on the engine parts greater than those for which they were designed. Similarly, a propeller which gives its best efficiency at 15,000 ft. will be comparatively inefficient at sea-level, unless the pitch can be changed. The aerofoil section too, the angle at which it is set and so on, all these can be selected for the specified height. In such cases, it may well happen that performance at sea-level is **inferior** to that at the height for which the machine was designed, and this is a feature of many modern aircraft. Above a certain critical height, 15,000 ft., 20,000 ft., or whatever it may be, performance will inevitably fall off and so the performance curves will be very similar, except that the highest curve of Horse Power Available will correspond to the critical height. In such aircraft it may well be that the advantages of flying high outweigh the disadvantages such as low temperatures, lack of oxygen, and so on.

Ceiling

This process of improving performance at altitude cannot be continued indefinitely and we shall eventually reach such a height that **there is only one possible speed for level flight** and the **rate of climb is nil.** This is called the **Ceiling.**

It requires extreme patience and time to reach such a ceiling, and, owing to the hopeless performance of the aeroplane when flying at this height, it is of little use for practical purposes, and therefore the idea of a **Service Ceiling** is introduced, this being defined as that height at which the rate of climb becomes less than 100 ft./min. (sometimes specified as 150 ft./min. or 200 ft./min.).

There is a story which dates from the early days of so-called "light aeroplanes," which relates how, in a competition in which marks were awarded for "speed range," competitors were required to fly between two points, first as fast as possible, and secondly as slowly as possible; one competitor succeeded in flying faster when he was flying as slowly as possible than when he was flying as fast as possible! Such an occurrence is not so strange as it may at first appear to be; it simply means that this machine, although flying but a few feet off the ground, was practically at its ceiling. As a matter of fact, such was the case with many of those first under-powered light aeroplanes, some of which succeeded in winning large prizes, although they often had considerable difficulty in leaving the ground.

Effect of Weight on Performance

It is sometimes important to be able to calculate what will be the effect on performance of increasing the total Weight of an aeroplane by carrying extra load. Here again the performance curves will help us.

If the Weight of an aeroplane is increased, the Lift will have to be increased also in order that the Lift may be equal to the new Weight. Thus we must either fly at a larger angle of attack or, if we keep the same angle of attack, at a higher speed. It is easy to calculate this speed—

Let old Weight $= W$ lb., new Weight $= W_1$ lb.

Let V ft./sec. be old speed, and V_1 ft./sec. be new speed at same angle of attack.

Since angle of attack is the same, C_L will be the same.

$$\therefore \quad W = C_L \cdot \tfrac{1}{2}\rho\, V^2 S$$

and

$$W_1 = C_L \cdot \tfrac{1}{2}\rho\, V_1^2 S$$

$$\therefore \quad \frac{V_1}{V} = \sqrt{\frac{W_1}{W}} \qquad . \qquad . \qquad . \qquad . \qquad . \qquad (1)$$

Such problems always become more interesting if we consider actual figures. Suppose, then, that we wish to carry an extra load of 2,000 lb. on our aeroplane which already weighs 10,000 lb.

Then

$$\frac{V_1}{V} = \sqrt{\frac{12,000}{10,000}} = \sqrt{1\cdot 2} = 1\cdot 096$$

This means that the stalling speed will be increased in this proportion, thus instead of 127 m.p.h. it will become $1\cdot096 \times 127 = 139$ m.p.h. The same will apply for each angle of attack from the stalling angle down to angles of normal flight, but it should be noted that **the maximum speed of flight will not be raised in this proportion.** This is because there will not be sufficient power available to give the extra speed at the same angle of attack, in other words the aeroplane will have to fly at a larger angle of attack, and so at a slower speed, or it will lose height.

To continue our problem, if the angle of attack is kept the same, C_D, as well as C_L, will remain the same.

Therefore if D lb. was old Drag of aeroplane, and D_1 lb. is new Drag—

$$D = C_D \cdot \tfrac{1}{2}\rho\, V^2 S$$

$$D_1 = C_D \cdot \tfrac{1}{2}\rho\, V_1^2 S$$

$$\therefore \quad D_1/D = V_1^2 / V^2$$

But, from (1), $V_1/V = \sqrt{W_1/W}$, i.e. $\dfrac{V_1^2}{V^2} = \dfrac{W_1}{W}$

$$\therefore \quad D_1/D = W_1/W \qquad . \qquad . \qquad . \qquad . \qquad . \qquad (2)$$

Now Power Required = Drag × Velocity

$\therefore$ if P is old power, and P_1 new power, then

$$\frac{P_1}{P} = \frac{D_1 V_1}{D V} = \frac{W_1}{W} \times \sqrt{\frac{W_1}{W}} = \left(\frac{W_1}{W}\right)^{\frac{3}{2}}$$

Translating this into figures and again considering flight at the stalling angle, if the power required at the old stalling speed of 127 m.p.h. was 900 h.p. $= P$, then—

$$\frac{P_1}{900} = \left(\frac{12000}{10000}\right)^{\frac{3}{2}} = 1\cdot 2^{\frac{3}{2}} = 1\cdot 315$$

$$\therefore \quad P_1 = 900 \times 1\cdot 315 = 1184 \text{ h.p.}$$

Thus at Stalling Angle new speed = 139 m.p.h.

and new horse power = 1184 h.p.

In a similar way, for each angle of attack, new speed and new horse power can be calculated, and thus a new curve of horse power required can be drawn for the new Weight of the aeroplane.

It is interesting to note that the net effects of the additional Weight are exactly the same as the effects of an increase of altitude, i.e.—

1. **Slight reduction in maximum speed.**
2. **Large reduction in rate of climb.**
3. **Increase in stalling speed.**

In short, the curve of horse power required is again displaced upwards and to the right. It will be noticed that this results in a **slight increase**

in the best speed to use for climbing. (This must not be confused with rate of climb.)

In spite of the similarity in effect of increase of weight and increase of altitude it should be noted that the increase of weight does not affect the reading of the air speed indicator, and so the results apply equally well whether we consider True or Indicated air speed.

Influence of Jet Propulsion on Performance

In this chapter we have considered the performance of an aircraft mainly from the point of view of the reciprocating-engine propeller-driven type. The substitution of a gas turbine driving a propeller will

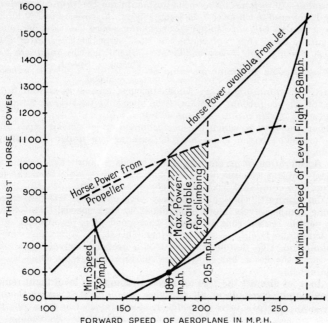

FIG. 133. HORSE POWER AVAILABLE AND HORSE POWER REQUIRED—JET PROPULSION

make very little difference to these considerations but, as with Range and Endurance, there will be certain differences for the pure jet-driven type. The differences all turn, as before, on the increase of propulsive efficiency with speed in the jet-driven aircraft.

As we have seen in Chapter V this increase in efficiency results in the Thrust remaining approximately constant at all speeds, and therefore the Thrust Horse Power available, i.e. Thrust × Speed, will rise in proportion to the speed. So the curve of Horse Power Available rises much more steeply than with the propeller-driven aircraft; it is, in fact, practically a straight line through the origin (Fig. 133). It will be evident from the figure that as a result of this difference **there is a tendency in the jet-driven type for all the speeds of best performance to be higher.** Assuming the same Horse Power Required curve as before (and since this only concerned the **aeroplane**, there is no reason why it should be different), the minimum Horse Power available at which it is possible to fly will be represented by the straight line which is tangential to the curve. With increase of r.p.m. the straight line will swing upwards. The maximum performance of the aircraft will, of course, depend on how much power is available at maximum r.p.m. If, as in the figure, we assume that the same power is available at 180 m.p.h. for both jet and propeller, it will be seen that the maximum speed of level flight is 268 m.p.h. (instead of 245 m.p.h.), the minimum speed of level flight is 132 m.p.h. (instead of 127 m.p.h.). The speed corresponding to best rate of climb is not very critical, but the average value is about 195 m.p.h. (instead of 170 m.p.h.). The speed for maximum Endurance has already been discovered in Chapter V as being 180 m.p.h. (instead of 160 m.p.h.). This of course will correspond to the point where the tangent touches the curve, since this represents the least slope to the line of Power against Speed; but Power is Thrust × Speed, so the minimum value of Power/Speed is minimum value of $\dfrac{\text{Thrust} \times \text{Speed}}{\text{Speed}}$, i.e. minimum Thrust, i.e. minimum Drag—which, in turn, means maximum Endurance for jet propulsion. Similarly the speed for maximum Range (see Chapter V) is 220 m.p.h. (instead of 180 m.p.h.).

Other features in which the performance of jet-driven types differs from propeller-driven types may be summed up under the following headings—

    1. **Acceleration of jet aircraft at low speeds is poor :** this applies particularly during take-off, when the speed of flow issuing from the jet is far too high compared with the speed of the aircraft.

    2. **Jet aircraft,** though hopelessly uneconomical at low speeds, **become comparatively more economical at high speeds.** This for the very simple reason that to double the speed of a jet aircraft means four times the Drag, i.e. four times the Thrust, i.e. four times the fuel consumption. To double the speed of a propeller-driven type means four times the Drag, but eight times the Power, so eight times the fuel consumption.

    3. **In a jet aircraft the true air speed attainable in level flight remains approximately constant at all altitudes** (the indicated speed therefore decreases), whereas in a propeller-driven aircraft the true air speed varies considerably, usually increasing and then decreasing, but depending especially on the methods of supercharging. In both types, of course, the air speed attainable at altitude may be influenced by compressibility effects (see Chapter X).

Now for some questions about performance—

    1. Why are split flaps of less value in the take-off and climb than in the approach and landing?

    2. "When an aeroplane is climbing, the Lift is less than the Weight." Explain why this statement is not so inconsistent as it sounds.

    3. How can we obtain a rough estimate of the performance of an aeroplane before it is built?

    4. What is the effect of altitude on the maximum and minimum speeds of an aeroplane?

    5. Distinguish between "Ceiling" and "Service Ceiling."

6. In attempting to climb to the ceiling, should the air speed be kept constant during the climb?

7. Discuss some of the advantages and disadvantages of flying at high altitudes.

8. If the load carried by an aeroplane is increased, what will be the effects on performance?

9. In what respects does the performance of a jet-driven aircraft differ from that of a propeller-driven type?

Numerical examples on Performance will be found on page 356.

CHAPTER VIII

MANOEUVRES

IN a sense, any motion of an aeroplane may be considered as a manoeuvre. In no other form of transport is there such freedom of movement. An aeroplane may be said to have six degrees of freedom
which are best described in relation to its three axes which may be
defined as follows—

The **Longitudinal Axis** (Fig. 134) is a straight line running fore and
aft through the centre of gravity of the aeroplane, and is horizontal
when the aeroplane is in "Rigging Position," i.e. in the attitude of
Straight and Level Flight.

The aeroplane may travel backwards or forwards along this axis.
Backward motion—such as a tail-slide—is one of the most rare of all
manoeuvres of an aeroplane but, in compensation for this, forward
movement along this axis is the most common of all, and is the main
feature of **straight and level flight.**

Any rotary motion of the aeroplane about this axis is called **Rolling.**

The **Normal Axis** (Fig. 134) is a straight line through the centre of
gravity, and is vertical when the aeroplane is in Rigging Position. It
is therefore at right angles to the Longitudinal axis as defined above.

The aeroplane may travel upwards or downwards along this axis,
as in **climbing** or **descending,** but in fact such movement is not very
common, the climb or descent being obtained chiefly by the inclination
of the longitudinal axis to the horizontal, followed by a straightforward
movement along that axis.

Rotary motion of the aeroplane about the Normal Axis is called
Yawing.

The **Lateral Axis** (Fig. 134) is a straight line through the centre of
gravity at right angles to both the Longitudinal and the Normal axes.
It will be horizontal when the aeroplane is in Rigging Position and
parallel to the line joining the wing tips.

The aeroplane may travel to right or left along the lateral axis;
such motion is called **sideslipping or skidding.**

Rotary motion of the aeroplane about the Lateral axis is called
Pitching.

These axes must be considered as moving with the aeroplane and
always remaining **fixed relative to the aeroplane,** e.g. the Lateral axis
will remain parallel to the line joining the wing tips in whatever attitude
the aeroplane may be, or, to take another example, during a vertical
nose-dive the Longitudinal axis will be vertical and the Lateral and
Normal axes horizontal.

So the manoeuvres of an aeroplane are made up of one or more, or
even of all the following—

1. Movement forwards or backwards.
2. Movement up or down.
3. Movement sideways, to right or left.
4. Rolling.
5. Yawing.
6. Pitching.

214

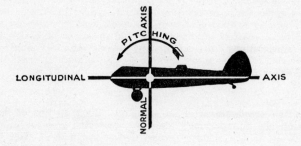

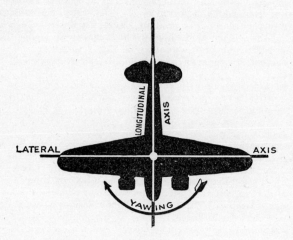

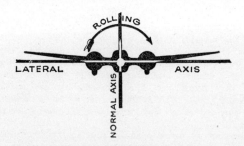

Fig. 134 The Three Axes

Some of these motions, or combinations of motion, are gentle in that they involve only a state of equilibrium. These have already been covered under the headings of level flight, gliding, climbing, and so on. In this chapter we will deal with the more thrilling manoeuvres, those that involve changes of direction, or of speed, or of both—in other words, **accelerations**. In such manoeuvres the aeroplane is no longer in equilibrium. There is more thrill for the pilot; more interest, but more complication, in thinking out the problems on the ground.

Accelerations

Now the **accelerations** of an aeroplane **along its line of flight are comparatively unimportant;** they are probably greatest during the take-off, or, in the negative sense, during the pull-up after landing, but in neither case are they as great as, for instance, the accelerations of a motor-car. But the **accelerations due to change in direction of flight are of tremendous importance.** In order to understand this part of the subject properly, the student should have some knowledge of that part of the science of Mechanics which deals with bodies travelling on curved paths. A brief summary of this was given in Chapter I, but the student to whom it is new should refer to any good book on Mechanics.

Here we can only sum up the main conclusions arrived at. When a body is compelled to move on a curved path, it is all the time trying to obey Newton's First Law and travel straight on in the direction in which it is going at any particular moment; therefore in order to keep it on a curve it is necessary to supply a "change of motion" or an "acceleration" towards the centre. This can only be done by supplying a force towards the centre, this force being directly proportional to the acceleration required (Newton's Second Law). Such a force is called the **" Centripetal Force."** The body will cause a reaction, that is to say an outward force, on whatever makes it travel on a curved path (Newton's Third Law). This reaction is called by some people the **" Centrifugal Force."**

If an aeroplane is travelling at a velocity of V ft./sec. on the circumference of a circle of radius r ft., then the acceleration towards the centre of the circle is V^2/r ft./sec./sec.

Therefore the centripetal (or centrifugal) force $= M \times$ acceleration, where M is the Mass of the aeroplane in slugs.

$$= \frac{M V^2}{r} \text{ lb.}$$

(If W is the weight of the aeroplane in pounds the corresponding formula is $W V^2/gr$ lb.)

In practice aeroplanes very rarely travel for any length of time on the arc of a **circle;** but that does not alter the principle in the least, since any **small** arc of a curve is, for all practical purposes, an arc of **some** circle with **some** radius, so all it means is that the centre and the radius of the circle keep changing as the aeroplane manoeuvres.

The acceleration being V^2/r shows that the two factors which decide the acceleration, and therefore the necessary force, are velocity and radius, the velocity being squared having the greatest effect. Thus curves at high speed, tight turns at small radius, need large forces towards the centre of the curve.

We can easily work out the acceleration, V^2/r. For instance, for an aeroplane travelling at 180 m.p.h. on a radius of 200 yards (180 m.p.h. = 264 ft./sec.; 200 yd. = 600 ft.) acceleration is $264 \times 264/600 = 116$ ft./sec./sec. (approx.) which is a little less than $4g$.

The force required to produce an acceleration of $4g$ is $M \times 4g$ or $W/g \times 4g$, i.e. $4W$ lb., so if the aeroplane weighs 2,000 lb. the necessary force is 8,000 lb.

Now imagine, for a moment, that the aeroplane is describing this circle in a vertical plane, a loop—but of an even curvature such as never occurs in practice! Then **the acceleration will be $4g$ all round the curve,** so the force **to produce the acceleration** will be $4W$ lb. all round the curve, **but** at the bottom of the curve there will **also be the weight to be lifted,** so the total Lift on the aeroplane wings will be $5W$ lb.; at the top of the loop, on the other hand, the Weight will help to produce the centripetal force, so the Lift on the wings will be $3W$ lb.—downward. At the sides of the loop it will be $4W$ lb.—in a horizontal direction. So it will be seen that while the acceleration is $4g$ all round the curve, the force varies between $3W$ and $5W$ lb. If it had been a horizontal curve, with the same acceleration of $4g$. the force towards the centre would have been $4W$ lb. all round the curve.

Now all this has been emphasized again because during recent years many pilots have grown into the habit of talking in terms of g's, and, as so often happens when a scientific word or symbol comes into popular use, the meaning of g is often—more often than not—misunderstood and misapplied. You will often hear people (unfortunately pilots are the worst offenders) saying that g stands for "gravity"—in a sense, of course, it does; but what they mean by "gravity" is "the force of gravity," and this it most certainly does **not** stand for; g is an acceleration, and it is measured in ft./sec./sec. Those who know a little more may justify their loose talk by saying that the force is **proportional** to the acceleration. That is quite correct, but there is all the difference in the world between proportionality and equality. Also, in the example of the loop given above, notice that the proportion is only true if we consider **only** the force to produce the acceleration. The acceleration is constant all round the circle but the **total** force is not. It would, of course, be very convenient if we could make the g's and the W's correspond, even in a vertical plane, that is to say if we could call the acceleration at the bottom of the curve $5g$ and at the top $3g$. This is the same as imagining the original **weight** as being **equivalent to an initial upward acceleration of** g, superimposing, as it were, an upward acceleration of g on the whole motion. This is quite legitimate, **provided we realize what we are doing** (there's the rub). It simplifies our thoughts and calculations, and the expert does it quite happily. But how many others do it, too, and how little do they know what they are doing!

Pulling Out of a Dive

In the light of what we have considered, let us take first the manoeuvre of pulling out of a nose-dive. Clearly this is a case of the aeroplane following a curved path at high velocity, with all consequent accelerations and forces. On the assumption that the aeroplane was diving at 60° to the horizontal—a very steep dive—and was travelling at 300 m.p.h. before pulling out, Fig. 135 gives some idea of the accelerations involved and their effects on pilot and aircraft if the pull-out is effected with various losses of height. Exact figures cannot be arrived at without making all kinds of doubtful assumptions, but the principle illustrated is true enough.

The effects of the increase of g's are as follows: Throughout the whole range the wing loading is going up; the "equivalent weight" of the aeroplane, of the pilot, of every part of aeroplane and pilot, is

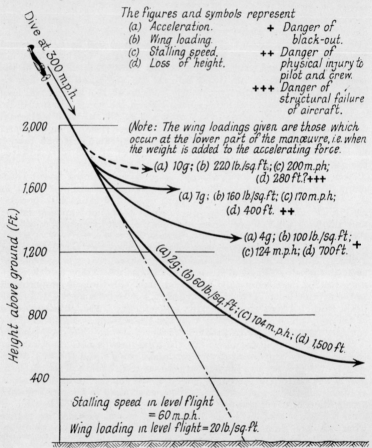

The figures and symbols represent
(a) Acceleration.   + Danger of
(b) Wing loading.   black-out.
(c) Stalling speed.   ++ Danger of
(d) Loss of height.   physical injury to
                              pilot and crew.
                           +++ Danger of
                              structural failure
                              of aircraft.

(Note: The wing loadings given are those which occur at the lower part of the manœuvre, i.e. when the weight is added to the accelerating force.

(a) 10g; (b) 220 lb./sq.ft.; (c) 200 m.ph; (d) 280 ft.?+++

(a) 7g; (b) 160 lb./sq.ft; (c) 170 m.p.h; (d) 400 ft. ++

(a) 4g; (b) 100 lb./sq.ft.; (c) 124 m.p.h; (d) 700 ft. +

(a) 2g; (b) 60 lb./sq.ft.; (c) 104 m.p.h; (d) 1,500 ft.

Dive at 300 m.p.h.

Stalling speed in level flight = 60 m.p.h.
Wing loading in level flight = 20 lb./sq.ft.

FIG. 135. PULLING OUT OF A DIVE

increasing; the stalling speed is getting higher and higher. At about $4g$ or $5g$ (we are ourselves offending by using g in its loose sense—it is really the loading that matters) the aeroplane is sitting on the air with four or five times its normal weight and the air is reacting on the structure in the same proportion, the pilot is sitting on his seat with four or five times his normal weight, his head feels heavy on his neck, but, most important of all, his heart, a pressure pump, is having difficulty in pumping the now heavy blood-stream to his head, and the lack of blood-pressure causes the sight to diminish and eventually the pilot "blacks out" altogether. This, in itself, is not serious, since he does not lose all his senses and usually completes the manoeuvre satisfactorily and recovers as soon as the g's are reduced. But if he goes up to 7 or $8g$ it is possible that more serious physical injury may result. For fighting purposes it is important that pilots should be able to stand as many g's as possible so that they can manoeuvre quickly, and experiments have been tried with this end in view. Perhaps we ought to take a lesson from the birds and fly with our bodies horizontal— even that has been suggested, and probably tried. When we reach $9g$ or $10g$—if we can reach $9g$ or $10g$—the loading on the aeroplane has become such that the structure itself is in a critical condition and may begin to show signs of breaking up. The designer has made it just a **little** stronger than the pilot, but there would be no point in making it **much** stronger.

All this time the stalling speed has been going up, in proportion to the square root of the Wing Loading (see page 187). The figure shows the increase of stalling speeds assuming a stalling speed in level flight of 60 m.p.h. Stalling at these high speeds is a very real danger; the aircraft may be very near the ground, when it stalls it will lose height very rapidly, and may even drop a wing and start a violent spin.

The moral of all this is that the pilot should allow plenty of height to pull out and should do so gently, while the designer must make the aircraft strong enough, and all who work on aeroplanes should understand the problem—that is why we have devoted so much space to it. We have also served our purpose because what has been said applies to nearly all the manoeuvres of an aircraft.

The Accelerometer

By means of an instrument called the **Accelerometer** these accelerations can be measured in flight, and, in this way, we can discover how the loads encountered during manoeuvres compare with the loads of normal flight. We will not attempt to describe the instrument used, but, in effect, the principle involved is that of hanging in the cockpit a weight on a spring balance. Suppose this weight is 1 lb., then at any time when the balance reads 1 lb. it means that there is no acceleration and the loads are those of normal flight. If the balance reads 2 lb., 3 lb., or 4 lb., then the loads are 2, 3 or 4 times respectively greater than those of normal flight; while if the balance reads less than 1 lb., the acceleration is in the opposite direction and the loads are less than those of normal flight. It is possible that the reading of the balance may be reduced to zero, or beyond, i.e. the weight of the 1 lb. would apparently become less than nothing; this would indicate that the loads were reversed, the landing wires of a biplane becoming loaded instead of the flying wires.

It is not, of course, suggested that this would in itself form a satisfactory instrument, but it does serve to illustrate the idea. In the actual instrument the "weight" is sometimes nothing more than a glass fibre, which, by virtue of its elasticity. also fulfils the function of the spring in the spring balance. In modern accelerometers a larger weight is used, supported on a diaphragm or long cantilever spring. The accelerometer might well become a standard instrument; it is useful or training pilots and also for fighting. Such an instrument sometimes takes the simple form of the spring balance itself and can be calibrated in loadings, or g's, or even in stalling speeds.

Results of Accelerometer Tests

Accelerometer tests have been carried out for nearly all standard manoeuvres, and the results are very interesting; they show that in ordinary manoeuvres performed by good pilots the loads very rarely

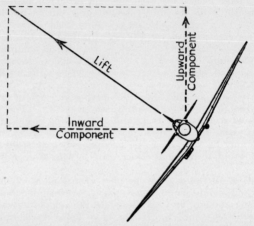

FIG. 136. DIRECTION OF LIFT DURING A PROPERLY BANKED TURN

exceed three times normal, although they may reach four times during a "mock fight," when the changes of direction are probably more sudden. Except for inverted flight, and the inverted manoeuvres mentioned later, the loads are very rarely less than half normal.

In order to allow for the extra loads likely to be encountered during aerobatics, every part of an aeroplane is given a "**Load Factor**," which varies according to conditions, being usually between 4 and 8. This means that the various parts are made from 4 to 8 times stronger than they need be for Straight and Level Flight.

Turning

In the case of the ordinary turn the inward Centripetal Force is provided by the aeroplane **banking** (like a motor-car on a racing track) so that the total Lift on the wings, in addition to lifting the aeroplane, can supply a component towards the centre of the turn (Fig. 136).

Angle of Bank

Suppose an aeroplane of weight W lb. to be travelling at a velocity of V ft./sec. on the circumference of a circle of radius r ft., then the acceleration towards the centre of the circle is V^2/r ft. per sec. per sec. Therefore the force required towards the centre $= W V^2/gr$ lb.

If the wings of the aeroplane are banked at an angle of $\theta°$ to the horizontal, and if this angle is such that the aeroplane has no tendency to slip either inwards or outwards, then the Lift L lb. will act at right angles to the wings (see Fig. 137), and it must provide a vertical component, equal to W lb., to balance the Weight, and an inward component, of $\dfrac{WV^2}{gr}$ lb., to provide the acceleration towards the centre.

This being so, it will be seen that, by Trigonometry—

$$\tan \theta = \frac{WV^2}{gr} \Big/ W = \frac{V^2}{gr}$$

This simple formula shows that there is a correct angle of bank, θ

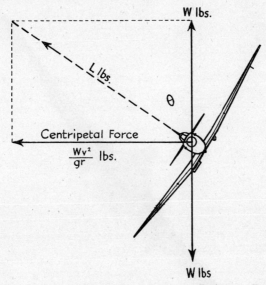

FIG. 137. FORCES ACTING ON AN AEROPLANE DURING A PROPERLY
BANKED TURN

for any turn of radius r ft. at a velocity of V ft. per sec., and that this angle of bank is quite independent of the weight of the aeroplane.

Consider a numerical example—

Find the correct angle of bank for an aeroplane travelling on a circle of radius 400 ft. at a velocity of 120 m.p.h. (Take the value of g as 32·2 ft./sec./sec.)

$$V = 120 \text{ m.p.h.} = 176 \text{ ft./sec.}$$
$$r = 400 \text{ ft.}$$
$$\tan \theta = \frac{V^2}{gr} = \frac{176 \times 176}{32\cdot2 \times 400} = 2\cdot405$$
$$\therefore \theta = 67\tfrac{1}{4}° \text{ approx.}$$

What would be the effect if the velocity were doubled, i.e. 240 m.p.h.?

$$\text{Tan } \theta \text{ would be } 4 \times 2\cdot405 = 9\cdot62.$$
$$\therefore \theta = 84° \text{ approx.}$$

What would be the effect if the velocity were 120 m.p.h. as in the first example, but the radius 800 ft. instead of 400 ft.?

$$\text{Tan } \theta \text{ would be } \frac{2 \cdot 405}{2} = 1 \cdot 2025.$$

$$\therefore \theta = 50\tfrac{1}{4}° \text{ approx.}$$

Thus we see that an increase in velocity needs an increase in the

PLATE XL. TURNING

The "Vampire III" going into a steep turn. Note the positions of the ailerons, which show that bank was still being applied when the photograph was taken
(*By courtesy of the De Havilland Aircraft Co. Ltd.*)

angle of bank, whereas if the radius of the turn is increased the angle of bank may be reduced, all of which is what we might expect from experiences of cornering by other means of transport. Fig. 138 shows the correct angle of bank for varying speeds and radii.

Loads during a Turn

It will be obvious from the figures that the Lift on the wings during the turn is greater than the Lift which the wings have to supply during straight flight; it is also very noticeable that the Lift increases considerably with the angle of bank. This means that all the lift bracing of the aeroplane, such as the Struts and Spars, will have to carry loads considerably greater than those of straight flight.

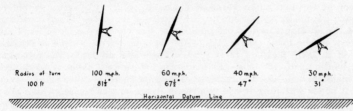

Radius of turn	100 m.p.h.	60 m.p.h.	40 m.p.h.	30 m.p.h.
100 ft	81½°	67½°	47°	31°

Horizontal Datum Line

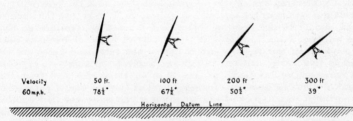

Velocity	50 ft.	100 ft	200 ft	300 ft
60 m.p.h.	78½°	67½°	50½°	39°

Horizontal Datum Line

FIG. 138. CORRECT ANGLES OF BANK

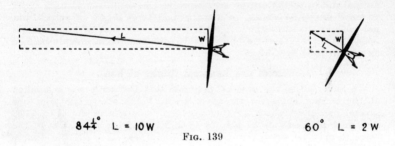

$84\frac{1}{4}°$ L = 10W $60°$ L = 2 W

FIG. 139

Mathematically, $W/L = \cos\theta$, or $L = W/\cos\theta$

i.e. at 60° Angle of Bank, Lift = $2W$, stalling speed, 85 m.p.h.
at 70½° Angle of Bank, Lift = $3W$, stalling speed, 104 m.p.h.
at 75½° Angle of Bank, Lift = $4W$, stalling speed, 120 m.p.h.
at 84¼° Angle of Bank, Lift = $10W$, stalling speed, 190 m.p.h.

These figures mean that at these angles of bank (Fig. 139) the loads on the wing structure are 2, 3, 4, and 10 times respectively the loads of Normal Flight. This is simply our old friend g again, but in this instance it is certainly better to talk in terms of Load than of g because the accelerations, and the corresponding loads, are in a horizontal plane while the initial Weight is vertical; it is no longer a question of adding by simple arithmetic.

Whatever the angle of bank, the Lift on the wings must be provided by $C_L \cdot \frac{1}{2}\rho V^2 \cdot S$. It follows, therefore, that the value of $C_L \cdot \frac{1}{2}\rho V^2 \cdot S$ must be greater during a turn than during Normal Flight, and this must be achieved either by increasing the velocity or increasing the value of C_L. Thus it follows that the stalling speed, which means the speed at the maximum value of C_L, must go up in a turn; as before it will go up in proportion to the square root of the Wing Loading, and the stalling speeds corresponding to the various angles of bank are shown in the table (assuming, as for the pull-out of a dive, a stalling speed in level flight of 60 m.p.h.). These are all fairly steep banks; for banks up to 45° or so the loads are not serious, there is no danger of blacking out, and the increase of stalling speed is quite small—even so, it needs watching if one is already flying or gliding anywhere near the normal stalling speed, and suddenly decides to turn. At steep angles of bank we have to contend not only with the considerable increase of stalling speeds but with all the same problems as arose with the pull-out, i.e. blacking out, injury to pilot and crew, and the possibility of structural failure in the aircraft. It may seem curious that the angle of bank should be the deciding factor, but it must be remembered that the angle of bank (provided it is the **correct** angle of bank) is itself dependent on the velocity and radius of the turn, and these are the factors that really matter. In fighting aircraft the ability to out-turn an opponent counts perhaps more than anything else, and from this point of view the question of steeply banked turns is one of paramount importance. An aspect of this question which must not be forgotten is that of engine power; **steep turns can only be accomplished if the engine is powerful enough to keep the aeroplane travelling at high speed and at large angles of attack, perhaps even at the stalling angle.** The normal duties of the engine are to propel the aeroplane at high speed at small angles of attack, or low speed at large angles of attack, but not both at the same time. Thus it is really only lack of engine power which prevents a slow-training aircraft from turning as steeply-banked as a high-speed fighter.

Correct and Incorrect Angles of Bank

We have, up to the present, assumed that the aeroplane is banked at the correct angle for the given turn. Fortunately, the pilot has several means of telling whether his bank is correct or not (Fig. 140), and since his methods all help us to understand the mechanics of the turn, it may be as well to mention them here. One old but simple device was a cross-level, sometimes rather incorrectly called an "inclinometer." This was nothing more than an ordinary spirit level, but with a more pronounced curve and a large bubble. If the bank was correct, this bubble would be in the centre, i.e. at the top of the curved tube, in exactly the same position as for normal flight. If, on the other hand, the bank was too steep, the bubble would go to the high side of the cross-level; while if the bank was not steep enough, the bubble would go to the low side. For this reason the pilot was told to "follow the bubble" with his control column, because this would cause him to move his ailerons in such a way as to correct the bank. Another good indicator is the wind itself, or a streamer tied to some exposed position. In normal flight and in a correct bank the wind will come from straight ahead (neglecting any local effects from the slip-stream); if the bank is too much, the aeroplane will sideslip inwards and the pilot will feel the wind striking his face from the inside of the turn, whereas if the bank is too small, the wind will come from the outside of the turn, due to an outward skid on the part of the aeroplane.

Yet another interesting indication is a plumb-bob hung in the cockpit out of contact with the wind. In normal flight this will, of course, hang vertically; **during a correct bank it will not hang vertically, but in exactly the same position relative to the aeroplane as it did in normal flight,** i.e. it will bank with the aeroplane. If over-banked the plumb-line will be inclined inwards; if under-banked, outwards from the above

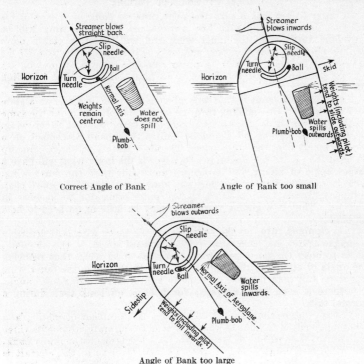

Correct Angle of Bank   Angle of Bank too small

Angle of Bank too large

FIG. 140. EFFECTS OF CORRECT AND INCORRECT ANGLES OF BANK

position. This plumb-bob idea, in the form of a pendulum, forms the basis of the modern sideslip indicator which is provided by the top pointer of the so-called "Turn and Bank Indicator." The pointer is geared so as to move in the opposite direction to the old bubble, and so the pilot must move the control column **away** from the direction of the pointer, this being considered a more instinctive method. Sometimes a curved transparent tube is used, as in the old cross-level, but a metal ball replaces the bubble and will, of course, move the opposite way to the bubble, so that in this case also the control column is moved away from the indication given on the instrument. The figure shows how a tumbler full of water would not spill even when tilted at 80° in a correct bank; if the bank were too small it would spill outwards over the top lip of the tumbler!

Lastly, during a correct bank the pilot will sit on his seat without any feeling of sliding either inwards or outwards; in fact, he will be sitting tighter on his seat than ever, his effective weight being magnified in the same proportions as the Lift so that if he weighs 14 stone in Normal Flight he will feel that he weighs 140 stone when banking at 84½°! If he over-banks he will tend to slide inwards, but outwards if the bank is insufficient.

Other Problems of Turning

In order to get into a turn the pilot puts on bank by means of his ailerons, but once the turn has commenced **the outer wing will be travelling faster than the inner wing and will therefore obtain more Lift,** so the pilot may find that not only is it necessary to take off his aileron control but actually to apply opposite aileron by moving his control column against the direction of bank—this is called " **holding off bank.**"

An interesting point is that this effect is different in turns on a glide and on a climb. On a **gliding turn** the whole aircraft will move the same distance downwards during one complete turn, but the inner wing, because it is turning on a smaller radius, will have descended on a steeper spiral than the outer wing; therefore the air will have come up to meet it at a steeper angle, in other words **the inner wing will have a larger angle of attack** and so obtain more Lift than the outer wing. The extra Lift obtained in this way may compensate, or more than compensate, the Lift obtained by the outer wing due to increase in velocity. **Thus in a gliding turn there may be little or no need to hold off bank.**

In a **climbing turn,** on the other hand, the inner wing still describes a steeper spiral, but this time it is an **upward** spiral, so the air comes down to meet the inner wing more than the outer wing, thus **reducing the angle of attack on the inner wing.** So, in this case, the outer wing has more Lift **both** because of velocity **and** because of increased angle, and **there is even more necessity for holding off bank than during a normal turn.**

Another interesting way of looking at the problem of gliding and climbing turns is to analyse the motion of an aircraft around its three axes during such turns. In a flat turn, i.e. a level turn without any bank, the aircraft is yawing only. In a banked level turn, the aircraft is yawing and pitching—in the extreme of a vertically banked turn it would be pitching only. But in a gliding or climbing turn the aircraft is pitching, yawing **and rolling.** In a **gliding** turn it is rolling **inwards,** as it were; in a **climbing** turn, **outwards.** The inward roll of the gliding turn causes the extra angle of attack on the inner wing, the outward roll of the climbing turn on the outer wing. Many people find it difficult to believe this. If the reader is in such difficulty he may be convinced by one of two methods; which will suit him best will depend upon his temperament. The mathematically-minded may like to analyse the motion in terms of the following (Fig. 141)—

The rate of turn of the complete aeroplane (about the vertical), Ω.
The angle of bank of the aeroplane, θ.
The angle of pitch of the aeroplane, ϕ.
A little thought will reveal the fact that the

$$\text{Rate of yaw} = \Omega \cdot \cos \phi \cdot \cos \theta.$$
$$\text{Rate of pitch} = \Omega \cdot \cos \phi \cdot \sin \theta.$$
$$\text{Rate of roll} = \Omega \cdot \sin \phi.$$

Translating this back into English, and taking one of the extreme examples, when $\theta = 0$, i.e. no bank, and $\phi = 0$, i.e. no pitch, cos θ and cos ϕ will be 1, sin θ and sin ϕ will be 0.

∴ Rate of yaw = Ω = rate of turn of complete aeroplane.

Rate of pitch and rate of roll are zero. All of which we had previously decided for the flat turn.

The reader (mathematically-minded) may like to work out for himself the other extremes such as the vertical bank ($\theta = 90°$) or vertical pitch ($\phi = 90°$), or better still the more real cases with reasonable values of θ and ϕ.

Notice that the rate of roll depends entirely on the angle of pitch, i.e. the inclination of the longitudinal axis to the vertical—if this is

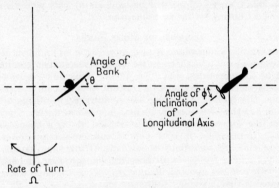

FIG. 141. GLIDING TURNS

zero, there is no rate of roll even though the aircraft may be descending or climbing.

What for the reader who does not like mathematics? Get hold of a model aeroplane, or, failing this, a waste-paper basket and spend a few minutes making it do upward and downward spirals; some people are convinced by doing gliding and climbing turns with their hand and wrist —and their friends may be amused in watching!

At large angles of bank there is less difference in velocity, and in angle, between inner and outer wings, and so the question of holding off bank becomes less important. But much more difficult problems arise to take its place.

First, though, let us go back to the other extreme and consider what is called a "flat turn," i.e. one that is all yaw and without any bank at all. In the older type of aircraft it was fairly easy to execute such a manoeuvre, the necessary inward force being provided by the airflow against the side of the fuselage and other side area of the machine, the airflow being caused by the violent outward skid of the aircraft. Slight turns of this kind were very useful when approaching a target for bombing purposes, but otherwise flat turns were in the nature of "crazy flying," and good pilots always try to keep their sideslip indicator in the central position.

Actually flat turns are not only incorrect flying, but they are rather difficult to execute for several reasons. First, the extra velocity of the outer wing tends to bank the aeroplane automatically (as explained above); secondly, the Lateral Stability (explained later) acts in such a way as to try to prevent the outward skid by banking the aeroplane; thirdly, the side area is often insufficient to provide enough inward force to cause a turn except on a very large radius; fourthly, the Directional Stability (also explained later) opposes the action of the rudder and tends to put the nose of the aircraft back so that it will continue on a straight path. Taking these four reasons together, it will be realized that an aeroplane has a strong objection to a flat turn!

Modern aircraft have a **very small side surface** and **very good Directional Stability,** and so, for the last two reasons particularly, a flat turn becomes virtually impossible. So much is this so that it is very little use applying rudder to start a turn, the modern technique being to put on bank only. More will be said about this when considering Stability and Control in the next chapter.

Controls on Steep Banks

The turning of an aeroplane is also interesting from the control point of view because as the bank becomes steeper **the rudder gradually takes the place of the elevators,** and vice versa. This idea, however, needs treating with a certain amount of caution because, in a vertical bank for instance, the rudder is nothing like so powerful in raising or lowering the nose as are the elevators in normal horizontal flight. Incidentally, the reader may have realized that a vertical bank, without sideslip, is theoretically impossible, since in such a bank the Lift will be horizontal and will provide no contribution towards lifting the Weight. If it is claimed that such a bank can, in practice, be executed, the explanation must be that a slight upward inclination of the fuselage together with the propeller thrust provides sufficient lift.

This only applies to a continuous vertical bank in which no height is to be lost; it is perfectly possible, both theoretically and practically, to execute a turn in which, for a few moments, the bank is vertical, or even over the vertical. In the latter case the manoeuvre is really a combination of a loop and a turn.

Generally speaking, the radius of turn can be reduced as the angle of bank is increased, but even with a vertical bank there is a limit to the smallness of the radius because, quite apart from the question of sideslipping, the Lift on the wings (represented by $C_L \cdot \frac{1}{2}\rho V^2 \cdot S$) must provide all the force towards the centre, i.e. $M \cdot \dfrac{V^2}{r}$ or $\dfrac{W\,V^2}{gr}$.

Thus
$$\frac{W V^2}{gr} = C_L \cdot \tfrac{1}{2}\rho V^2 \cdot S$$

or
$$r = \frac{2W}{C_L \cdot \rho S \cdot g}$$

Now, in straight and level flight the stalling speed (V_s) is given by the equation
$$W = L = C_L \,\text{max.}\, \tfrac{1}{2}\rho V_s{}^2 \cdot S$$

If we substitute this value of W into our formula for the radius we get

$$r = \frac{2 \cdot C_L \,\text{max.}\, \tfrac{1}{2}\rho V_s{}^2 \cdot S}{C_L \cdot \rho \cdot S \cdot g}$$

i.e.
$$r = \frac{V_s{}^2}{g} \times \frac{C_L \,\text{max.}}{C_L}$$

This shows that the radius of turn will be least when C_L is equal to C_L max., i.e. when the angle of attack is the stalling angle, and radius of turn $= \dfrac{V_s^2}{g}$. It is rather interesting to note that the minimum radius of turn is quite independent of the **actual** speed during the vertical banks, it is settled only by the stalling speed of the particular aeroplane; thus, to turn at minimum radius, one must fly at the stalling angle, but any speed may be employed provided the engine power is sufficient to

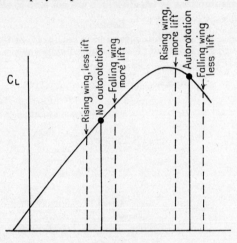

ANGLE OF ATTACK

FIG. 142. CAUSE OF AUTO-ROTATION

maintain it. In actual practice, the engine power is the deciding factor in settling the minimum radius of turn whether in a vertical bank or any other bank, and it must be admitted that it is not usually possible to turn on such a small radius as the above formulae would indicate.

The formula above applies to some extent to all steep turns and shows that the aeroplane with the lower stalling speed can make a tighter turn than one with a higher stalling speed. (We are referring, as explained above, to the stalling speed in straight and level flight.)   But in order to take advantage of this we must be able to stand the g's involved in the steep banks, and we must have engine power sufficient to maintain turns at such angles of bank.

Aerobatics

The usual aerobatics are Loops, Spins, including Auto-rotation (Fig. 142), Rolls, Sideslips, and Nose-dives, to which may be added Upside-down Flight, the Inverted Spin, and the Inverted Loop. The manoeuvres may also be combined in various ways, e.g. a half loop followed by a half roll, or a half roll followed by the second half of a loop.

There are many reasons why aerobatics should be performed in those types of aircraft which are suitable for them. They provide excellent training for accuracy and precision in manoeuvre, and give a feeling of complete mastery of the aircraft, which is invaluable in all combat flying. They may also be used for exhibition purposes, but modern aircraft are so fast and the radius on which they can turn or manoeuvre is so large that, in many ways, they provide less of a spectacle than older types. Not least, aerobatics increase the joy and sensations of flight to the pilot himself—not quite so much to other occupants of the aircraft!

The movements of the aeroplane during these aerobatics are so complicated that they baffle any attempt to reduce them to the terms of simple mechanics and, indeed, to more advanced theoretical consideration, unless assumptions are made which are not true to the facts.

Loop

Figs. 143 and 144 show the approximate path travelled by a slow type of biplane during a **loop** and the corresponding accelerometer diagram.

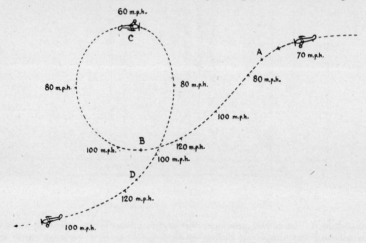

FIG. 143. A LOOP

From this it will be seen that, as in many manoeuvres, the greatest loads occur at the moment of entry. Notice also that even at the top of the loop the load is very little less than normal—that is to say, that the pilot is sitting firmly on his seat in the upward direction, the loads will still be on the flying wires, and our weight on its spring balance will be hanging upwards! Only in a bad loop will the loads at the top become negative, causing the loads on the aircraft structure to be reversed and the pilot to rely on his straps to prevent him from falling out.

Simple theoretical problems can be worked out on such assumptions as that a loop is in the form of a circle or that the velocity remains constant during the loop, but the error in these assumptions is so great that very little practical information can be obtained by attempting to solve such problems, and it is much better to rely on accelerometer tests and the results of practical experiments.

Spin

A **Spin** (Fig. 145) is an interesting manoeuvre, if only for the reason that there stands to its discredit a large proportion of all aeroplane accidents that have ever occurred. It differs from other manoeuvres

in the fact that the wings are "stalled,"—i.e. are beyond the critical
Angle of Attack, and this accounts for the lack of control which the
pilot experiences over the movements of the aeroplane while spinning;
it is, in fact, a form of "auto-rotation," which means that there is a
natural tendency for the aeroplane to rotate of its own accord. This
tendency will be explained a little more fully when dealing with the
subject of control at slow speeds in the next chapter. In a spin the

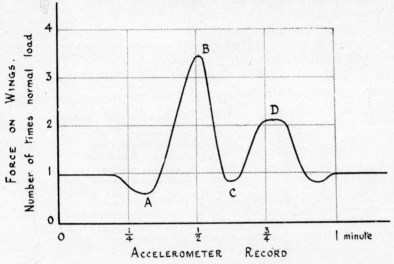

FIG. 144. ACCELEROMETER DIAGRAM FOR A LOOP

aeroplane follows a steep spiral path, but the attitude while spinning
may vary from the almost horizontal position of the "flat" spin to the
almost vertical position of the "spinning nose-dive." In other words
the spin, like a gliding turn or steep spiral is composed of varying
degrees of yaw, pitch and roll. A flat spin is chiefly yaw, a spinning
nose-dive chiefly roll. The amount of pitch depends on how much the
wings are banked from the horizontal. In general, the air speed during
a spin is comparatively slow, and the rate of descent is also slow.
Any device, such as the use of slots, which tend to prevent stalling,
will also tend to minimize the danger of the accidental spin and may,
in some cases, make it impossible to carry out deliberately. The area
and disposition of the fin, rudder, and tail plane exert considerable
influence on the susceptibility of the aeroplane to spinning.

Many of the terrors of a spin were banished once it was known just
what it was. We then realized that in order to get out of a spin we must
get it out of the stalled state by putting the nose down, and we must
stop it rotating by applying "opposite rudder." In practice, the latter
is usually done first, because it is found that the elevators are not
really effective until the rotation is stopped. The farther back the
Centre of Gravity, and the more weights that are distributed along the
length of the fuselage, the flatter and faster does the spin tend to
become and the more difficult is it to recover. This flattening of the

spin is due to the centrifugal forces that act on the masses at the various parts of the aircraft (Fig. 146); it has a distinct similarity to the Centrifugal Turning Moment that tends to turn a propeller blade to

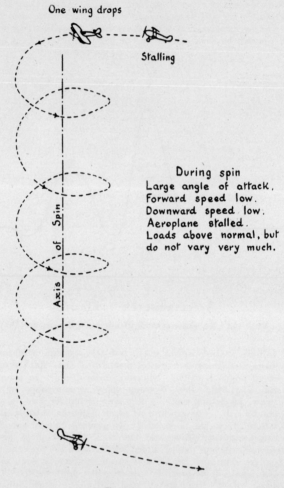

One wing drops

Stalling

During spin
Large angle of attack.
Forward speed low.
Downward speed low.
Aeroplane stalled.
Loads above normal, but
do not vary very much.

Axis of Spin

FIG. 145. A SPIN

fine pitch (page 134). A spin is no longer a useful combat manoeuvre, nor is it really a pleasant form of aerobatics, but since it is liable to occur accidentally, especially during a fight, pilots are taught how to recover from a spin.

Roll

During a **roll** (Fig. 147) the aeroplane rotates laterally through 360°, but the actual path is in the nature of a horizontal corkscrew, there being varying degrees of pitch and yaw. In the so-called slow roll the loads in the 180° position are reversed, as in inverted flight, whereas in the other extreme, the barrel roll, which is a cross between a roll and a loop, the loads are never reversed.

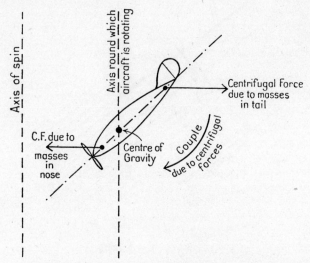

FIG. 146. TENDENCY OF A SPIN TO FLATTEN OWING TO CENTRIFUGAL FORCES

Sideslip

In a **sideslip** (Fig. 148) there will be considerable wind pressure on all the side surfaces of the aeroplane, notably the fuselage, the fin and the rudder, while if the planes have a dihedral angle the pressure on

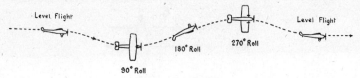

FIG. 147. A ROLL

the wings will tend to bring the machine on to an even keel. The sideslip is a useful manoeuvre for losing height or for compensating a sideways drift just prior to landing, but, as already mentioned, modern types of aircraft do not take very kindly to sideslipping. The small side area means that they drop very quickly if the sideslip is at all steep, and the Directional Stability is so strong that it may be impossible to hold the nose of the machine up (by means of the rudder), and the dropping of the nose causes even more increase of speed.

Nose-dive

A **nose-dive** is really an exaggerated form of gliding; the gliding angle may be as great as 90°—i.e. vertical descent—although such a steep dive is rarely performed in practice. If an aeroplane is dived vertically it will eventually reach a steady velocity called the "terminal velocity." In such a dive the Weight is entirely balanced by the

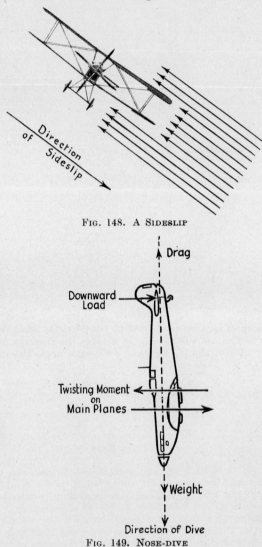

Fig. 148. A Sideslip

Fig. 149. Nose-dive

Drag, while the Lift has disappeared. The Angle of Attack is very small or even negative, there is a large positive pressure near the leading edge on the top surface of the aerofoil, tending to turn the areoplane on to its back, and this is balanced by a considerable "down" load on the tail plane (Fig. 149). In such extreme conditions the terms

PLATE XLI. INVERTED FLIGHT

Hawker "Hurricane." Notice the tail-down attitude that is usually associated with inverted flight.

(*By courtesy of "Flight."*)

used are apt to be very misleading; for instance, the "down" load referred to is horizontal, while the Lift, if any such exists, will also be horizontal. The terminal velocity of the average aeroplane is in the neighbourhood of 400 or 500 m.p.h., and it makes very little difference whether the engine is running or not. It is interesting to note that some aeroplanes cannot reach, even in vertical descent, the horizontal speeds attained by modern fighting aircraft, the terminal velocity of which is as high as 600 or 700 m.p.h.—so fast, in fact, that you would not hear them coming. But they lose so much height in attaining the terminal velocity that, in practice, it is doubtful whether it can ever be reached. As was only to be expected, the problems which accompany the attainment of a speed near to the speed of sound are first making themselves felt in connection with the nose-dive, especially at high altitudes. Test pilots in all countries have reported violent changes of trim, stiffness of the controls, and have even "seen things" on the wings! Little is known about it all as yet, but there is one consoling feature—as one gets nearer the earth, terminal velocities are lower (owing to the greater density), and the speed of sound is higher (owing to the higher temperature). So if one gets into trouble high up, there is always a chance of getting out of it lower down. This is further explained in Chapter X.

The nose-dive, and the pulling-out of a nose-dive, are two entirely different problems, and the latter has already been fully dealt with.

Upside-down Flight

Real **upside-down flight** (Fig. 150) is not so often attempted as is commonly supposed, and should be distinguished from a **glide** in the inverted position, which does not involve problems affecting the engine. If height is to be maintained during inverted flight, the engine must,

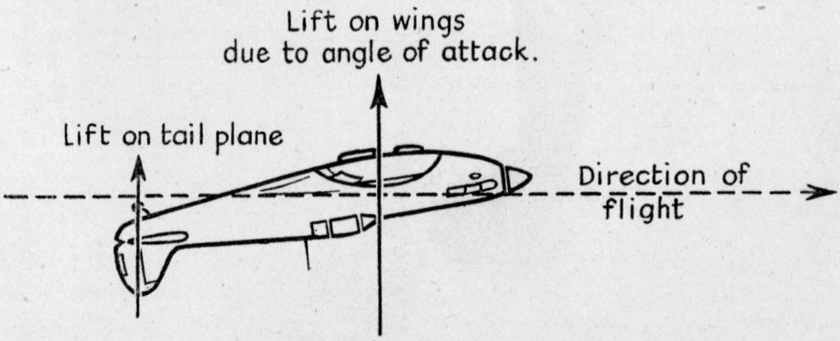

FIG. 150. UPSIDE-DOWN FLIGHT

of course, continue to run, and this necessitates precautions being taken to ensure a supply of petrol and the proper functioning of the carburettor. The aerofoil will be inverted, and therefore, unless of the symmetrical type, will certainly be inefficient; while in order to produce an Angle of Attack, the fuselage will have to be in a very much "tail-down" attitude. The stability will be affected, although in certain cases aeroplanes have been more stable when upside-down than the right way up, and considerable difficulty has been experienced in restoring them to normal flight. In spite of all the disabilities involved, some aeroplanes are capable of maintaining height in the inverted position.

Inverted Spin

The **inverted spin** is in most of its characteristics similar to the normal spin; in fact, in some instances pilots report that the motion is more steady and therefore more comfortable. As in inverted flight, however, the loads on the aeroplane structure are reversed and the pilot must rely on his straps to hold him in the machine.

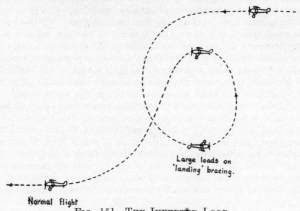

Large loads on 'landing' bracing.

Normal flight

FIG. 151. THE INVERTED LOOP

Inverted Loop

The **inverted loop,** or "double bunt," in which the pilot is on the outside of the loop (Fig. 151), is a manoeuvre of extreme difficulty and danger. The difficulty arises from the fact that whereas in the normal loop the climb to the top of the loop is completed while there is speed and power in hand and engines and aerofoils are functioning in the normal fashion, in the inverted loop the climb to the top is required during the second portion of the loop, when the engine and aerofoils are in the inefficient inverted positions. The danger is incurred because of the large reversed loads which affect all the landing bracing, which is not usually designed to the same strength as the ordinary flying bracing. It was a long time before this manoeuvre was successfully accomplished, and once it had been, so many foolhardy pilots began to attempt it—often with fatal results—that it had to be forbidden.

" Bumpy " Weather

In addition to the loads incurred during definite aerobatics, all aeroplanes are required to face the effects of **unsteady weather conditions.** Accelerometer records show that these may be quite considerable, and they must certainly be reckoned with when designing ordinary commercial aeroplanes. Where aeroplanes are, in any case, required to perform aerobatics, they will probably be amply strong enough to withstand any loads due to adverse weather. The conditions of weather which are likely to inflict the most severe loads on an aeroplane consist in strong gusty winds, hot sun, intermittent clouds and uneven ground conditions: a combination of all these factors will, almost certainly, spell a "rough passage" that will rival any crossing of the Atlantic by sea. The turbulence and up-currents that may be encountered in severe thunderstorms and in cumulo-nimbus clouds can sometimes be such as to tax the strength of the aeroplane and the flying skill of the pilot.

Manoeuvrability

Before leaving the subject of manoeuvres we ought to mention that the Inertia of an aeroplane—or, to be more correct, the Moment of Inertia of the various parts—will largely determine the ease or otherwise of handling the machine during manoeuvres. Without entering into the mathematical meaning of Moment of Inertia, we can say that, in effect, it means the natural resistance of the machine to any form of rotation about its Centre of Gravity. Any heavy weights which are a long distance away from a particular axis of rotation will make it more difficult to cause any rapid movement around that axis; thus weights on the wing tips or, what amounts to much the same thing, a large span will result in a resistance to Rolling about the longitudinal axis. Similarly, a long fuselage will mean a resistance to Pitching and Yawing.

In this question of quick manoeuvrability the Biplane has a decided advantage over the Monoplane, since it is in every way more compact, the weights being concentrated nearer to the Centre of Gravity. Another advantage of the Biplane from the point of view of manoeuvrability is its greater rigidity, which prevents dangerous distortion of the structure taking place during manoeuvres. It was largely for these reasons that the Biplane was for so long the more popular type for military purposes, where quick manoeuvrability is an essential feature. Modern high-speed monoplanes have very high wing loading and thus a small area of wing which makes them nearly as good as a biplane for purposes of manoeuvrability.

_____

See if you can answer these questions about the various manoeuvres which an aeroplane can perform—

1. What are the three axes, fixed in the aeroplane, round which an aircraft may rotate, and what is the name of each rotation?

2. What are the six degrees of freedom of an aeroplane?

3. Explain what is meant by Centripetal and Centrifugal Force?

4. What is meant by saying that $4g$ may be reached in pulling out of a dive?

5. Why does an aeroplane bank when taking a corner?

6. Why is there a danger that a pupil may stall an aeroplane during a turn?

7. Why is there a definite limit to the smallness of the radius on which an aeroplane can turn?

8. Two aircraft turn through 360° in the same time, i.e. at the same rate of turn, but the radius of turn of one is twice that of the other. Will they have the same angle of bank? If not, which will have the greater?

9. Discuss the possibilities of executing a "vertical bank."

10. Explain the difference between a gliding and climbing turn from the point of view of holding off bank.

11. Why is a sideslip a difficult manoeuvre on some types of modern aircraft?

12. Why is the tail well down in inverted (level) flight?

13. Why does the biplane have advantages as regards manoeuvrability?

14. What is an Accelerometer?

15. What are the forces acting upon an aeroplane during a steep nose-dive?

16. Why is a "load factor" allowed when designing an aeroplane?

17. What is meant by the reversal of loads in the aeroplane structure?

18. In what manoeuvres are the loads on the structure likely to be reversed?

_____

Numerical examples on Manoeuvres will be found on page 359.

CHAPTER IX

STABILITY AND CONTROL

Meaning of Stability

THE **Stability of an aeroplane means its ability to return to some particular condition of flight** (after having been slightly disturbed from that condition) **without any efforts on the part of the pilot.** An aeroplane may be stable under some conditions of flight and unstable under other conditions. For instance, an aeroplane which is stable during

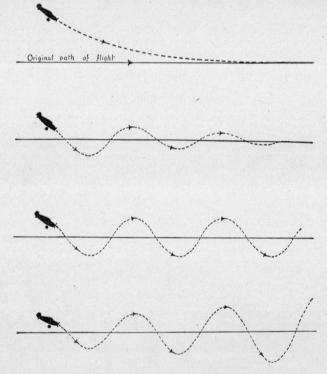

Original path of flight

FIG. 152. DEGREES OF STABILITY

Straight and Level Flight may be unstable when inverted, and vice versa. If an aeroplane were stable during a nose-dive, it would mean that it would resist efforts on the part of the pilot to extricate it from the nose-dive. The stability which is definitely due to features incorporated in the design of the aircraft is sometimes called **Inherent Stability.**

Stability is often confused with Balance, and the student should be careful to distinguish between the two. An aeroplane which flies with one wing lower than the other may often, when disturbed from this attitude, return to it. Such an aeroplane is out of its proper balance, but it is not unstable.

There is a half-way house between Stability and Instability, for, as already stated, an aeroplane which, when disturbed, tends to return to its original position is said to be Stable; if, on the other hand, it tends to move farther away from the original position, it is Unstable. But it may tend to do neither of these and prefer to remain in its new position. This is called **Neutral Stability,** and is sometimes a very desirable feature.

Fig. 152 illustrates some of the ways in which an aeroplane may behave when it is left to itself. The top diagram shows complete dead-beat stability which is very rarely achieved in practice. The second is the usual type of stability, that is to say an oscillation which is gradually damped out. The steady oscillation shown next is really a form of neutral stability, while the bottom diagram shows the kind of thing which may easily occur in certain types of aircraft, an oscillation which steadily grows worse. Even this is not so bad as the case when an aeroplane makes no attempt to return but simply departs farther and farther away from its original path. That is complete instability.

The stability of an aeroplane must be considered about all three axes, and it is possible for an aeroplane to be stable about one axis, but unstable about another.

Control

Control means the power of the pilot to manoeuvre the aeroplane into any desired position. It is not by any means the same thing as stability; in fact, the two characteristics may directly oppose each other. It is only when the pilot and the aeroplane agree as to what alterations should be made in their method of flight that control and stability can be said to work hand in hand.

The Stability or Control of an aeroplane in so far as it concerns **Rolling** about the Longitudinal axis is called **Lateral** Stability or Control respectively. Students are sometimes confused as to why it is called Lateral Stability when the rotation is about the Longitudinal axis; the term, however, is a purely common-sense one, since it is the Lateral axis which is disturbed, and if this is realized there should be no reason for confusion.

Stability or Control which concerns **Yawing** about the Normal axis is called **Directional** Stability or Control.

Stability or Control which concerns **Pitching** about the Lateral axis is called **Longitudinal** Stability or Control.

Lateral and Directional Stability are so closely inter-connected that it is impossible to consider one without the other, and they are therefore often grouped together under the single term of Lateral Stability.

Mathematical Difficulties

Before we attempt to explore this subject any further we feel it our duty to warn the reader that the **problems involved in the consideration of Stability and Control of aeroplanes are sufficient to baffle the greatest mathematicians of the day,** and that any attempt at "simple" explanation of such problems may, at the best, be incomplete and possibly incorrect. The reader need have no fear of the mathematics, as we shall not even attempt to tackle them, but he must be prepared, if and when he acquires greater knowledge of the subject from more advanced works, to readjust his ideas accordingly.

After this very necessary apology we will try to explain, at any rate, the practical considerations which affect Stability.

Longitudinal Stability

We will start with **Longitudinal Stability,** since this can be considered independently of the other two. In order to obtain this stability in pitching, we must ensure that **if the Angle of Attack is temporarily increased, forces will act on the aeroplane in such a way as to depress the nose and thus decrease the Angle of Attack once again.** To a great extent we have already tackled this problem while dealing with the movement of the Centre of Pressure on aerofoils and the necessity for the tail plane. In general we can say that the Longitudinal Stability of the aeroplane is dependent on four factors—

1. **The position of the Centre of Gravity** of the aeroplane, which must not be too far back. This is probably the most important consideration.

2. **The movement of the Centre of Pressure on the Main Planes.**

This, as we have seen, usually tends towards instability, although this effect is minimized in the case of aerofoils with convex cambers on the under-surface.

3. **The movement of the Centre of Pressure on the Fuselage or body of the Aeroplane.**

When a modern aeroplane is presented at any angle of attack to the air there may be considerable air forces on fuselage, body, nacelles, etc. The centre of pressure of such forces is apt to move as the angle of attack alters, and it nearly always moves in the unstable direction, thus adding to the instability effect of the main planes.

4. **The Area of the Tail Plane, the Angle at which it is set, its Aspect Ratio, and its Distance from the Centre of Gravity.**

Of these the angle is not so important as is often supposed, the setting being decided more from considerations of equilibrium than of stability.

Longitudinal Dihedral

The Tail Plane is usually set at an angle less than that of the Main Planes, the angle between the chord of the Tail Plane and the chord of the Main Planes being known as the **Longitudinal Dihedral** (Fig. 153).

Main Plane

Tail Plane

FIG. 153. LONGITUDINAL DIHEDRAL ANGLE

This Longitudinal Dihedral is a practical characteristic of most types of aeroplane, but so many considerations enter into the problem that it cannot be said that an aeroplane which does not possess this feature is necessarily unstable longitudinally. In any case, it is really the Angle of Attack, the actual angle at which the Tail Plane strikes the airflow, which matters; therefore we must not forget the downwash from the Main Planes. This downwash will cause the actual Angle of Attack to be less than the angle at which the Rigger sets the Tail Plane (Fig. 107). For this reason, even if the Tail Plane is set at the same angle as the Main Planes, there will in effect be a Longitudinal Dihedral angle, and this may help the aeroplane to be longitudinally stable. The range of angle on adjustable Tail Planes may allow the Tail Plane angle to be increased to such an extent that it is greater than that on the Main Planes, but these large Tail Plane angles are normally only used when the Angle of Attack of the Main Planes is large and therefore the angle of downwash is greater than usual. An indiscriminate use of the adjustable Tail Plane by the pilot might, in fact, lead to longitudinal instability.

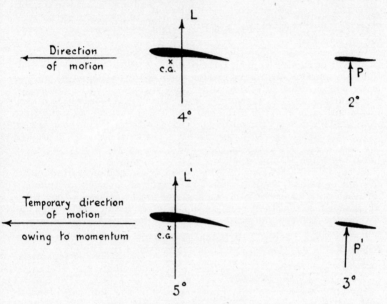

FIG. 154. LONGITUDINAL STABILITY

Suppose an aeroplane to be flying so that the Angle of Attack of the Main Planes is 4° and the Angle of Attack of the Tail Plane is 2°; a sudden gust causes the nose to rise, inclining the longitudinal axis of the aeroplane by 1°. What will happen? The momentum of the aeroplane will cause it temporarily to continue moving practically in its original direction and at its previous speed. Therefore the Angle of Attack of the Main Planes will become nearly 5° and the Tail Plane nearly 3° (Fig. 154). The Lift on the Main Planes will increase and probably move slightly forward, while the Lift on the Tail Plane will increase in an even greater proportion. (The Tail Plane Lift may also move forward, but, compared with the original leverage, the movement is so small as to be negligible.) **If the restoring Moment caused by the increase in the Tail Plane Lift multiplied by the distance to the Centre of Gravity is greater than the upsetting movement caused by the increase in Main Plane Lift and its new distance from the Centre of Gravity, then the aeroplane will be stable.** This last sentence puts the whole thing in a nutshell, but unfortunately it is not quite so easy to analyse the practical characteristics which will bring about such a state of affairs. In some instances there may be very little, if any, movement of the Centre of Pressure on the main planes, and even the condition of the Longitudinal Dihedral is not an absolute essential for Longitudinal Stability. Thus the forward position of the centre of gravity and the area and leverage of the tail plane will probably have the greatest influence.

An apparently simpler explanation is sometimes given by taking into account only the fact that the Lift on the Tail Plane is increased in greater proportion to that on the Main Plane, and therefore the Tail will be lifted. This, however, is incomplete, and may even be incorrect, since it does not take into account the very important movement of the Lift on the Main Planes, which is, in fact, what causes the necessity for the Tail Plane.

In the rare cases where the Tail Plane is in front of the Main Planes there will probably still be a Longitudinal Dihedral, which means that this front surface must have greater angle than the Main Planes. The latter will naturally still be at an efficient angle, such as 4°, so that the front surface may be at, say, 6° or 8°. Thus it is working at a very inefficient angle and will stall some few degrees sooner than the Main Planes. This fact is claimed by the enthusiasts for this type of design as its main advantage, since the stalling of the front surface will prevent the nose being raised any further, and therefore the Main Planes will never reach the Stalling Angle.

In the Pterodactyl type, in which there is no separate surface either in front or behind, the wings must be heavily swept back, and there is a "wash-out" or decrease in the angle of incidence as the wing tip is approached, so that these wing tips do, in effect, act in exactly the same way as the ordinary tail plane (Plates XXVII and XXVIII).

Lateral Stability

Lateral and Directional Stability will first be considered separately, and then we will try to see how they affect each other.

To secure **Lateral Stability** we must so arrange things that when a slight Roll takes place the forces acting on the aeroplane tend to restore it to an even keel. To a certain extent this is a property of all aeroplanes **provided they are flying at a small Angle of Attack,** for suppose one wing were to drop, **while it was dropping the air would come up to meet it,** and therefore the effective Angle of Attack would be increased, so increasing the Lift on that wing. By the same argument the Angle of Attack and Lift on the rising wing would be decreased. Such changes will obviously tend to prevent the aeroplane from rolling, but **the righting effect will only last while the aeroplane is actually rolling.** The fact must also be emphasized that this effect will only take place while the Angle of Attack is small; if the Angle of Attack is at or beyond the stalling angle, then the increased angle on the falling wing will cause a **decrease** in Lift, while the corresponding decrease of angle on the other side may actually cause an increase; thus the new forces will tend to roll the aeroplane still further, and the process will continue, this being the cause of the auto-rotation previously mentioned (Fig. 142 on page 229).

The danger of auto-rotation can be practically eliminated by the use of automatic slots near the wing tips. This is because, when one of the wings begins to drop, the increase in the effective Angle of Attack will cause the slot on that wing to open, thus increasing the lift and

restoring that wing to its normal position. Automatic slots are, therefore, a considerable aid to the natural lateral stability of the aeroplane.

Dihedral Angle

Lateral Stability will be improved by the use of a **Dihedral Angle**
on the Main Planes (see Fig. 155). For rigging purposes the Dihedral
Angle is taken as being the angle between **each** plane and the horizontal,

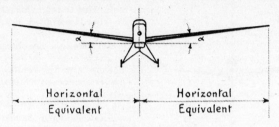

α° = Dihedral Angle

FIG. 155. LATERAL DIHEDRAL ANGLE

not the total angle between the two planes, which is really the geo-
metrical meaning of a Dihedral angle. If the planes are inclined
upwards towards the wing tips, the Dihedral is Positive; if downwards, it is Negative; but the latter arrangement is hardly ever used in
practice.

The effect of the Dihedral Angle in securing Lateral Stability is
sometimes dismissed by saying that if one wing drops the Horizontal

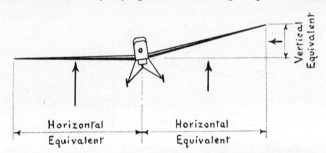

FIG. 156. HORIZONTAL EQUIVALENT AND VERTICAL EQUIVALENT

Equivalent on that wing is increased and therefore the Lift is increased,
whereas the Horizontal Equivalent and the Lift of the wing which
rises is decreased, therefore **obviously** the forces will tend to right the
aeroplane.

Unfortunately, it is not all quite so obvious as that.

It is quite true that the **vertical** force on the lower wing will be
greater than the **vertical** force on the raised wing, owing to the change
in Horizontal Equivalents; but, once the rolling has ceased, the **total**
force on each wing will be the same, and will be at right angles to
each plane, and will act at the same distance from the centre of

gravity. Each force will therefore have the same moment, and therefore the forces will **not** tend to return the aeroplane to its normal position! Looking at it in another way, the Horizontal Equivalent on the lower wing has become greater, but the **vertical equivalent** on the raised wing has increased, causing a force tending further to upset the aeroplane, and thus balancing the righting effect due to the Horizontal Equivalent (Fig. 156).

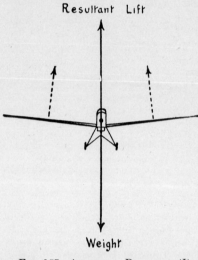

Resultant Lift

Weight

Fig. 157. Action of Dihedral (I)

An attempt has been made to explain this in some detail because the apparently simple explanation is so often accepted without thought. The fact is that if we consider a model aeroplane—with Dihedral—to be travelling so that its centre of gravity travels along a wire, and **cannot slip sideways,** then if one wing of the model is lowered, the **dihedral will not restore it to its original position.** Also, according to the simple explanation, an aeroplane—with dihedral—which is exe-cuting a properly banked turn would tend to return to an even keel, and the pilot would have to "hold on" the bank (the author

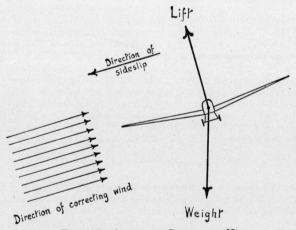

Lift

Direction of sideslip

Direction of correcting wind

Weight

Fig. 158. Action of Dihedral (II)

has actually seen this stated in a book on Theory of Flight). **This, however, is not what occurs,** for, owing to the increased velocity of the outer wing during a turn, it is more usual to have to "hold off" the bank.

What, then, is the real explanation as to why a Dihedral Angle is an aid to Lateral Stability? When the wings are both equally inclined (Fig. 157) the resultant Lift on the Wings will be vertically upward and will exactly balance the Weight. If, however, one wing becomes lower than the other (Fig. 158), then the resultant Lift on the wings will be slightly inclined in the direction of the lower wing, while the Weight will remain vertical. Therefore the two forces will not balance each other and there will be a small resultant force acting on the aeroplane in a sideways and downwards direction. This force is temporarily unbalanced and therefore the aeroplane will move in the direction of this force—i.e. it will sideslip—and this will cause a flow of air in the opposite direction to the slip. This wind will strike the lower plane at a greater angle than the upper plane, also the wing tip of the lower plane will become, as it were, the leading edge so far as the slip is concerned; and just as the centre of pressure across the chord is nearer the leading edge, so the centre of the pressure distribution along the span will now be on the lower plane; for both these reasons the lower plane will receive more Lift, and after a slight slip sideways the aeroplane will roll back into its proper position. As a matter of fact, owing to the protection of the fuselage, it is probable that the flow of air created by the sideslip will not reach a large portion of the raised wing at all; this may help the correction, but the whole problem becomes so complicated that we may be well advised not to investigate further. It remains, however, that a Dihedral Angle of 3° or more does produce a reasonable amount of Lateral Stability, and we had better let it rest at that.

High Wing and Low Centre of Gravity

Although the Dihedral Angle is the best and the most usually adopted method of obtaining Lateral Stability, other methods have been tried with varying degrees of success. If the wings are placed in a high position and the Centre of Gravity in a correspondingly low position, a type of lateral stability is introduced which has sometimes been given the rather misleading name of pendulum stability. The word "pendulum" implies that the weight is hung on a fixed support, but the wings of an aeroplane are not by any means fixed and they sideslip with the rest of the machine, so that it only acts as a pendulum in so far as the wings are held back by the air resistance produced by the sideslip. The parachute is the only true example of this kind of lateral stability (Fig. 159). As the word "pendulum" rather implies, this method is apt to lead to the aeroplane swinging first to one side and then to the other during recovery, but the low weight is inclined to swing over too far in the other direction, causing the other wing to drop; then a sideslip follows in that direction, and so on. This method is usually adopted in the High Wing or Parasol type of monoplane, which often has no Dihedral Angle. The Low Wing Monoplane, on the other hand, must usually have a Dihedral Angle.

Sweepback and Lateral Stability

A considerable angle of sweepback, such as is used in the Pterodactyl type, will in itself promote Lateral Stability, for, supposing the left wing to drop, as in the two previous cases, there will be a sideslip to the left and the left-hand wing will present, in effect, a higher aspect ratio than the right wing to the correcting airflow (Fig. 160). It will therefore receive more Lift and, as before, recovery will take place after sideslip.

Fin Area and Lateral Stability

One factor which may influence Lateral Stability is the position of the

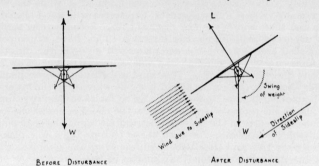

FIG. 159. HIGH WING AND LOW CENTRE OF GRAVITY

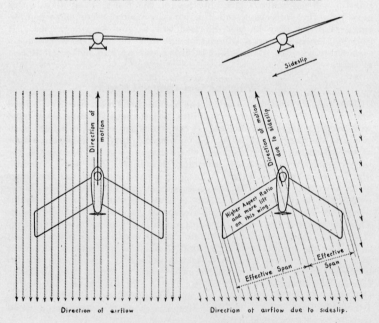

FIG. 160. SWEEPBACK AND LATERAL STABILITY

various "side surfaces," such as the fuselage, fin and rudder, wheels, and especially the floats or hull of a seaplane. All these will present areas at right angles to any sideslip, therefore there will be considerable pressure upon them which, if they are high above the Centre of Gravity, will tend to restore the aeroplane to an even keel (Fig. 161); but if these surfaces are low, like the floats or hull of a seaplane, the pressure upon them will tend to roll the machine over still more and so cause Lateral Instability (Fig. 162). In order to counteract this effect, vertical fins have sometimes been placed above the top planes of flying boats, but it is only in very rare cases that a high vertical fin has been used with the sole object of promoting Lateral Stability.

The reader will have noticed that, whatever the method of obtaining

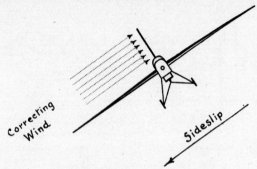

FIG. 161. EFFECT OF HIGH FIN ON LATERAL STABILITY

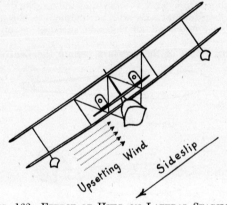

FIG. 162. EFFECT OF HULL ON LATERAL STABILITY

stability, once the rolling motion is completed and the aeroplane is flying with one wing low, correction only takes place after a sideslip towards this low wing.

It is this sideslip which affects the Directional Stability.

Directional Stability

We will first try to consider **Directional Stability** by itself, if only as a means of convincing ourselves that the two are so inter-linked one with the other that they cannot be disposed of separately. In order to establish Directional Stability we must ensure that, if the aeroplane is temporarily deflected from its course, it will, of its own accord, tend to return to that course again. This is almost entirely a question of the "side surface" or "fin area" which has already been mentioned when dealing with Lateral Stability, but here it is not a question of the relative height of this side surface, but whether it is in front of or behind the Centre of Gravity. When the aeroplane is flying in the normal way the airflow will approach it directly from the front, i.e. parallel to its longitudinal axis. Now imagine the aeroplane to be

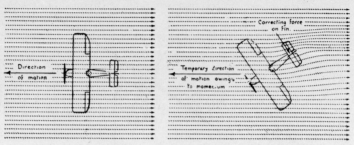

BEFORE DISTURBANCE   AFTER DISTURBANCE

FIG. 163. DIRECTIONAL STABILITY

deflected from its course as in Fig. 163; owing to its natural momentum it will for a short time tend to continue moving in its old direction, therefore the longitudinal axis will be inclined to the airflow, and a pressure will be created on all the side surfaces on one side of the aeroplane.

If the turning effect of the pressure behind the Centre of Gravity is

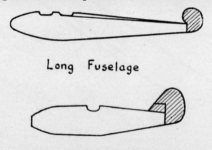

Long Fuselage

Short Fuselage

FIG. 164

greater than the turning effect in front of the Centre of Gravity, then the aeroplane will tend to return to its original course.

If, on the other hand, the turning effect in front is greater than that behind, the aeroplane will turn still further off its course. Notice that it is the turning effect or the moment that matters, and not the actual pressure; therefore it is not merely a question of how much side surface is in front of or behind the Centre of Gravity, but also of the distance from the Centre of Gravity of each side surface. For instance, a small fin at the end of a long fuselage may be just as effective in producing directional stability as a large fin at the end of a short fuselage (Fig. 164).

PLATE XLII. DIRECTIONAL STABILITY

American heavy bomber, "Fortress II," showing the large fin, which is augmented by the dorsal fin along the top of the fuselage.

(By courtesy of "The Aeroplane.")

Also, in certain cases there may be actually more side surface in the front than in the rear, but the rear surfaces will be at a greater distance. All the side surfaces of an aeroplane, including that presented by wings with dihedral, affect the Directional Stability, but to the fin is allotted the particular task of finally adjusting matters and its area is settled accordingly. In cases where there is already sufficient side surface to the rear provided by the fuselage and rudder, no fixed fin may be necessary.

There is a very close resemblance between the Directional Stability of an aeroplane and the action of a weathercock which always turns into the wind; in fact, one often sees a model aeroplane used as a weathercock. The simile, however, should not be carried too far, and the student must remember that there are two essential differences between the aeroplane and the weathercock—first, that the aeroplane is not only free to yaw, **but also to move bodily sideways;** and, secondly, that the "wind," in the case of the aeroplane, is not the wind we speak of when on the ground, **but the wind caused by the original motion of the aeroplane through the air.** This point is emphasized because of the idea which sometimes exists that an aeroplane desires to turn head to wind. If such were the case, Directional Stability would be a very mixed blessing.

Lateral and Directional Stability

Now we are, at last, in a position to connect these two forms of stability—the sideslip essential to Lateral Stability will cause an air pressure on the side surfaces which have been provided for Directional Stability. As explained above, the effect of this pressure will be to turn the nose of the aeroplane into the relative wind, i.e. in this case, **towards the direction of sideslip.** The aeroplane, therefore, will turn off its original course and in the direction of the lower wing. It is rather curious to note that the greater the Directional Stability of the aircraft the greater will be the tendency to turn off course in a sideslip. This turn will cause the raised wing, now on the outside of the turn, to travel faster than the inner or lower wing, and therefore to obtain more lift and so bank the aeroplane still further. By this time the nose of the aeroplane has probably dropped and the fat is properly in the fire with all three stabilities involved! The best way of seeing all this happen in real life is to watch a model aeroplane flying on a gusty day; the light loading and slow speed of the model make it possible to watch each step in the proceedings, whereas in the full-sized aeroplane it all happens more quickly, and also the pilot usually interferes by using his controls. If, for instance, the left wing drops and he applies rudder so as to turn the machine to the right, he will probably prevent it from departing appreciably from its course.

We can now explain the new technique of turning an aeroplane— this has already been hinted at in the previous chapter. Suppose, when we want to turn to the left, **instead of applying any rudder we simply bank the aeroplane to the left,** as we have already seen it will slip inwards and **turn to the left.** That is all there is in it. So effective is this method with modern aircraft that it has become unnecessary to use the rudder at all for turning purposes; unfortunately this fact has led people to think that a modern aeroplane turns in some new and mysterious way, and it has become almost a sin to suggest that the rudder turns an aeroplane or even that it causes yaw. The heretics

who suggest such things are not really so wrong as their would-be
teachers would have them believe. So far as the yaw is concerned—
and a turn must involve a yaw—the rudder (with the help of the fin)
is still responsible, just as (with the help of the fin) it always was. The
difference is simply that the rudder and fin are brought into effect
by the inward sideslip, instead of by **application** of rudder which tends
to cause an outward skid. The pilot may do nothing about it, but the
stability of the aeroplane puts a force on the rudder for him. It should
also be emphasized that although it may be most practical, and most
sensible, to commence a turn in certain aircraft without application of

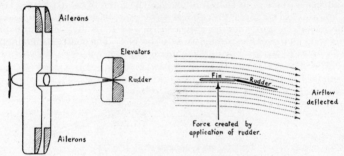

Ailerons

Elevators

Rudder

Fin

Rudder

Airflow
deflected

Force created by
application of rudder.

Ailerons

FIG. 165. CONTROL SURFACES

rudder, **such a turn cannot be absolutely perfect, there must be an inward
sideslip**—the pilot may not notice it, the sideslip indicator may not
detect it; but it is there just the same, **otherwise the aircraft would
not turn.**

Just as a slight roll results in a sideslip and then a yawing motion so
if an aircraft moves in a yawed position, as in Fig. 163, that is if it moves
crabwise (which is really the same thing as slipping or skidding) Lateral
Stability will come into play and cause the aircraft to roll away from the
leading wing. Also, while the aircraft is actually yawing the outer wing
will move faster than the inner, obtain more lift and thus cause a rolling
motion. Thus a **roll causes a yaw,** and a **yaw causes a roll,** and the study
of the two cannot be separated.

If the stability characteristics of an aeroplane are such that it is
very stable directionally and **not very stable laterally,** e.g. if it has large
fin and rudder and little or no dihedral angle, it will have such a marked
tendency to turn into a sideslip, and to bank at steeper and steeper
angles, that it may get into an uncontrollable spiral—this is sometimes
called **spiral instability,** but note that it is caused by too much stability
(directional).

If, on the other hand, the aeroplane is **very stable laterally** and **not
very stable directionally,** it will sideslip without any marked tendency
to turn into the sideslip. Such an aircraft is easily controllable by the
rudder, and if the rudder only is used for a turn the aircraft will bank
and make quite a nice turn.

The reader will find it interesting to think out the other characteristics
which these two extremes would cause in an aeroplane.

Controls of an Aeroplane

Whether an aeroplane is stable or unstable, it is necessary for the pilot to be able to "control" it, so that he can manoeuvre it into any desired position.

Longitudinal Control is provided by the **elevators,** i.e. flaps hinged behind the tail plane.

Lateral Control is provided by the **ailerons,** i.e. flaps hinged at the rear of the aerofoils near each wing tip.

Directional Control is provided by the **rudder,** i.e. a vertical flap hinged to the stern post.

The system of control is the same in each case, i.e. if the control surface is moved it will, in effect, alter the Angle of Attack and the camber of the complete surface, and therefore change the force upon it (see Fig. 165).

The control surfaces are connected to controls in the pilot's cockpit. The elevators and ailerons are both moved by a single column on a universal joint and the rudder by a rudder bar. **The control is instinctive,** i.e. a forward movement of the control column depresses the elevators,

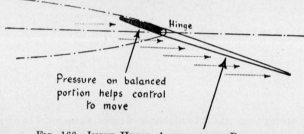

Pressure on balanced portion helps control to move

FIG. 166. INSET HINGE AERODYNAMIC BALANCE

increases the lift on the tail, and so causes the nose of the aeroplane to drop. If the control column is pushed to the left, the right-hand aileron will be depressed and the right-hand wing lifted, while, at the same time, the left-hand aileron will be raised and the left-hand wing will drop; thus the whole aeroplane will bank to the left. Both the forward and sideways movement of the control column can be carried out simultaneously, causing both the nose and the left wing to be depressed. In some aeroplanes the control column can only move in a fore-and-aft direction, lateral control being provided by a wheel similar to the steering wheel of a motor-car; an anti-clockwise rotation of the wheel will cause the left wing to drop. As an alternative to the wheel there may be some form of "spectacles," i.e. a horizontal bar fitted to the top of the control column, with a hand grip at each end so that it can be tilted to right or left; this is really a variation of the wheel system, the principle being exactly the same. In the case of the rudder, if the right foot is pressed forward the rear of the rudder will be moved to the right (called "right rudder") and the aeroplane will turn to the right. Some pilots claim that the rudder control is **not** instinctive, and it certainly does not correspond to the steering, say, of a bicycle.

In each instance it will be noticed that the control surfaces are placed as far as possible away from the centre of gravity so as to provide sufficient leverage to alter the position of the aeroplane.

Balanced Controls

Although, in general, the forces which the pilot has to exert in order to move the controls are small, the continuous movement required in "bumpy" weather becomes tiring during long flights, especially when the control surfaces are large and the speeds fairly high. For this reason controls are often " **balanced,**" or, more correctly, partially balanced.

Several methods have been employed for balancing control surfaces. Fig. 166 shows what is perhaps the most simple kind of aerodynamic balance.

The hinge is set back so that **the air striking the surface in front of**

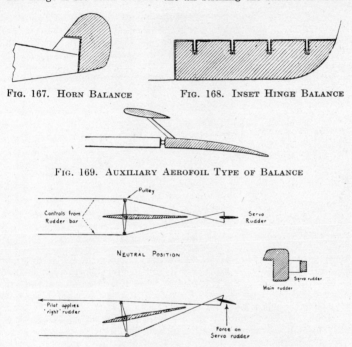

FIG. 167. HORN BALANCE   FIG. 168. INSET HINGE BALANCE

FIG. 169. AUXILIARY AEROFOIL TYPE OF BALANCE

FIG. 170. SERVO SYSTEM OF BALANCE

the hinge causes a pressure which tends to make the control move over still further ; this **partially balances** the effect of the air which strikes the rear portion. This method of balancing is effective but it must be carried out very carefully; over-balancing is dangerous since it may remove all "feel" of the control from the pilot. It must be remembered that when the control surface is set at a small angle, the Centre of Pressure on the surface is well forward of the centre of the area, and if at any angle the Centre of Pressure is in front of the hinge it will tend to take the control out of the pilot's hands (or feet). Usually not more than one-fifth of the surface may be in front of the hinge.

Figs. 167, 168, and 169 show practical applications of this type of balance. In all of these some part of the surface is in front of the hinge, and each method has its own advantages.

Fig. 170 shows the servo type of balance which differs in principle since the pilot in this case only moves the small extra surface (**in the**

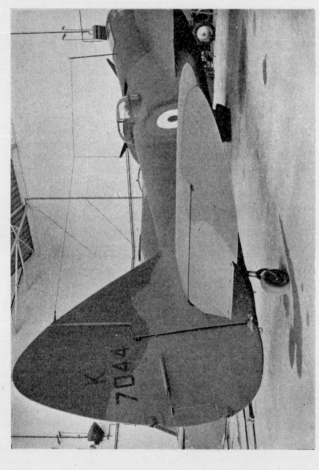

PLATE XLIII. BALANCED CONTROLS

Rear view of the Bristol "Blenheim," showing the horn balance of both rudder and elevators
Notice also the trimming tabs on both surfaces.
(By courtesy of the Bristol Aeroplane Co., Ltd.)

opposite direction to normal), and, owing to the leverage, the force on the small surface helps to move the main control in the required direction. It is, in effect, a system of gearing.

Perhaps the chief interest in the servo system of balance is that it was the forerunner of the balancing "tabs" and trimming "tabs" which have largely displaced the older systems. The development of these control tabs has been very rapid and has formed an interesting little bit of aviation history. As now used, they are so effective and so simple that one is inclined to wonder why we put up with the old-fashioned and clumsy methods for so long.

The servo system suffered from many defects, but it did show how powerful is the effect of a small surface used to deflect the air in the opposite direction to that in which it is desired to move the control surface. The next step was to apply this idea to an aileron when a machine was inclined to fly with one wing lower than the other. The method may have been crude, but the idea was sound. On the aileron of the wing which was flying low, a length of cable was placed along the top surface near the trailing edge, then a piece of fabric was stuck on to hold it in position (Fig. 171). The slight curl up thus produced at the trailing edge deflected the air upwards, causing a downward force which had sufficient turning effect about the hinge to depress the whole aileron, thus increasing the lift on that wing and curing the fault in flying. This little "trick," as it might almost be called, not only did the job, but it became very popular among riggers because it saved them the trouble of altering the whole wing incidence for the same purpose. To them it was but a labour-saving device, but, looked at from a wider point of view, it arrived at a most appropriate time because aeroplane construction was tending in such a way—towards rigid monoplane wings—that the alteration of wing incidence was becoming not only difficult but impossible.

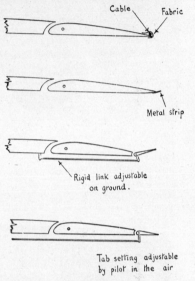

FIG. 171. EVOLUTION OF CONTROL TABS

It was a small step to the next stage of development—a strip of flexible metal attached to the trailing edge of the control surface (Fig. 171). This could be bent upwards or downwards as required and was most effective in correcting flying faults without alteration of rigging. It was used on the S.6.b. Schneider Trophy machine, and subsequently on many other types.

So far, the deflection of the air has only been in one direction and thus we have obtained a **bias** on the controls rather than a balancing system. The next step gave us both balance and bias; the strip of metal became a **tab**, i.e. an actual flap hinged to the control surface.

PLATE XLIV. MORE TABS

Here the tabs on the rudder and elevators of the "Meteor." Note, on the rudder tab, the desensitizer at the trailing edge (see page 260).

(By courtesy of the Gloster Aircraft Co. Ltd.)

PLATE XLIV. TABS

The tail unit of the Bristol Freighter. On the rudder the upper tab is a trimming tab and the lower one a spring tab. The starboard elevator tab is operated by the pilot, the port tab automatically.

(By courtesy of the Bristol Aeroplane Co., Ltd.)

This tab was connected by a link to a fixed surface (the tail plane, fin or main plane), the length of this link being adjustable on the ground (Fig. 171). When the main control surface moved in one direction, the tab moved in the other and thus experienced a force which tended to help the main surface to move—hence the balance. By adjusting the link, the tab could be set to give an initial force in one direction or the other—hence the bias.

Sometimes a spring is inserted between the tab and main control

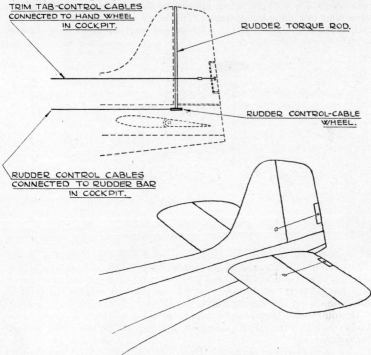

FIG. 172. CONTROL TABS

system. The spring may be used to modify the system in two possible ways—

1. So that the amount of tab movement decreases with speed, thus preventing the action being too violent at high speeds.

2. So that the tab does not operate at all until the main control surface has been moved through a certain angle, or until a certain control force is exerted. Tabs of this kind are called **Spring Tabs.**

The final step (Figs. 171, 172 and Plates XLIII, XLIV, and XLV) required a little mechanical ingenuity, but otherwise it was a natural development. The pilot was given the means of adjusting the bias while **in the air,** and thus he was enabled to correct any flying faults, or out-of-balance effects, as and when they occurred.

It would be difficult to over-estimate the value of these control tabs in modern design. They have most of the virtues and few of the vices of other inventions and gadgets. They are simple, light in weight and effective; they give balance which is never too violent and which has the very desirable feature of becoming more effective as the control surface is moved through larger angles; for all practical purposes they replace the old methods of "rigging" by tightening and slackening wires and twisting the machine into some new shape; and they provide the pilot with a means of correcting the faults while flying instead of waiting until he is on the ground. It cannot even be said that they add "something extra to go wrong" because, although they need small controls in the cockpit, when applied to the elevators **they make the adjustable tail plane unnecessary.** This alone causes a saving in weight, the loss of one control in the cockpit and, perhaps most important of

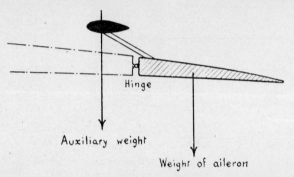

Fig. 173. Mass Balance

all. enables the designer to make a simpler and more efficient design of the tail unit. The tabs on the rudder have saved us from the adjustable fin, which would have been another complication, and the aileron tabs have, for the first time, enabled the pilot to correct the fault of flying one wing low **during flight.**

It would seem that control tabs have come to stay; but one never knows in this subject. At one time the adjustable tail plane seemed indispensable.

The cross-sectional shape of the control surface itself may have an important effect on aerodynamic balance. A convex shape tends towards over-balance, whereas a concave or hollow-ground shape has the opposite effect. This is illustrated by the "de-sensitizer," a device which sometimes has to be fitted to the trailing edge of a control surface to prevent over-balance, and which consists of a narrow flat plate giving a hollow-ground effect (Plate XLV).

Mass Balance

Control surfaces are often balanced in quite a different sense. A **mass** (usually a lump of lead) is fitted in front of the hinge in such a way as to prevent the "flutter" of control surfaces which is liable to occur at very high speeds of flight (Fig. 173). This flutter is a kind of vibration which is caused by the combined effects of the changes in air pressure distribution over the surface as the angle of attack is altered, and the elastic forces set up by the distortion of the structure itself. All structures are distorted when loads are applied, bridges bend under the weights that go over them, church towers and New York skyscrapers sway in the wind; and the aeroplane structure is no exception. If the structure is elastic, as all good structures should be, it will tend to spring back as soon as the load is removed, or changes its point of application. In short, a distorted structure is like a spring that has been wound up and is ready to spring back. An aeroplane wing or fuselage can be distorted in two ways, by bending and by twisting, and

PLATE XLVI. MASS BALANCE

"Supermarine S.6," one-time winner of the Schneider Trophy and holder of the world's speed record. Ancestor of the " Spitfire." Notice the large mass balance weight on the ailerons to prevent flutter at high speeds.

(By courtesy of " The Aeroplane.")

each distortion can result in an independent vibration. Like all vibrations, this flutter is liable to become dangerous if the two effects add up. The flutter may affect the control surfaces such as an aileron, or the main planes, or both. The whole problem is very complicated, and not yet properly understood, but we do know of two features which help to prevent it—a **rigid structure** and **mass balance of the control surfaces.** When the old types of aerodynamic balance were used, e.g. the inset hinge or horn balance, the mass could be concealed inside the forward portion of the control surface and thus two birds were killed with one stone; but with the tab type of balance the mass must be placed on a special arm sticking out in front of the control surface. One point at last against tabs!

Perhaps it should be emphasized that the **mass** is **not** simply a weight for the purpose of balancing the control surface "statically," e.g. to keep the aileron floating when control wires are not attached; it may have this effect, but its real purpose is to alter what are called the "moments of inertia" of the surface, and thus alter the period of vibration and the liability to flutter. It may help to make this clear if we realize that mass balance is just as effective on a rudder, where the weight is not involved, as on an elevator or aileron.

PLATE XLVII. CONTROL AT LOW SPEEDS
The "Auster III" in   steep turn near the ground.
(*By courtesy of "The Aeroplane."*)

So important is the exact distribution of the mass on a control surface that strict orders have had to be introduced concerning the application of paint and dope to these surfaces. It is for this reason that the red, white and blue stripes which used to be painted on the rudders of Royal Air Force machines were removed (they have now been restored, but only on the **fixed** fin), and why the circles on the wings may not overlap the ailerons. Rumour has it that when this order was first promulgated, some units in their eagerness to comply with the order, but ignorant as to its purpose, painted over the circles and stripes with further coats of dope!

Control at Low Speeds

We now turn our attention to an important and interesting problem— namely, that of control at low speeds or, what amounts to the same thing, at large Angles of Attack. It is obviously of little use to enable a machine to fly slowly unless we can ensure that the pilot will still have adequate control over it.

Let us first state the problem by giving an example. Suppose, owing to engine failure, a pilot has to make a forced landing. If he is inexperienced—and indeed it has been known to happen to pilots of considerable experience—he will often tend to stall his aeroplane in an attempt to reach a distant field or to climb over some obstacle. Now the use of slots or flaps may postpone the stall, may help him to obtain lift at slow speeds, but they will not give him what he most needs—namely, efficient control.

In the first place, owing to the decreased speed of the airflow over all the control surfaces, the forces acting on them will be less and they will feel "sloppy." **But this is not all.** Suppose while he is thus flying near the stalling angle he decides that he must turn to the left, he will apply "left rudder," and at the same time he will move his control column over to the left, which will cause the right aileron to go down and the left one to go up. The rudder will make a feeble effort to turn the aeroplane to the left. What will be the effect of the movement of the ailerons?

The effect of the right aileron going down should be to increase the Lift on the right wing, but in actual practice it may decrease it, as it may increase the Angle of Attack beyond that angle which gives the greatest Lift. **But what is quite certain is that the Drag will be considerably increased on the right wing, so tending to pull the aeroplane round to the right.** (This "yawing effect," caused by the ailerons, is present at nearly all Angles of Attack, but it becomes particularly marked near the Stalling Angle; it is called **Aileron Drag.**) Meanwhile, what of the left wing? The Lift may either have decreased or increased according to the exact Angle of Attack, but in any case the change in Lift will be small. The Drag, on the other hand, will almost certainly have decreased as the aileron moved upwards. To sum it all up, the result of the pilot's attempt to turn to the left is that there may or may not be a slight tendency to roll into the left bank required for an ordinary left-hand turn, while at the same time the Drag on the wings will produce a strong tendency to turn to the **right** which may completely overcome the rudder's efforts in the opposite direction (Fig. 174). The conditions are, in fact, very favourable for a spin (both literally and metaphorically); the pilot could hardly have done better had he deliberately attempted to get the aeroplane into a spin.

So much for the problem. What solution can be found? We must endeavour to ensure that when the stalling angle is reached, or even exceeded, the movement of the controls by the pilot will cause the same effect on the aeroplane as in normal flight. The following improvements would all help to attain this end—

1. **Increased turning effect from the rudder.**
2. **Down-going aileron should not increase the Drag.**

3. **Up-going aileron should increase the Drag.**
4. **Down-going aileron should increase the Lift at all angles.**
5. **Up-going aileron should cause a loss of Lift at all angles.**

A large number of practical devices have been tried out in the attempt to satisfy these conditions; most of them have been partially successful, but in hardly any case can they be said to have solved the problem completely.

Let us consider a few of these and see to what extent they meet our requirements.

(a) The use of **very large rudders** with sufficient power to overcome the yawing effect of the ailerons in the wrong direction.

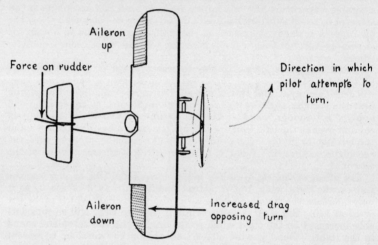

FIG. 174. RESULT OF THE ATTEMPT TO TURN AT LARGE ANGLES OF ATTACK

The disadvantage is that the size of rudder required to obtain the desired result is excessive for normal flight. Also this seems to be a method of tackling the problem from the wrong standpoint—instead of curing the disease, it allows the disease to remain while endeavouring to make the patient strong enough to withstand it.

(b) A **wash-out,** or decrease of the Riggers' Angle of Incidence, towards the wing tips.

This will mean that when the centre portions of the wings are at their Stalling Angle, the outer portions are well below the angle, and therefore the aileron will function in the normal way. The obvious defect of this arrangement is that the wash-out must be considerable to have any appreciable effect on the control, and the result will be a corresponding loss of lift from the outer portions of the wing in normal flight. The same effect can be obtained by rigging up the ailerons so that the trailing edge of the ailerons is above the trailing edge of the wing.

(c) "**Frise,**" or other **specially shaped ailerons** (Fig. 175). This is a patented device, the idea being so to shape the aileron that when it is moved downwards the complete top surface of the main plane and the aileron will have a smooth, uninterrupted contour causing very little Drag, but when it is moved upwards the aileron, which is of the balanced variety, will project below the bottom surface of the main plane and cause excessive Drag. This method has the great advantage of being simple, and it undoubtedly serves to decrease the bad yawing effect of the ailerons, and therefore it is often used. Unfortunately, its effects are not drastic enough.

(d) **Differential Ailerons** (Fig. 176). Here, again, is a delightfully simple device suffering only from the same defect that, although it provides a step in the right direction, it does not go far enough to satisfy our needs. Instead of the two ailerons moving equally up and down, a simple mechanical arrangement of the controls causes the

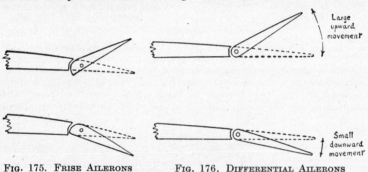

FIG. 175. FRISE AILERONS   FIG. 176. DIFFERENTIAL AILERONS

aileron which moves upwards to move through a larger angle than the aileron which moves downwards, the idea being to increase the Drag and decrease the Lift on the wing with the up-going aileron, while at the same time the down-going aileron, owing to its smaller movement, will not cause excessive Drag.

(e) **Slot-cum-Aileron Control** (Fig. 177). The slots, which need only be at the outer portions of the wings in front of the ailerons, may be of the automatic type, or the slot may be inter-connected to the aileron in such a way that **when the aileron is lowered the slot is opened,** while when the aileron is raised, or in its neutral position, the slot is closed. By this means the down-going aileron will certainly serve to increase the lift for several degrees beyond the stalling angle, nor will the Drag on this wing become very large since the open slot will lessen the formation of eddies. We shall therefore obtain a greater tendency to roll in the right direction and less tendency to yaw in the wrong direction. This is exactly what is required, and the system has been proved to be very effective in practice. The automatic slot has the great merit of simplicity, and it has the additional advantage that it tends to provide a certain degree of automatic lateral stability, especially when flying near the stalling angle.

Sometimes there is also a slot between the main plane and the aileron.

(f) **Spoiler Control** (Fig. 178). The Spoiler, or Interceptor, is a long, narrow plate fitted near to the Leading Edge of the aerofoil. In the ordinary way it lies flush with the surface and has no effect on the performance of the aerofoil, but it is connected to the aileron controls in such a way that when the aileron is moved up beyond a certain angle the

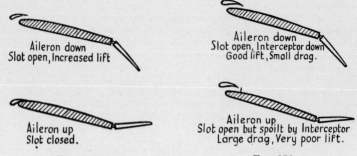

FIG. 177.
SLOT-CUM-AILERON CONTROL

FIG. 178.
SLOT-CUM-INTERCEPTOR CONTROL

Spoiler is raised at right angles to the airflow. This will naturally cause eddies over the top surface of the aerofoil, resulting in a very appreciable decrease in Lift and increase in Drag. This, when combined with the automatic slot, will mean that the wing on which the aileron

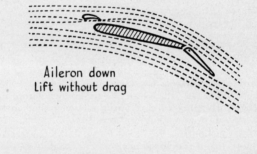

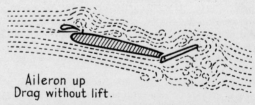

FIG. 179. A POSSIBLE COMBINATION OF DEVICES TO MAKE AILERON
CONTROL EFFECTIVE AT ALL ANGLES OF ATTACK
Slot-cum-Interceptor-cum-Frise-cum-Differential Ailerons.

goes down obtains increased Lift and very little extra Drag, while on the other wing the Lift is "spoilt" and the Drag greatly increased. **Thus we have a large rolling effect in the right direction combined with a yawing effect also in the right direction.**

This is what we aimed at, and there is the further advantage that the mechanical operation of the Spoiler is easy, since the forces acting upon it are very small. It may be fitted close behind the slot, and is so arranged that when it is in the down position it will lie underneath the slot. The effect of the Spoiler was found to be too violent when flying at high speeds, and therefore it was so arranged that it did not come into play until the aileron had been raised through a considerable angle and, even then, only when the slot was open. This method of control feels strange to the pilot who is unaccustomed to it because the loss of Lift caused by the Spoiler will result in a decided drop of that wing, which may be alarming when near the ground. But any such strangeness can soon be overcome and the pilot begins to realize the advantages of maintaining good lateral control, up to and beyond the normal stalling angle. The improvement in manoeuvrability is particularly noticeable when the aeroplane approaches its ceiling. But, whatever its merits, the Spoiler has not yet become popular as a means of control. It is used extensively as an air brake (see Chapter III).

It may be noticed that the elevator control has not been mentioned in dealing with this problem: the elevators usually remain fairly efficient since the Angle of Attack of the Tail Plane will be less than that of the Main Planes, and therefore there will not be the same tendency to stall as in the case of the ailerons. Also, when the engine is running the extra velocity of the slipstream will add to the effectiveness of both rudder and elevators provided they are in the slipstream.

It would be rash to prophesy what will be the control of the future, but so far as the present is concerned it is possible to combine the good effects of Slots, Interceptor, Frise, and Differential Ailerons (Fig. 179), and such a combination, together with an efficient rudder, should leave little to be desired. In point of fact, the average modern aircraft suffers very little from "aileron drag," although it has neither slots nor interceptors, but only a combination of Frise and Differential aileron. It is interesting to note, however, that when flying inverted the "adverse yaw" set up is even worse than with the old type of ailerons—just what one would expect, if one thinks it out.

Questions on stability and control—

1. What is meant by "inherent" stability?
2. What are the main factors which influence Longitudinal Stability?
3. Why does a dihedral angle not tend to eliminate the bank when an aeroplane is executing a correctly banked turn?
4. In what ways may Lateral Stability be secured without the use of the dihedral angle?
5. Why are Lateral Stability and Directional Stability really inseparable?
6. What would be the characteristics of an aircraft with extreme directional stability and little lateral stability?
7. What would be the characteristics of an aircraft with extreme lateral stability and little directional stability?
8. What is the object of balancing controls?
9. Why is the surface of an inset-hinge type of balanced control considerably less in front of the hinge than behind it?
10. Explain the action of control "tabs" in providing balance to controls and as a means of correcting flying faults.
11. What are spring tabs?

12. Distinguish between "mass" balance and "aerodynamic" balance.

13. Explain the difficulty of obtaining satisfactory lateral control at large angles of attack.

14. Describe some of the methods which have been tried with a view to overcoming this difficulty.

CHAPTER X

HIGH-SPEED FLIGHT

Introduction

IN the first nine chapters of this book frequent references have been made to the problems of high-speed flight, but detail consideration of these problems has been deferred to the present chapter. Why? Is there then some reason why high-speed flight should be considered on its own, as a separate subject? Are different principles involved? What is all the mystery surrounding this subject, or this part of the subject? What is it all about? Well, we shall try to answer these questions in the course of the chapter, so here goes!

The Speed of Sound

It is hardly necessary to tell the reader that it has all got something to do with the speed of sound or, more correctly, with the speed at which sound travels in air. If he reads the daily newspapers he cannot fail to have discovered that much, though he may well be confused as to the meaning of such terms as compressibility and sonic barriers. He may well wonder whether there really is some "barrier" to motion through the air, still more may he wonder whether such barrier is impassable— as has so often been stated in the popular press—when he knows that shells and rifle bullets have for many years succeeded in penetrating this so-called barrier, and apparently without any great difficulty.

What, then, is the significance of the speed of sound?

Simply this. **When a body moves through the air at speeds well below that at which sound travels in air, there is, as it were, a message sent ahead of the body to say that it is coming.** When this message is received, the air streams begin to divide to make way for the body, and **there is very little, if any, change in the density of the air as it flows past the body.** The way in which air is thus "warned" of the presence of the body which is approaching, or of changes in the shape or attitude of that body, can be clearly illustrated in a smoke tunnel in which the air flows over an aerofoil fitted with a flap. If the smoke streams are allowed to settle when the flap is in the closed position, and the flap is then lowered, all the streams of smoke many chords length in front of the aerofoil immediately change course, and streams which previously flowed below the aerofoil, now flow above it—seeking in fact the easiest path over the body. Once again, if we could "see the air" in front of an approaching aeroplane, this fact would be immediately obvious, and the air would begin to be disturbed perhaps 100 yards or more in front of the aeroplane of the approach of which it must have had some warning.

What we have called a "message" or "warning" is really due to a wave-motion in the air set up by the areas of increased and decreased pressures around the body. **These pressures are communicated in all directions to the surrounding air by means of " waves."** These waves are similar to sound waves, and they travel at the speed of sound, which is about 1,100 ft. per sec. (760 m.p.h.) in air at sea level conditions. There is no mystery in this relationship between pressure waves and sound waves because sound is, in fact, a pressure wave set up by some local compression of the air.

Suppose, then, that the body itself travels through the air at the speed of sound, there will be no time for the message to get ahead and **the air will come up against the body with a " shock."** This shock causes local compressions and **sudden changes in the density, pressure, and velocity of the air,** together with a **tendency for the air flow to break away from the surface of the body,** with **consequent changes in Lift, Drag, and other aerodynamic forces and moments.** These changes are so marked that they make it necessary for us to modify considerably the aerodynamic laws that we have so far learnt.

Compressibility and Incompressibility

It was emphasized in the early chapters that **air is compressible ;** it was also emphasized, though perhaps not emphatically enough, that though it is compressible it does, in fact, **behave at ordinary speeds almost as though it were incompressible.** That really is the strange part of the subject, and that is what we have assumed throughout our elementary aerodynamics, namely that air behaves like water, that its density does not change as it flows over a body. Of course such an assumption is not true, air is really compressible at all speeds and the density does change as the wings and bodies of aeroplanes move through air at quite ordinary speeds, but the point is that the error in making the assumption is so small as to be negligible, while the simplification that the assumption gives to the whole subject is by no means negligible.

As we approach the speed of sound the error in making this assumption of incompressibility can no longer be justified, the air is definitely compressed, it no longer behaves like water and all the theory—and practice —of the subject is different. We are now dealing with a compressible fluid.

It should be clear from this explanation that **the change is gradual, not sudden ;** it is all a question of deciding when the error becomes appreciable, and a rough idea of the error involved may be obtained from the following figures which represent the error in assuming the ordinary laws of aerodynamics when estimating the drag of a body moving through air at the speeds mentioned—

Speed (m.p.h.)	Error in Assuming Incompressibility
100	About $\frac{1}{2}\%$
200	Less than 2%
300	4%
400	7%
500	11%
600	16%

It will be sufficiently clear from this that **we must begin to change our ideas some time before we reach 760 m.p.h.**

Shock Waves and Shock Stall

Let us see if we can find out a little more of what actually happens during this change from incompressible flow to compressible flow, and so discover the cause of the mounting error in making the assumption of incompressibility.

The first indication would seem to be a breakaway of the airflow from the surface of the body, usually some way back, setting up a turbulent wake (Fig. 180). This may occur at speeds less than half that of sound

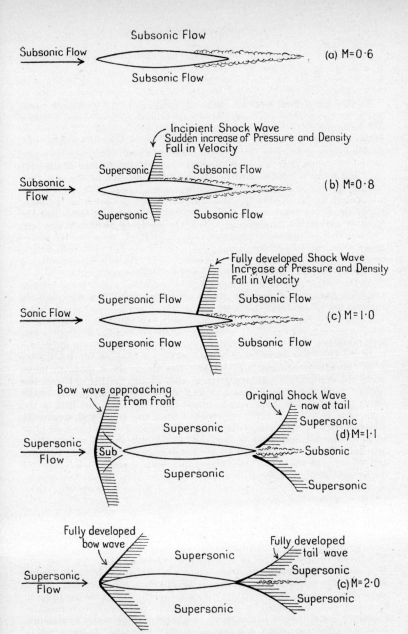

FIG. 180. DEVELOPMENT OF SHOCK WAVES AT INCREASING
MACH NUMBERS

(a) Subsonic Speeds. No shock wave. Breakaway at transition point.
(b) At critical Mach Number. First shock wave develops.
(c) At speed of sound. Shock wave stronger and moving back.
(d) Transonic speeds. Bow wave appears from front. Original wave
at tail
(e) Fully supersonic flow. Fully developed waves at bow and tail,

and has already been dealt with when considering the boundary layer. It will, of course, cause an increase of drag over and above that which is to be expected at the particular speed as reckoned on the speed-squared law.

As the speed increases the point of breakaway, or transition point, tends to creep forward, resulting in turbulent airflow over a larger proportion of the surface and a thicker turbulent wake.

When we reach about three-quarters of the speed of sound a new phenomenon appears in the form of a **shock wave.** This can be represented by **a line approximately at right angles to the surface of the body and signifying a sudden rise in pressure and density of the air, thus holding up the air flow and causing a decrease of speed of flow. There is a tendency for the breakaway and turbulent wake to start from the point where the shock wave meets the surface which is usually at or near the point of maximum camber, i.e. where the speed of airflow is greatest.** These shock waves are not merely imaginary lines, they can be photographed in the laboratory by suitable optical means, and claims have been made that they have been seen in flight, though more probably what has been seen is the result of the turbulent wake.

At the speed at which the shock waves begin to appear there is **quite a sudden rise in drag, and the results of the turbulent flow and pressure changes are known as a shock stall,** since there are many characteristics in common with the ordinary stall—and a few important differences. To avoid confusion we shall in future refer to the ordinary stall as the **high incidence stall,** a name which in itself indicates the main difference since the shock stall can occur at any incidence or angle of attack.

As the speed increases still further, the shock wave tends to move back, but in doing so becomes stronger and extends farther out from the surface while there is even more violent turbulence behind it. At speeds above that of sound there may be more than one wave, the first in the form of a bow wave which approaches from the front and eventually attaches itself to the nose of the body. The second wave has now gone back to the tail and tends to become curved and shaped rather like a fish-tail. Each wave represents a sudden change in the density, pressure, and velocity of the air. The figures may help to make the effects of increasing speed more clear; the final figure reminds one of photographs of shock waves on shells and bullets, which is hardly surprising since we are approaching the same speeds.

Effects of Shock Stall

From what has been said the reader will have realized that the shock stall is not necessarily a phenomenon that occurs on the wings alone; it may apply to any part of the aeroplane. Whenever it occurs there will be a **considerable increase in drag**—that much is fairly obvious. Owing to the turbulence of the wake there is also likely to be **buffeting.** When the shock stall begins on lifting surfaces such as wings the increase in drag will be accompanied by a **loss of lift** and a completely new pressure distribution resulting in a **change of the positions of the centre of pressure,** thus upsetting the balance of the aeroplane. All these features are in common with the high incidence stall.

Mach Number

The time has come to introduce a term that is now on everybody's lips in connection with high-speed flight—**Mach Number.** The term is a compliment not, as one might expect, to some modern research worker, but to the Austrian, Professor Ernst Mach (1838–1916), who was professor of the history and theory of science in the University of Vienna. Incidentally, his *Science of Mechanics*, which was published in English in 1893, throws much light on the work of Newton and others, and is well worth reading.

Fortunately the definition of Mach Number is simple, though, as always, people have tried to wrap it in mystery and complicate it by introducing such terms as equivalent air speeds, indicated Mach Numbers, and so on. **The Mach Number (M) refers to the speed at which an aircraft is travelling in relation to the speed of sound.** Thus a Mach Number of $\frac{1}{2}$ means that the aircraft is travelling at half the speed of sound. **Both the speed of the aircraft and the speed of sound are true speeds, i.e. the only real speeds.**

Variation of Speed of Sound

There is one small complication that must be introduced into the definition of Mach Number even at this stage. **The speed of sound varies according to the temperature of the air,** and therefore we must add to the definition the fact that **the speed of sound must be that corresponding to the temperature of the air in which the aircraft is actually travelling.** People are often surprised to hear that the speed of sound in air depends on temperature alone. As a matter of fact it doesn't! But the other properties, such as the density, on which it also depends, are so related that the temperature is the controlling factor.

The actual relationship is that the **speed of sound is proportional to the square root of the absolute temperature.** It is a solemn thought, therefore, that the speed of sound would be zero in air at the absolute zero of temperature; such a thought opens up possibilities of testing "high-speed phenomena" at very low speeds in wind tunnels at very low temperatures. Not a very practical proposition probably, but it serves as an illustration of the point that **what we are concerned with is not really high-speed flight at all, but flight at speeds in the neighbourhood of the speed of sound, in other words at Mach Numbers approaching 1.** It may not be practical to experiment at the absolute zero of temperature, but **it is very practical to consider flight in the stratosphere where, at a temperature of about − 60° C., the speed of sound will have fallen from about 760 m.p.h. at sea-level to about 660 m.p.h.**

Perhaps it should be emphasized again that this drop in the speed of sound is not really a function of the height at all; at a temperature of − 60° C., such as may occur at sea-level in, say, the North of Canada in winter, the speed of sound would also be about 660 m.p.h., while in tropical climates it might be well over 760 m.p.h. even at considerable heights.

This variation of the speed of sound with temperature accounts for the rather surprising feature of recent speed record attempts in that the pilots have waited for hot weather, or gone to places where they expect hot weather, in order to make the attempts. Surprising because it has always been considered, and is in fact true, that high temperatures act **against** the performance of both aircraft and engine. The point, of course, is that the record breakers **wanted to go as fast as possible while keeping as far away as possible from the speed of sound**—so they wanted the speed of sound to be as high as possible. The time will come, and may come soon, when they will want just the opposite again, so that they can get **above** the speed of sound as soon as possible—but we are anticipating.

Critical Mach Number

It has already been made clear that the onset of compressibility is a gradual effect, and that things begin to happen at speeds considerably lower than the speed of sound, that is at Mach Numbers of less than 1. One reason for this is that, as explained in earlier chapters, **there is an increase in the speed of airflow over certain parts of the aeroplane** as, for instance, over the point of greatest camber of an aerofoil. This means that although the aeroplane itself may be travelling at well below the speed of sound, the airflow relative to some parts of the aeroplane may attain that value. In short, there may be a **local increase of velocity up to that of sound and a shock wave may form at this point.** This, in turn, may have the results already mentioned, an increase of drag, decrease of lift, movement of centre of pressure, and buffeting. In an aeroplane in flight the results may be such as to cause the aircraft to become uncontrollable, in much the same way as it becomes uncontrollable at the high incidence stall at the other end of the speed range.

All this will occur at a certain Mach Number, which will be different for different types of aircraft, and which is called the **Critical Mach Number** (M_{cr}) of the type.

If the reader has followed the argument so far he will not be surprised to learn that the general characteristic of a type of aircraft that has a high Critical Mach Number is **slimness,** because over such an aircraft the local increases of velocity will not be very great. This was well illustrated by the Spitfire, a "slim" aircraft that was originally designed without much thought as to its performance near the speed of sound, yet which has proved to have a Critical Mach Number of nearly 0·9, one of the highest ever achieved.

The Critical Mach Number or, as it might be called, the **Shock Stalling Speed,** corresponds at the high speed end of the flight range to the **High Incidence Stalling Speed** at the other end—and there is some of the same looseness of definition about it. We had some difficulty in deciding whether the ordinary stalling speed should be defined as the speed at which the Lift coefficient is a maximum, or at which the airflow burbles over the wing, or at which the pilot loses control over the aircraft. They are all related, but they do not necessarily all occur at the same speed. So now with the Critical Mach Number—is it the Mach Number at which the local airflow at some point reaches the velocity of sound? or at which a shock wave is formed? or at which the air burbles? or at which the drag coefficient begins to rise?—or, again, when the pilot loses control? I do not know—nor, apparently, does anyone else! Authorities differ on the matter, each looking at it according to his own point of view, or sometimes according to whether he wants to claim a high Critical Mach Number for his pet type of aircraft. However, it doesn't matter very much; they are really all part of the same phenomenon, and there is not a great deal of difference between them.

Since there is sometimes misunderstanding on the point it may be as well to mention that it is quite sensible to speak of an aircraft flying at Mach Numbers other than its Critical Mach Number. Thus an aircraft with M_{cr} of 0·85 can be spoken of as flying at $M = 0·8$ or $M = 0·7$ or, for that matter, at any Mach Number between that of the High

Incidence Stall and that of the Shock Stall. But it would not be wise to use the term Mach Number instead of air speed at the low speed end of the range—the reader will probably see the reason for this himself, and it will be explained later in the chapter.

Is it possible for an aircraft to fly at a Mach Number higher than its Critical Mach Number? Is it possible for an aircraft to have a Critical Mach Number higher than 1? These two questions may at first sound silly, but they are not. The answers to both depend entirely on which of the many definitions of Critical Mach Number we adopt. If the Critical Mach Number is when the pilot loses control, then he can hardly fly beyond it; but if it is when a shock wave is formed, or when the drag coefficient begins to rise, why shouldn't he? He may not even know that it has happened, any more than he knows whether he is at the maximum lift coefficient in an ordinary stall. Graphs of lift and drag coefficients are all very well on a blackboard, but one cannot see them on the instrument panel when flying—the more's the pity perhaps! Also, supposing he can maintain control through all the shock waves, increases of drag coefficient and so on—and why should he not?—then he will surely find that his Critical Mach Number is higher than 1 or, to be more correct, that the aircraft has not got a Critical Mach Number at all in any of the senses that we have so far defined it.

The Sonic Barrier

If we are to use the term "barrier" at all as a description of our difficulties in approaching and exceeding the speed of sound in flight, then it is fair to say that **the Critical Mach Number represents the near side of the barrier. What of the problems of getting over, or through, the barrier? And what are the prospects of flight on the far side?** In other words, we have found out something about flight at subsonic speeds, what about transonic and supersonic speeds?

Well, from the Drag point of view it is possible to give a reasonable answer to these questions largely because they have been studied for many years, both theoretically and practically, in connection with the flight of shells and bullets. The answer can be given most reasonably in terms of the Drag Coefficient which, for a body of given shape, should remain constant—according to the elementary principles of flight. The Drag would then go up with the square of the velocity. Any change in the Drag Coefficient means that the velocity-squared law has broken down.

The actual behaviour of the Drag Coefficient, for a thin aerofoil shape, can best be illustrated by a diagram (Fig. 181). This **shows that up to a Mach Number of about 0·7 the Drag Coefficient remains constant—** which means that our elementary principles are true—**then it begins to rise.** According to one definition the Mach Number at which it begins to rise, in this example 0·7, is the Critical Mach Number. **At M of 0·8 and 0·85 C_D is rising rapidly.** Note that the curve then becomes dotted and the full line is resumed again at an M of about 1·2. The reason for this is interesting. It is possible to operate high-speed wind tunnels up to an M of about 0·85, and again at M of 1·2 or more, but in the region of the speed of sound a shock wave develops right across the wind tunnel itself, the tunnel becomes "choked" and the speed cannot be maintained. Thus there are no reliable wind tunnel results in this region, and **the dotted part of the curve is really an intelligent guess.** Experiments are now being made by other means, by dropping bodies, or propelling them with rockets and also, of course, by full scale flight tests, and it should not be long before our guess can be confirmed—or otherwise. Previous experiments on shells suggest that there is nothing much wrong with it.

After a Mach Number of about 1·2 experimental evidence is again available, and it suggests that C_D **drops and eventually, at M of 2 or more becomes constant again though at a higher value than the original,** variously quoted as 2 or 3 times. Incidentally, there is no evidence that a body with a high Critical Mach Number will maintain its superiority at still higher Mach Numbers. In fact, the present evidence is

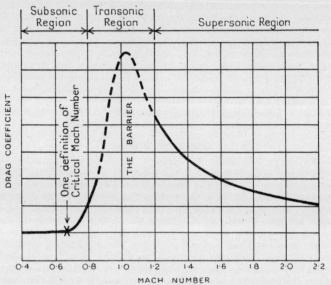

FIG. 181. THE SONIC BARRIER

rather the reverse, and this is an important point when considering the possibilities of exceeding Mach Numbers of 1. The good old Spitfire may be well advised to make the best of its sub-sonic glory.

The diagram shows that there is some justification for the use of the term "barrier." There is a definite hurdle to be got over. But it also shows that conditions on the other side are again reasonable and that supersonic flight is a practical proposition.

The reader is advised to work through Example No. 296 (page 361) in which he will plot the actual Drag, as distinct from the Coefficient, and it will then be clear that the Drag also actually falls after $M = 1$, but that the barrier itself is not quite so evident in terms of Drag.

What about Lift and Centre of Pressure? In these matters we are really ignorant so far as the transonic region is concerned, and the nature of the curves before and after the barrier is such that he would be a brave man who could guess how to join them up and, further, we have no evidence or experience from knowledge about shells and bullets since research on them has been largely confined to the supersonic region. So flight tests seem to be the best hope of exploring the transonic region and of finding out just what the penetration of the barrier involves, but in view of our present ignorance such tests are apt to be somewhat hazardous.

Solutions to the Problem

So much for the problem of flight at high speeds. What are our prospects of solving it?

There was a time when the prospects seemed poor owing to the lack of engines with the necessary power to overcome the rapid rise in Drag which begins at the Critical Mach Number. Even without compressibility effects the Drag would rise with the square of the velocity, and the Power—which is Drag × Velocity—with the cube of the velocity. The effect of compressibility is to increase these values still further in accordance with the following table, which shows the approximate figures for a Spitfire—

Velocity (m.p.h.)	300	400	500	600	700
Horse Power (without compressibility)	1,000	2,500	4,600	8,000	13,000
Actual Power Required	1,000	2,500	4,700	10,000	30,000

Actually the problem is much more serious than this, **if we assume that the aircraft will be driven by propellers.** As was explained in the chapter on Thrust, the efficiency of a good propeller is about 80 per cent **at its best, but its " best " is at speeds of 300 to 400 m.p.h., after which the efficiency falls off very rapidly**—this happens for various reasons, but chiefly because the propeller tips are the first part of the aircraft to suffer from compressibility. With the high forward speed of the aeroplane combined with the rotary speed of the circumference of the propeller disc, Mach Number troubles begin to occur at aircraft speeds of 400 m.p.h., and **the result is so disastrous that the horse power which would have to be supplied to the propeller by the engine in order to attain the speeds given in the table would look something more like this—**

Velocity (m.p.h.)	300	400	500	600	700
Power to be given to propeller	1,100	3,200	8,000	20,000	100,000 ?

When one looks at these figures one realizes why it was that people who knew what they were talking about forecast only a few years ago that it would be a long, long time before we could exceed 600 m.p.h.

Yet they were wrong. And for one simple reason—**the advent of the gas turbine and the first flight of a jet driven aircraft in 1941.** This made all the difference, partly because of the elimination of the propeller and its compressibility problems (it is true that there are similar problems with the turbine blades in the jet engine), but mainly because, as explained in Chapter IV, **the efficiency of the jet increases rapidly over just those speeds, 400 m.p.h. to 600 m.p.h., when the efficiency of the propeller is falling rapidly.** The net result is that whereas the reciprocating-engine-propeller combination requires nearly twenty times as much power to fly at 600 m.p.h. compared with 300 m.p.h., the jet engine only requires about five times the thrust, and it is thrust that matters in a jet engine. Further, **the weight of the jet engine is only a small fraction of that of the reciprocating-engine-propeller combination,** and at this speed **even the fuel consumption is less.**

Maybe the prophets ought to have foreseen the jet engine—but they didn't, at least not within anything like the time during which it actually appeared. Of course there were good reasons too why they didn't foresee it, for no metal could then possibly stand up to the temperatures of the gas turbine blades. And there were good reasons

why metals could not be found to do so. Yes, there are always good
reasons why progress should be halted in our time—but it never is.

**The jet engine, then, was the first step in solving the problem of high-
speed flight.** And while on the subject of engines, the rocket system of
propulsion takes us even a step further and no man now, who knows
what he is talking about, dare predict
the limits of speed that may be reached
with rockets.

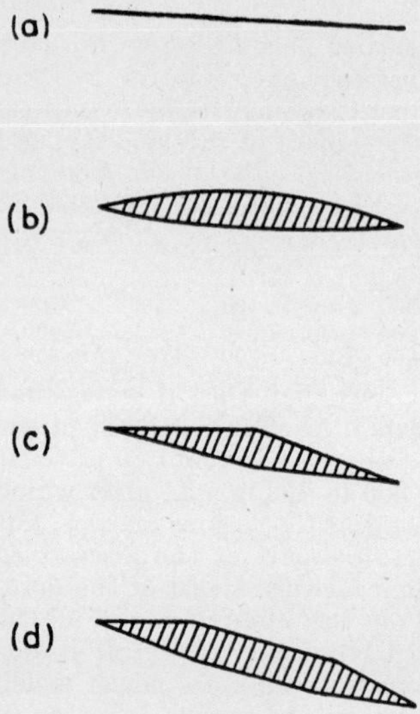

(a) ─────────────────────

Aerofoil and Body Shapes

As has already been suggested, the
aircraft must be slim if it is to approach
or penetrate the sonic barrier. The
slimness applies to all parts—the aerofoil section, the body, the engine
nacelles and perhaps most of all to
small excrescences (if there must be
such things) on the aircraft.

(b)

So far as aerofoil sections are concerned there are really two steps to be
considered ; first, to reach high speeds
at all the low-drag laminar-flow section
discussed in an earlier chapter must be
employed ; but for actual penetration
of the barrier, and for supersonic flight,

(c)

there is evidence in favour of **bi-convex
sections, both top and bottom surfaces
forming circular arcs** (Fig. 182), or even
**of straight lines. A flat plate would be
best of all**—back to the good old

(d)

days !—but this is obviously impractic-
able for reasons of strength, and **there
are possibilities in the double-wedge
type of section** (Fig. 182). The aerofoil

FIG. 182. SUPERSONIC AERO-
FOIL SHAPES

(a) Flat Plate (not practicable)
(b) Bi-convex (circular arcs)
(c) Double Wedge
(d) Hexagonal

is likely to be **thin—and symmetrical, or nearly so.**
**The advantage of high aspect ratio disappears altogether at high Mach
Numbers,** and aspect ratios may be as low as 1.

Sweep-back

During the 1939–45 war the Germans went far ahead of other countries
in their research work on the aerodynamic problems of high-speed
flight. The results of their work took practical form in the V weapons,
and in jet- and rocket-propelled fighters. Their experiments suggest the
possibilities of **a considerable degree of sweep-back,** or even sweep-
forward, **as a means of raising the Critical Mach Number.**

Theoretical arguments can be produced to show that about 35° to
40° of sweep-back should raise the Critical Mach Number by 0·2, e.g.
from 0·8 to 1·0—something to be reckoned with. The theory is based on
the idea **that it is only the component of the airflow at right angles to the
leading edge that will cause the shock effects,** and on heavily swept-back
wings this component is of course appreciably less than the forward
speed of the aircraft. **Practical tests confirm that there is considerable
improvement,** though rather less than the theory would indicate.

Both full-scale aircraft and models were built with sweep-back of this order, some of them as tail-less types, but some with sweep-back on both wings and tailplane. An extreme example was the **Delta wing** shape (Fig. 183).

One reason for the failure to realize in practice the possible theoretical improvement is the effect of " **centre interference.**" This phenomenon is shown in Fig. 184, which gives some indication of the type of flow over a heavily swept-back wing.

There seems to be little doubt that this is a promising line of research. **The difficulties,** as the Germans fully realized, **are in the other problems connected with heavily swept-back wings.** These may be summarized as—

1. **Tip stalling**—an old problem.
2. **Low** C_L **max., and therefore high stalling speed, and** C_L **max. is obtained at too large an angle to be suitable for landing.** This is another old problem

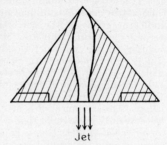

FIG. 183. DELTA WING FOR SUPERSONIC FLIGHT
(Aspect Ratio 1)

and one that might be overcome by special slots, flaps or suction devices.

3. **Control problems.** In attempting to solve these the Germans used

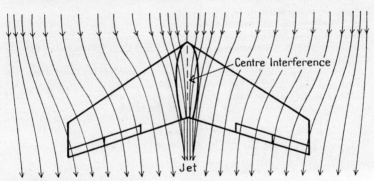

FIG. 184. HEAVILY SWEPT-BACK WING FOR HIGH-SPEED FLIGHT
(Aspect Ratio 3)

very complicated control systems sometimes with three separate elevons (combined elevator and ailerons) on each wing, each with different movements, and sometimes with various spoiler devices.

The Pilot's Point of View

We have so far discussed the problems of high speed very much from the point of view of the designer—but what about the pilot? Well, if he wants to know what is going on, or what is likely to happen, **the first thing that he needs is an instrument to tell him at what Mach Number he is flying.** Various types of **Machmeter** are already in existence, and no doubt they will be improved in accuracy and reliability. For a Mach-meter to give a reliable indication of the Mach Number it must measure, in effect, the true speed of the aircraft and the true speed of sound for the actual temperature of the air. The first is usually done via the indicated speed, which can be corrected for air density by a compensating device within the instrument, but which still includes position error. A temperature compensating device can be used to give the true speed of sound, but in modern instruments this has been eliminated, and a combination of aneroid barometer and air speed indicator gives all the corrections required—except that of position error. The term "Indicated Mach Number" is sometimes used for the reading of the Machmeter, but it is an unsatisfactory term since it differs from Indicated Air Speed in that the main correction, that of density, has already beem made in the instrument itself.

In the absence of a Machmeter the pilot will find that the Air Speed Indicator is apt to give very misleading ideas—even more so than usual. This assumes, of course, that he is not one of those pilots who have already discovered that what the Air Speed Indicator reads is not an air speed at all! Unless he is such a pilot, he may reason that if the speed of sound is around 760 m.p.h. **he cannot possibly run into trouble with say 200 m.p.h. on the clock. A shock stall at this speed might come as a real shock.**

Yet such a shock is possible, and may well become even more possible. Let us see why—

1. In the first place, the speed of sound is a real speed, a true speed.
2. Secondly, it decreases with fall of temperature, down to **660 m.p.h.,** or less, in the stratosphere.
3. Thirdly, the Air Speed Indicator does not of course read the true speed, and the error is more than 100 per cent in the stratosphere, so that at 40,000 ft. for instance, it will read **less than 330 m.p.h.** when the real speed is 660 m.p.h.
4. Fourthly, trouble begins at speeds considerably less than the speed of sound itself. Assuming, for instance, that the Critical Mach Number is 0·7 (a low value but by no means unknown) then a shock stall may occur at 0·7 × 330 = **231 on the clock.**
5. Fifthly—and a point not so far mentioned—a shock stall occurs at an even lower Critical Mach Number during manoeuvres, so that in a turn for instance **the 231 might well be reduced to 200.**

And there we are!

The figures are all possible, and they might be even worse.

There is one compensating point; that the pitot head is, after the propeller tips, one of the first parts of an aeroplane to experience the effects of compressibility, and this may cause the Air Speed Indicator to over-read at very high speeds. This, however, is not likely to be important because it is usually allowed for in calibration.

The following table may be a help to a pilot in realizing what is

Height (feet)	True Speed of Sound (m.p.h.)	True Speed at which Shock Stall will occur assuming M_{cr} of 0·7	Reading of A.S.I. at this speed (omitting position error)
0	760	532	532
10,000	735	514	443
20,000	705	493	360
30,000	680	476	292
40,000	660	462	230
50,000	660	462	180

going on ; the figures are calculated of course on the assumption of the International Standard Atmosphere and will vary to some extent according to how much actual conditions differ from the conditions assumed.

The figures in the last column are the readings of the Air Speed Indicator at which a shock stall may occur (it may even occur at lower indicated speeds because the figures given do not allow for manoeuvres), and they are apt to be rather alarming. There is, however, another way of looking at it—and one that is much more heartening.

Suppose one **dives** from 50,000 ft. **at a constant true speed of, say, 500 m.p.h., that is, at a rapidly increasing speed on the clock,** of

195 m.p.h. at 50,000 ft.
250 m.p.h. at 40,000 ft.
307 m.p.h. at 30,000 ft.
365 m.p.h. at 20,000 ft.
430 m.p.h. at 10,000 ft.
and 500 m.p.h. at sea-level—

strange as it may seem, the actual Mach Numbers would be **decreasing—**

$$\frac{500}{660} \text{ or } 0.76 \text{ at } 50,000 \text{ ft.}$$

$$\frac{500}{660} \text{ or } 0.76 \text{ at } 40,000 \text{ ft.}$$

$$\frac{500}{600} \text{ or } 0.735 \text{ at } 30,000 \text{ ft.}$$

$$\frac{500}{705} \text{ or } 0.71 \text{ at } 20,000 \text{ ft.}$$

$$\frac{500}{735} \text{ or } 0.68 \text{ at } 10,000 \text{ ft.}$$

$$\frac{500}{760} \text{ or } 0.66 \text{ at sea-level.}$$

This means that if the critical Mach Number were 0.7 an aircraft that was shock stalled at 50,000 ft. would become unstalled at a height of about 15,000 ft.

Even if the true speed were to increase during the dive, as would probably happen in practice, there might still be a drop in Mach Number.

This consoling feature of the problem is based on the assumption of rise in temperature with loss of height—if the temperature does **not** rise that is to say, if there is an inversion, well the reader—and the pilot—can calculate what will happen !

Behaviour of Aeroplane at Shock Stall

All this rather assumes that there is something to be feared about a shock stall, and that pilots try to avoid it. Well, in our present state of knowledge—or ignorance—of the transonic region, it must be admitted that there is something to be said for that point of view. After all, there was a time when we looked upon the high incidence stall in the same way—something to be avoided at all costs. Now, however, it is practised by all pilots in the very early stages of learning. Much the same will no doubt happen to the shock stall—it is all a question of knowledge, and this is being rapidly gained.

As it seems at present, **by far the most important effect is a considerable change of longitudinal trim**—usually, but not always, towards nose-heaviness, and sometimes first one way then the other. Unfortunately the change of trim is made even worse by the **very large forces required to move the controls,** and the **ineffectiveness of the trimmers.** There is also likely to be **buffeting, vibration of the ailerons,** and **pitching and yawing oscillations** which may become uncontrollable.

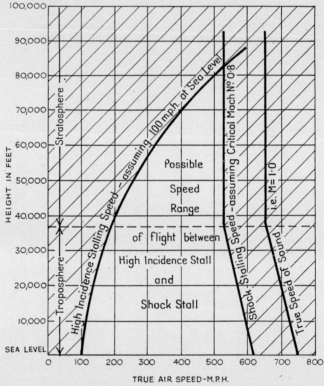

FIG. 185A. SPEED RANGE OF FLIGHT—TRUE SPEEDS

Altogether not a very desirable state of affairs, and certainly something to be avoided, or got out of as soon as possible. The best way of avoiding trouble is to **keep an eye on the Machmeter**—if there is one—and, if the worst comes to the worst, to **get into regions of higher temperature.** The best way of getting out of trouble is **to stop going so fast!** In a climb this is easy—just throttle back. That is why the safest and best research work can be done in climbing flight—and it is already possible to reach Critical Mach Numbers on the climb in some types. In level flight it may not be quite so easy to lose speed, especially if the controls cannot be moved; and in a dive, which is where these troubles are most likely to occur, it will be even more difficult. It is essential therefore that **all aircraft capable of these speeds should have some kind of dive**

brake, or spoiler, which can safely be used at high Mach Numbers. We have had to go very fast on aeroplanes before the need for a brake was recognized!

From the pilot's point of view, just as from the designer's point of view, there are reasons to hope that the supersonic region will be more pleasant than the transonic, so it is all a question of penetrating the barrier, and this is now becoming one of the first priorities in aeronautical research work.

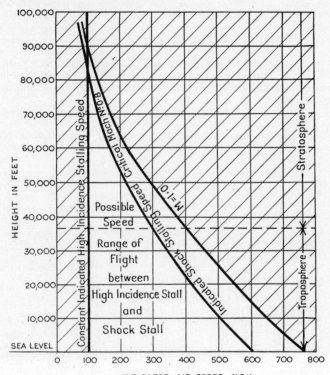

FIG. 185B. SPEED RANGE OF FLIGHT —INDICATED SPEEDS

Height and Speed Range

It was explained in an earlier chapter that owing to limitations of engine power the speed range of an aircraft narrows with height, until, at the absolute ceiling, there is only one possible speed of flight. This speed, however, was not the stalling speed, but rather the speed of best endurance, and the absolute ceiling was simply a question of engine power; for a given aircraft, the greater the power supplied, the higher would be the ceiling.

Now, however, **with almost unlimited thrust available** in the form of jets or rockets, or eventually perhaps atomic energy, there is **an altogether new aspect of the limitation of height at which an aircraft can fly.** If we assume that flight is not possible at speeds below that of the high incidence stall, nor above that of the shock stall, then we are faced with the fact that, irrespective of engine power, **the true speed of the high incidence stall will increase with height,** while **the true speed of the shock stall will fall from sea-level to the base of the stratosphere, and then remain constant.** The result, assuming a sea-level stalling speed (high incidence) of 100 m.p.h. and a Critical Mach Number of 0·8 is shown in Fig. 185A, the shaded portions being the regions in which flight is not possible. It will be evident that this aeroplane cannot fly above 83,000 ft., whatever the power available, while if it flies at 83,000 ft., it can only fly at the stalling speed. If it flies any slower it will stall (high incidence), and if it flies any faster it will stall (shock). Surely a modern interpretation of being between the devil and the deep sea! Fig. 185B shows exactly the same thing from the point of view of indicated speeds. Thus, **quite apart from engine power, there is a limitation to the height of flight, and a narrowing of the speed range as the limiting height is approached.**

This curious coming together of the two stalls will occur at considerably lower heights during manoeuvres, which will cause the high incidence stalling speed to increase, and the shock stalling speed to decrease. The following figures are quite reasonable for 40,000 ft.—

High Incidence Stall (True Air Speeds)				Shock Stall (True Air Speeds)			
Normal stall, sea-level	Normal stall at 40,000 ft.	Stall at 4g, at 40,000 ft.	Further increased at high M to, say,	At 4g this may be reduced to, say	M = 0·7. 40,000 ft.	M = 1. 40,000 ft.	M = 1. Sea-level
m.p.h. 100	200	400	420	420	462	660	760 m.p.h.

Increase of high incidence stalling speed ⟶ ⟵ Decrease of shock stalling speed

One must always be careful in interpreting results of this kind, and in making forecasts for the future from them, to **remember what assumptions have been made.** We have surely seen the danger of forecasting in the false prediction that aircraft could not exceed 600 m.p.h.—a prediction based on assumptions which themselves proved false. So now let it be clear that we are making assumptions—and these in turn may be proved false—and the main one is that the aircraft cannot fly above a certain Critical Mach Number. This Critical Mach Number may be raised, and once it becomes supersonic it may disappear altogether as a limiting factor or even as a hurdle. Then the picture will be entirely different.

So long as the present conditions prevail the limit of high speed is decided entirely by the Critical Mach Number. This applies to all types of aeroplane, and there seems to be no logical reason why the Critical Mach Numbers of Bombers or Transport aircraft should be any lower than that of Fighters—in fact, if it is assumed that Fighters must manoeuvre and that Bombers need not (beware of these curious assumptions) we soon see the origin of the prediction that has so often been made that **Bombers will soon be able to fly as fast, or faster, than Fighters.** Maybe they will, maybe they will not. In the meantime the pilotless fighter, the guided missile, need have little fear of the sonic barrier, and with its sweep-back and rocket propulsion it is already exploring the supersonic regions of flight. Whether these things are aeroplanes, I do not know; whether they take us beyond the limits of what we have called "Mechanics of Flight," I know still less; but, whatever they are, and whatever their future as weapons of war, they are likely to prove an invaluable means of extending our knowledge, or should we say removing our ignorance, about the problems of really high-speed flight.

Other Problems of High-speed Flight

As we learn to conquer the problems of high-speed flight that have been outlined in this chapter, we may be sure that new and perhaps more baffling problems will confront us. Aerodynamically, difficulties of stability and control are already on the horizon.

But it may be that the time is not far ahead when the limits set to flight are not aerodynamic at all. There is the problem of the distortion of the structure under the colossal loads that will be involved, there are indications that the human body may be affected in curious ways and there is the question of the rise of temperature of the aircraft. The last is one of those little practical things that may hinder progress more than other problems that seem more profound. The temperature rise in degrees Centigrade is represented approximately by the formula ($V/100$)^2 where V is the speed in m.p.h.; so what is merely 1° C. at 100 m.p.h., or 4° C. at 200 m.p.h., becomes 36° C. at 600 m.p.h. and 100° C. at 1,000 m.p.h. There will no longer be any difficulty in keeping warm in the stratosphere—the problem will be to keep cool!

But whatever the problems of the more distant future, we are now on the threshold of the most important and the most interesting era in the history of flying—and the door ahead is wide open for brave men to enter in.

CHAPTER XI

THE TEST FLIGHT

In the preceding chapters I have tried to explain the principles upon which the flight of an aeroplane depends. I hope that you have been able to learn something from my explanations, but I know only too well that they have been incomplete, that however carefully you may have read you may still feel that something is lacking. If this be so, then it is I, your instructor, who have failed in my task. Fortunately I think I know the cause of the failure, and in this last chapter I am going to try to make amends.

Let me explain. If you are one of those for whom I have written, then your chief interest probably lies in technical matters connected with aviation rather than in flying as flying. It may be that you are a draughtsman, or an apprentice, or a ground engineer, a fitter or a rigger, or perhaps just a schoolboy; your ambition may be to become a designer, a foreman, an inspector or a works manager, or just an aeronautical engineer—a delightfully vague term which might mean anything. You may, of course, be a pilot—and I hope you are—but whichever of these you may be, I want you to fly, and for this final lesson in the principles of flight I am going to hand you over to a new instructor, and the lesson will be conducted in a new and unusual classroon.

The new instructor is the aeroplane itself, and the classroom is its cockpit.

It was not as a mere idle jest that Captain Barber chose *The Aeroplane Speaks* as title for a book published during the First Great War —a book, incidentally, which must surely be considered as a classic of aviation literature. Assuredly an aeroplane **does** speak, but only to those who fly in it; on the ground it is dumb. It tells the pilot just what it likes to do, and what it does not like to do; it talks confidentially to the rigger about the uncomfortable feeling caused by the nuts he has tightened too much, it reprimands the fitter if the engine does not give forth the power of all its horses. The aeroplane is no respecter of persons where bad workmanship is concerned, and works manager and apprentice will equally be held responsible for a loose rivet or a faulty weld; even the designer is not free from criticism, if he ever dares to fly in his own creation. But though the aeroplane is a stern master, it is also the most obliging of servants to those who give it sympathetic understanding, and that you cannot do unless you fly in it.

In a few moments I shall leave you, and this new master will take you under his wing. He will lift you up into the air, he will show you how to fly. It may be your first flight, it may be your thousandth; but there will be plenty to learn. You will find the cockpit of an aeroplane a noisy classroom, the blackboard will be covered with instruments and dials and pointers, instead of pencil and paper you will have a control column and a throttle lever, and outside the window what sights there will be to distract you, the sky and the clouds and the earth! But this is the laboratory of flying, the only place where the practical experiments can be conducted, and I beseech you, all of you, whether it be your ambition to work in drawing office, workshop, or hangar, to take every opportunity of gaining that great experience of being borne on wings through the air. Without such experience you may learn to design, to build, and to take care of aeroplanes, but there will always be something missing in your work, a something which is difficult to define, but which results in an absence of sympathy between yourself and the aeroplane which you help to create. During your flights, during your lessons in the air, you will meet again all the old familiar things to which you have been introduced in this book—Angles of Attack, Lifts, Drags, Wind Gradients and so on; but at first you may not recognize them. You will not be able to see the air coming up to meet the wings, nor the Centre of Pressure wandering about on the aerofoil, nor arrows serving as signposts to show where the forces are acting, **but all these things will be happening just the same,** and as you listen to your new instructor I want you to try to **visualize** them, to link up what you have learnt on the ground and what you learn in the air, for then, **and only then,** will you begin to **understand** flying.

But let us be going. I hear the engines running, and look!—the wind-sock is beginning to stir as if waking from its night's rest, a breeze is springing up, and the mist is rolling away from the aerodrome; it is going to be a perfect day for the Test Flight. Leave your slide-rules and your mathematics, your Lifts, your Drags, and your tan θ's—all those can wait. On with your flying suits—you will hardly need them, since nowadays you fly in a greenhouse—and here are some earpieces and a microphone, so that you will be able to listen to all that your instructor has to say—Oh, and a parachute; yes, just in case. Ready? Good. Sing me a song of the air, my lads, oh! Sing me a song of the air.

There are some who sing of the raging sea,
Of the wind and the tide a-flowing free,
Of a life on the ocean wave ;
There are some who sing of the huntsman bold,
Of the thrills of the search for hidden gold,
Of the sword and the soldier brave.
There are songs that are merry, and songs that are sad,
There are songs of the good and songs of the bad,
And rollicking songs of the fair, my lad,
Yes, rollicking songs of the fair.
But sing me a song of the Air, my lad,
A care-free song of the Air, my lad,
Oh ! sing me a song of the Air, my lad,
Oh ! sing me a song of the Air.

But here we are on the tarmac, and here, dear readers, our ways must part. You are the fortunate ones who will start on the great adventure, whereas I, alas!, must stay on this unhappy earth, consoled only by the thought that I have brought you to this jumping-off point and must now return and endeavour to bring others to the same point. In bidding you good-bye, I can only wish you the best of luck on your journey and hand you over to a much better instructor than myself.

So we'll open the throttle and gather speed,
For an Airman's life is a life indeed,
As the engine roars away ;
Gone are the cares of the earth below,
As up through a gap in the clouds we go,
With an ever-increasing sway.

" The Aeroplane Calling "

Hullo, the Designer who conceived and created me—Hullo, the Draughtsmen who gave me shape and form—Hullo, all Craftsmen and Mechanics who bent me to shape and assembled me in the workshops —Hullo, Fitters who gave me power for flight—Hullo, Riggers who checked and adjusted all my dimensions—Hullo, Pilot, my jockey and friend—Hullo, all my passengers! This is the Aeroplane calling you.

Gentlemen, I feel highly honoured to carry so many distinguished passengers on this Test Flight. I have often complained, at times rather bitterly, that some of you do not take sufficient interest in me once I am out of your hands; but now that you have left your office chairs I shall have a chance of telling you some home truths. But take your seats, gentlemen, please—I'm longing to get off the ground. What a load! I have never carried so many passengers before. I hope you have allowed for all this, Designer, and that my C.G. is going to be in the right place, otherwise I shall be nose-heavy or tail-heavy or something. Buckle up the straps of your harness, because I may feel like some inverted flying later on, and I don't want you all to fall out. Make yourselves comfortable—that's half the battle in flying.

Now, Pilot, just check up on my controls and see that they all work the right way—no, it is not very likely that they will be wrong, but it **has** happened, you know. Now open up my engine and make quite sure that it is going to give me full power, because I shall need every bit of it for the take-off. By Jove! don't be in too much of a hurry, I nearly went over on my nose then. Don't you realize that the chocks and the brakes are holding my wheels back, and the Thrust is so high up that it tries to pull me over? That's better; hold the stick back, that puts a downward force on my tail. If I had an adjustable tail plane you could have pulled the lever back and put my tail at the smallest possible angle; but I am too modern to have things like that, and while congratulating you, Designer, on inventing control tabs, I must submit that they don't help much in preventing my nose going over now, do they? Yes, there could have been men to hold my tail down, but don't you think that it would be better to make me self-supporting, as it were, on the ground, just as I am self-supporting in flight? But I see that the Pilot is satisfied with my engine, and I'm not sorry either. The chocks have been removed, the rigger is saluting to show that all is clear, so I am ready when you are, Pilot.

Taxying

Open the throttle a little and let us get going. Bump, bump, bump! Honestly, Designer, you have not done much to make my journey over the ground very pleasant; you have made it **possible,** but that is about the best that can be said. But where are you going, Pilot? we seem to be swinging all over the place. The wind is blowing from behind us, and it is moving over the ground as fast as we are, so my rudder is no use at all. It's all very peculiar, this taxying business, so unlike flying; but **unless you treat me properly on the ground you will never be considered a really good pilot.** Try my wheel brakes, they work differentially, so that once you have put them on, if you press with your right foot my right-hand wheel will be held back and I shall turn round to the right. That's the idea. Now keep me straight like that.

But here we are at the edge of the aerodrome, so turn me round, Pilot, I don't want to run into that wall. That's the way, you know how to do it now. What a help the brakes are, and you used to think that aeroplanes didn't need brakes! Yes, that's a good idea, too, opening up the throttle a little; I feel the slipstream over my rudder, and that is helping me round. Let's pause before we turn head into wind; this gives us a chance to see that we have attended to everything and to have a good look round to see that all is clear. Yes, all is well. Are you all ready, Pilot? Now for the great moment. Flaps? Yes, just a little, it really does help me to get off, you know, though I often hear you chaps arguing about it. Now open the throttle—steadily and surely—and turn direct into wind. That's it. It is quite easy to turn me into wind, because you see I'm designed that way—I always like to face the wind. Now for it!

Taking Off

That's the way, Pilot, stick forward just a little so that the wind can get under my elevators and tail plane and lift it up; now there is less resistance, and I'm beginning to dart forward. It's good to feel the wind in my face, to be able to breathe again. 30, 35 m.p.h. already, but don't forget that we really started at 20 m.p.h., owing to the head wind. I can get moving much more quickly than my ancestors, and that's chiefly thanks to you, Propeller Designer; you really were a clever man to invent this constant-speed propeller. I can feel it now, slowly changing to coarser and coarser pitch so that it can pull me farther forward in each revolution.

Now my wings are stretching; what a glorious feeling after having to hold them up all by myself—I can actually feel the Lift on them now and less pressure on my wheels. Lighter and lighter I feel as we bump over this horrible rough ground. Oh, my poor legs!—bump, bump, bump—all my knee joints are feeling it; it's a good thing that the safety catch is well home, or my legs might collapse under me at this critical moment. Keep me straight, Pilot, straight, man, for heaven's sake! Yes, I know we are getting rather near the hangars, but just keep me straight until I'm off, then you watch me clear the hangars for you! That's better; I do tend to swing a bit, don't I? Cannot you prevent that, Designer? You don't quite know what is the cause of the trouble—can I tell you where I feel the pressure? Yes, I think it's all on one side of my fin and rudder. It must be the slipstream, I think; you see, my propeller is going round anti-clockwise so the slipstream is going anti-clockwise too, and the top of it is hitting my fin and rudder. I can feel the pressure on the right-hand side, and that makes me want to turn to the right. You cannot help that, you say? But surely you could offset my fin a little so that the slipstream would hit it head on? No? Oh, I see, you **want** it to hit one side so that when we are in the air it will balance the torque which tends to make me roll over the opposite way to the rotation of the propeller—well, well, I never thought of that, I suppose we can't have it all ways. Now we are nearly off, I think I left the ground then. 45 m.p.h.? No, just a little more speed—48, 50, 53—that's better, now I can fly. Give me a little bit more Angle of Attack—stick back just a little more—that's it—steady, now. Off the ground at last—and what's the speed? 55 m.p.h. Not so bad, but I could have got off sooner if you had given me a little more Angle of Attack. No, not now! Yes, we all want to get over those hangars, but that's not the way to set about it. Don't take any liberties with me—I'm dangerous, you know, when I get rattled, and I **shall** get rattled if you don't keep my nose down a bit and allow me to pick up speed.

That's better—60, 65 m.p.h. But you've forgotten something, Pilot—there's a colossal Drag on my undercarriage, **why don't you pull it up?** Designer, I've a little quarrel with you there—my ancestors may not have had such luxuries as retractable undercarriages, but their legs were streamlined; as for mine—well, look at them! And they hold me back a lot when I'm taking off, and just after I've taken off, and that's when I most want to pick up speed. But now I've got my legs tucked up—that makes a difference, doesn't it? 70, 75, 80 m.p.h. I can feel the propeller responding, too, really getting into its stride, the pitch angle increasing steadily as the speed goes up. You may as well put the lever into coarse pitch now, Pilot. No; it does not mark coarse or fine pitch on the quadrant—just Low r.p.m. and High r.p.m., which is really much better. For take-off, we set it to high r.p.m. to get maximum power, and the propeller pitch was first very fine, then gradually got coarser as the aeroplane's speed increased. Now we can put the lever to lower r.p.m. for economy, and the pitch will still adjust itself, so that the propeller works efficiently. Now, gently, up over the hangars—yes, I thought so, cleared them easily. You can put the flaps up now, Pilot; press the knob, that's the way, my hydraulic system does it all for you; I feel half human with all my veins and arteries, and oil flowing through them just like blood; and the pump, like a heart, pushing the oil out to my extremities, to my wings and my legs. Be careful, Pilot, I'm dropping. When you put my flaps up, I lost Lift, and had no time to gain speed to make up for it. That's better, a little more Angle of Attack.

Hullo! Hullo! What's happened now? What's the meaning of this, Fitter? Surely you are not going to let the engine fail me just when I most need it? **Oh, no, Pilot, you must not turn back.** That's a very, very old habit of Pilots. You know that I shall need more speed for the turn, and you are sure to stall me; and besides, suppose I did turn, I should then be flying down wind, and travelling very fast over the ground with hardly any air speed to keep me in flight. No, if the Fitter really is going to let us down you must put me as gently as you can in that field ahead there. That's right, keep my nose down a little, just in case; no, no, don't let my legs down, I could never get into that field on my wheels, land me as gently as you can on my belly, and neither you nor I will come to much harm. Yes, I think you had better put the flaps down. No, wait a moment, my engine is picking up—I can feel the Thrust again. You gave my engine a tough time of it during that take-off, and just for the moment it hesitated; but there is nothing seriously wrong. Ease the throttle back just a little; we don't need so much power now, and you can afford to give my engine a rest. As you move the throttle, watch my revolution indicator—that's clever, isn't it? My engine is giving less power, but my propeller is going round just as fast.

Ugh!—what was that? Only a bump. Shook you up a bit? Yes, and me too. You couldn't see it coming? No, nor could I. That's the worst of this air, you cannot see the beastly stuff; on the ground and the water you can at least see what is coming to you. But you ought to have been expecting that bump; I was. Look at those factories down there—acres and acres of roofs in the blazing sunshine, chimneys, too, belching forth hot air; if anything was likely to cause an up-current, that was it. Down we go again; we are over those woods now, and the sun cannot heat them up like the factory roofs. We are in the shadow of that cloud, too. It looks to me as though we are going to have a bumpy time of it down here; let us do a circuit and try a landing, and then, if all goes well, we can climb up above the clouds and see what it's like up there. Let us turn round to the left—there's one-way traffic round the aerodrome, and it's always to the left unless there's a right-hand arrow on the tarmac down there.

Turning

Height, 2,000 ft. Air speed, 120 m.p.h. That's excellent—we don't want to cruise round the aerodrome at a high speed, there are too many others flying about. Now, Pilot, round to the left—you have learnt all about it in your lectures on the ground, so you ought to find it quite easy. That's the way, stick to the left and over I go, banking to the left. Just a little left rudder; that's a good idea, it is not as necessary as it used to be when the old-fashioned aileron would have held my right wing back, but the Designer has altered all that, and I have nearly forgotten what Aileron Drag means. Do you see? I am slipping in a little and feel the wind on the left of my fin and rudder, and that is turning me to the left even if you don't move the rudder at all. Now pull the stick back a little, because now my elevators are beginning to turn me, and look! my nose is dropping, and the elevators will help to hold it up. You were going to do that by using "top rudder"? Yes, that was the old-fashioned way, and it still works—up to a point. But the rudder is not so effective for this purpose on modern aeroplanes and now, even on fairly steep banks, we think of the elevator as controlling the position of the nose, and only use the rudder to prevent slip or skid. It is very easy—and it works.

Steady, I am beginning to bank too much; have you forgotten that my right wing is now going faster than my left wing, and is getting more Lift, and I shall roll right over unless you stop me? That's better—more than that, stick over to the right a little—hold off my bank; that's it. Perfect! Look at my instruments: sideslip needle dead in the centre, rate of turn needle well over to the left; look at the artificial horizon, you can actually see me banking without looking at the real horizon. Why, I've even got an accelerometer, that must be specially for this Test Flight. What does it say? 4½g. How do you feel, Pilot? All fit? Spendid! Designer? No reply. Rigger? Fitter? —what, all of you blacked out! Well, perhaps it is just as well, because you might not like to see all my spars and rivets and bolts and skin, all stretching and straining all over the place. How would you like to carry 4½ times your own weight? But you needn't worry about me; I'm doing fine—I can take it, even if you cannot. Why, I believe I could stand double this. All the same, Pilot, I think we might let them off now; we have been round three times already. That's it, straighten up, take off the bank, get the nose level again—not easy to do, is it, without skidding or slipping one way or the other? Hullo— they are all awake again. It is quite all right, gentlemen; you'll be none the worse for it, and next time you talk about g's and things, you may realize what they mean.

Straight and Level

Now, Pilot, just a gentle circuit of the aerodrome—a spot of straight and level flight; we have not tried that yet. 120 m.p.h.? Yes, that is just the speed I like for this local flying; besides, it is my best range speed and so it is excellent practice in flying for economy. My tail is feeling a bit heavy, though; what about adjusting my elevator trimming tabs? Which way? The instinctive way—that's it; push the lever forward, the same way as you would move the control column to lift my tail. Have a look behind you—do you see the little tabs on my elevator that have now gone **up**?—Yes, those little things! They feel the wind on the top and so push my elevators **down,** then my elevators feel the Lift and hold my tail **up.** I'm not flying quite straight, Pilot, but I rather suspect that that is because you won't leave my rudder alone. Take your feet off, hands off, too—I can fly by myself, you know; you are sometimes much too inclined to forget that. Do you see? Straight and level—no need to adjust my rudder or aileron tabs.

Ah, another bump, down goes my left wing—no, don't touch anything. We slip to the left, just a wee bit, you hardly notice it, do you? but it has made the wind blow sideways on to my wings, and thanks to my dihedral I feel more Lift on my left wing and I am getting level again. Yes, I am a little off my course; that was because the wind also hit my fin and rudder on the left side. That's a pity, Designer; but you cannot help it, you had to make me Directionally Stable also. Another bump—that one hit my tail and lifted it up—watch me put this right. The wind hits the top of my tail, and down it goes again! Whoa! that was a strange bump—it seemed to hit the tail end of my fuselage all on one side and has put my nose off its course, but do you see how it's swinging back again? You've got something there, Designer. And, Pilot, when you write your report you can say that my Directional Stability is excellent and, in future, don't forget how well I can fly by myself—sometimes better than you can fly me. But there is the aerodrome, a little behind us now, and over on our left, so let us make a trial landing.

Approach and Landing

We are still at 2,000 ft., so we will lose a little height first—throttle the engine back a little. That's clever, isn't it?—I take up a natural angle of glide; that is because the Designer arranged the forces acting on me so that all would be well if the engine were to stop unexpectedly. Do you remember those diagrams on the blackboard? Good! Now let us think about our proper glide. There is the aerodrome still over on the left, and the windsock shows that we are flying down wind. Let us turn across the wind and keep the aerodrome in view. That's fine. Now, Pilot, remember all the things you have to do to get me ready for landing. That's right—legs down. Oh, they do feel the Drag—going at this speed, 110 m.p.h.! I can feel them slowing me up already; also, being underneath me, they are pushing my nose even farther down, but that is all to the good. Now the propeller—make sure about that. It will adjust itself within limits, but to be certain that it will be in fine pitch if we make a bad approach and wish to take off again in a hurry, put the lever into the "high r.p.m." position. Good! Now, it seems to me, Pilot, that I am going to glide too far—even with my undercart down I still have a Lift/Drag ratio of 8 to 1, so I would glide at an angle of 1 in 8 even without my engine to help me—but with my engine assisting I shall never get down at all if we go on like this. **So, flaps down, please!** That is more like it— about half-way down, that will do; we'll keep the rest in hand in case we find that we are overshooting. That has moved my C.P. back, too, tilting me right up on my nose—no, don't pull the stick back; I am only doing 80 m.p.h., in spite of the steep angle and in spite of the engine pulling me; and I want quite a lot of speed in hand so that I can do the flattening-out, and in case we meet any wind gradients or other unpleasant things near the ground.

Now we are only a few hundred feet up; so turn in to land. That's splendid—keep me just like that. Trimmer back a wee bit so that my tail will go down easily when you want it to do so. Keep me steady at 80 m.p.h. 50 ft. up, and over the aerodrome boundary—excellent! Stick back—gently, gently, I have got a little speed in hand, but not much, so don't put my stalling speed up by giving me g's at this stage. There is a nice gentle force on top of my tail now, and I'm flying nearly level—75, 70, 65 m.p.h. I lost a lot of speed during that flattening-out, gentle though it was. Now my speed is dropping even more quickly— my wheels are skimming the blades of grass—this is good fun—flaps are pulling me back—60 m.p.h., 55 m.p.h., speed is going down, and I'm going down, too, but only an inch at a time—now—no—now— yes—**both** my legs **and** my tail wheel at the same time, a perfect three-pointer. Well done, Pilot.

Throttle back now, we don't need my engine any more, but it helped me considerably during that approach. I felt the slipstream over my rudder and elevators, and they work much better like that; besides, although we seemed to come down steep, we should have come down much steeper **without** the engine, and then we should have had to flatten out more, and that would have needed more speed. Notice, too, that I was only doing 50 m.p.h. when I touched down; I can fly a wee bit slower with my engine running. What is my speed now?— 45, 40—flaps holding me back splendidly, they help me to stop without the harshness of the wheel brakes, but now that the speed is low try my brakes, Pilot. Steady, steady, I nearly went on my nose, and I feel like swinging to one side or another. You are not so clever, Designer, about this braking business—a little bit slow with the tricycle under-carriage idea, aren't you? Yes, I know there are snags, but you said that about retractable undercarriages, and variable-pitch propellers, didn't you? But, look, I have stopped. A good landing, Pilot.

Off Again!

But this is not the time or place for talking, so let us get going again. There's plenty of room ahead, so we need not turn round—but that is only because of my brakes and flaps and things, and because you used them properly, Pilot. No need to tell you how to take off this time— it should all be automatic; I am going to keep quiet until we are over and beyond those hangars. . . .

Yes, that was a good take-off—everything done systematically, that is the way to fly nowadays. And what a change from the "good old days"! Your fathers used to be told to fly by "instinct" or, more literally, by "the seat of their pants." Instinct be blowed! They used to go round and round in small circles when they got into a cloud, and then blame the compass for it! No, there wasn't much flying by instinct; but they did fly quite a lot by eye, and that is why they got lost when they could not see. But even when you **can** see, the eye may be deceptive—let us do a little low flying, and you will soon discover what I mean. The people living down below don't like this— one cannot blame them—so let us go and try it over those marshes. What is the height, 200 ft.? That is quite low enough. Now we are still going against the wind, just as we took off, and our air speed, what is it, 100 m.p.h.? Just a little slower, a bit of flap down, if you like—90, 80. That's about it; nice safe, steady speed. Now have a look at the ground below—seems to be moving quite fast, doesn't it? Yes, it is going past us at about 60 m.p.h., and, being close to it, we notice it. Now, Pilot, make a turn, just as I explained to you earlier on. To the right? That suits me. Stick to right—good—wee bit of right rudder—good! Hullo, hullo, why are you taking the bank off? **Hold** it off, yes; but don't **take** it off. Thought you were slipping inwards? Good heavens, it's all very well for you, shut up in a glass house like that, but if you could have felt the wind blowing against my left side! Look at your sideslip indicator, well over to the left. Pilot, for the first time I must reprimand you—you have not done as I told you, you did **not** turn as I taught you. You looked at the ground—and you were deceived, deceived by your eye. Have you never heard of optical illusions? Well, that was one. We were turning to the right, and as we turned the wind was first ahead, then was on my left, then behind me, so it **looked** as though we were drifting to the right across the ground, slipping inwards—**but we were not slipping inwards,** we were making a perfect turn—until you spoilt it. But what are you doing **now**? Look at my air speed—50 m.p.h. Horror upon horrors! I am just going to stall—and at 200 ft., too! I can feel the air beginning to burble over my wings, and buffeting my tail, I am beginning to shudder all over, and if you moved my ailerons I'm sure they wouldn't have much effect. Ah, the Designer has saved us this time, not because of the cleverness of his design, but because he wasn't going to be fooled by what he saw. He knew what keeps me flying, and he had the presence of mind to shove the throttle open and give me more Thrust. **Air speed,** Pilot, **air speed** is what matters—**not ground speed.** We were going down wind—we **were** going faster over the ground than before, yes, even when we were only doing 50 m.p.h. air speed and in danger of losing our lives. So now do you see what I mean about flying by eye and instinct and seats of pants and such like things? You didn't notice all this higher up? No, that's the strange part about it. We only notice relative speed when we are close to a thing. Have you ever been in an aeroplane and seen a bomb dropped from a great height? You have? Well, what does it do? Drops straight down under the machine, falling a little behind, until it gets near the ground—then it suddenly shoots forward and hits the target! No, Pilot, it doesn't **really** do that, it only **appears** to do that. It is really going forward all the time (because it was going forward when it was on the aeroplane). Its forward speed gets a little lower because of its Drag, so that it lags a little behind the aeroplane; but as soon as it is close to the ground, you compare it with the ground and realize for the first time that it is going forward—in other words, the bomb is then doing a little bit of low flying!

After all that sermon, turn me up wind again and see what happens this time. Good—a perfect turn! But you were struggling with

PLATE XLVIII. "BELOW THE CLOUDS"
(By courtesy of " Flight ")

yourself, weren't you. You thought we were skidding outwards, but I knew I wasn't because no wind hit my sides. Thank goodness you didn't bank me too much, as I feared you would, or I might have slipped into the ground. Oh, yes, we were moving sideways **relative to the ground,** that was **not** an optical illusion; and I quite agree that if there had been a high obstacle on the outside of our turn, we might have had to bank more steeply to avoid it.

But look at those clouds, getting thicker and thicker. I believe it's going to rain down here—let us go up above them. Now for a nice long steady climb.

Climbing

That's it. Not too steep. Give me a little more power, please; after all, the Engine Designer has given you a lot of surplus for occasions like these. Remember that I now have two enemies, Drag and Weight. That is better, but still rather steep. You think that because you **point** me to the stars, I am going to climb to the stars; but you make a great mistake. Why, my wings are now hitting the air at 12°—give me 5° or 6° and I shall be much happier, and climb much better. What's that? I'm talking Greek to you? No—but I was forgetting that you have no instrument to tell you my Angle of Attack. But remember that the air speed is always a guide, because I have a definite air speed for a definite Angle of Attack. Now, for instance, I want my wings to hit the air at 6° so as to climb, and if the Designer looks at his Horse Power Available and Horse Power Required curves he will tell you at what forward speed I shall have most surplus power and so will climb best—140 m.p.h., the Designer says. That's a good speed, but I suppose he's right, he ought to know. Put me at that and try—120, 130, 140. Seems strange, doesn't it—putting my nose down in order to climb, but have a look at the altimeter, and time me for 1,000 ft. Ten, twenty, thirty seconds—not quite thirty seconds. Over 2,000 ft. a minute—not too bad for a large fellow like me, and without really exerting all my power. And do you realize that I was only climbing at 1,000 ft. a minute when you were pointing me upwards so steeply? Now that you know that I'm climbing at my best, just trim my elevators and I'll fly hands off—that's it. Now up to the clouds—by Jove! it's getting black and miserable down here—not a sign of blue sky anywhere, we'll have to go through the thick of them. It's raining, too; watch the poor old earth getting soaked—it's turning into a typical English summer day after all! Ugh!—what a bump!—and another!—leave it to me, Pilot, I'll correct them. Oh, it's damp and cold! Now for the plunge!

Through the Clouds

In the thick of it now—horrible! Steady, Pilot, where are you going? No—you think you can, but you can't—your instinct isn't clever enough for that. You have only two hopes now—my instruments and my natural stability. I could climb through this cloud by myself if you would leave me alone, but I don't think you will. No, I thought you wouldn't. All right, Pilot, I'll let you have your own way for a few moments. Just try to keep me straight and level—steady, not so bad—my left wing has dropped a bit, you know—or don't you?— and I'm turning to the left. Why don't you correct me? My nose is going up—what **are** you doing? Now you are turning me to the left and trying to bank me to the right, **and** I'm stalling—I don't really know what I am doing—oh, over I go, I thought so, into a spin—and you were trying to fly me straight and level. Round we go, round and round, round and round, round and round—out of the cloud again. Now, Pilot—ah, you know what to do at last! That's it, right rudder —I was spinning to the left, but you didn't know I was, did you? I don't believe you knew I was spinning at all, you were probably expecting me to poke my nose out at the top of the clouds. Well,

PLATE XLIX. "THROUGH THE CLOUDS"
(*By courtesy of A. V. Roe & Co., Ltd.*)

there's nothing for it but to try again. That's right, back into the old climb, and this time start flying by instruments even before we reach the cloud. Look at the artificial horizon, it shows I'm climbing a little, but my wings are level. What does the clock say, 140 m.p.h.? I will climb better at 130 now, so put me at that. No, it isn't **really** that I need less speed (actually I need rather **more** as I climb); it is only that the air is thinner at this height. so the clock reads wrong. What does the Directional Gyro say, 270°? that means that I am pointing west, because you will remember that you set the Directional Gyro to read the same as the compass. Turn Indicator? Top needle central, that tells us that there is no slip—bottom needle central, that means that we are not turning. Altimeter?—5,200 ft. Into the cloud we go again, so keep all the readings constant. It's not so difficult as it sounds if only you will remember two things—first, that I can almost fly by myself—secondly, that you need not concentrate on **all** the instruments—after all, if I am level on the artificial horizon, and the turn indicator tells you that I am not turning. I cannot be doing much wrong, can I? That's splendid this time. Look at the altimeter, 5,500, 6,000 ft. Air speed 125, nose down a little, 130. Keep it at that. Now turning a wee bit to left—that's better. Easy, isn't it? Just leave everything alone for a few seconds. Now—do you see? Alone I did it, even though I do feel like a drowned rat. Thank goodness it's not cold enough for ice to form on my wings. But look, it's getting lighter—there's daylight above—blue sky at last. We're through.

Above the Clouds

What a sight! What a joy! Look, my Passengers, especially those of you who have never been up before. There are many fair sights on earth, but there is nothing to compare with this. The sun and the blue sky above, and just below us a sea of rolling white clouds extending in all directions as far as the eye can see.

> *And the air is crisp, and the wind is keen,*
> *And the clouds are all lit with a silvery sheen,*
> *It's the finest sight that I've ever seen,*
> *For there's nothing on earth so fair.*
> *But now we are up in the Air, my lad,*
> *We're care-free men of the Air, my lad,*
> *And I am the King of the Air, my lad,*
> *Yes, I am the King of the Air.*

Look at my shadow floating over the clouds—do you see how it is framed with the colours of the rainbow? Think of the earth down below, the rain and the gloom and the wars and then look again at this wonderful world of ours.

Now let us climb a few more thousand feet, Pilot—up to about ten thousand, then we can do some experiments. At the moment I feel as though I could go on climbing for ever, and that's a change from the old days, isn't it? As the air gets thinner, my engine cylinders need more air—more boost, as you call it. How's that going to be done? Automatic boost control! Sounds simple; it is simple, and that's why it's clever. My mixture of air to petrol goes all wrong—automatic mixture control! My propeller loses grip—automatic pitch control! And the real merit of all these is that the Designers have harnessed the changes in pressure and density and have made them do the work. Thus the disease itself effects the cure, and that is always the best way, then we don't get cures when we haven't got diseases.

But time me for a thousand feet now—we are just passing the 8,000 mark. Ten, twenty, thirty and one, two, three seconds—not much difference from what it was down below. We might have done a little better, too, because you ought to be going a little slower now—try 125 on the clock, Pilot. But all this climbing cannot go on for ever— I'm rated at 10,000 ft., which means that I shall be at my best then, speed and climb and everything—after that, well, the inevitable happens. We won't try it now, but you would find that you would have to lower and lower my speed on the indicator until at my Service Ceiling it was down to about 100 m.p.h.—about the same as my best endurance speed—but it wouldn't **really** be 100—much more than that; if it were at 40,000 ft., it would be twice as much. My rate of climb would get less and less, my maximum speed would decrease. In short, I would deteriorate in every way until if I ever reached the Absolute Ceiling, I could only fly at one speed—it would be both my fastest and

my slowest—I could only have one Angle of Attack, I could not turn,
I couldn't do anything except stagger along. But, anyway, it would be
terribly cold up there, and all of you would pass out if you hadn't got
oxygen—and here we are at ten thousand, and that's a much more
gentlemanly height at which to do things.

Speed

Now put me through my paces, Pilot. First, open the throttle
steadily—that's the way; the engine won't object if it's only for a
minute or two. Full open, good. By Jove! I can feel the Thrust—
the pull in my propeller shaft is terrific, and what an acceleration it is
causing—140, 160, 180, 200 m.p.h., over 3 miles a minute—but we are
still gaining speed, it takes time. Now it is largely up to you, Pilot—
I only need about 1° Angle of Attack. Oh, I again forgot, you cannot
judge the angles. Well, watch the clock—**no**, not **that** clock, the Air
Speed Indicator, I mean—**and** watch that funny little instrument we
haven't used yet, the Rate of Climb Indicator—you see, we are still
climbing a little. That's better, but now my angle is getting too small;
don't you remember that I need a downward force on my tail at high
speed? So trim me again—that's it, not too far; it's very sensitive now. What are we doing?—280, 290, 295, 300—5 miles a minute—
oh boy, that feels good, doesn't it?—305, 310, 312, 313, 314, 315,
315, 314—ah, that's about the limit, I think—nose down a bit—no. I'm
losing height now. Let's call it 315, and let's call it a day, too; my
engines have had quite enough of this for the present. 315 on the
clock, that's——? Oh, what is it—got a computer, Pilot? I never
could work out square roots and things—What's that, Designer?
You've got a slide-rule? What is it then?—True speed just over
350 m.p.h. Well, well, and they talk about the Blue Riband of the
Atlantic!

Slow Speed

Now let us try the other end of the scale—how slowly can I fly?
Throttle down a little, Pilot. What a sigh of relief from my engine!
No, not much, Pilot; actually I could have done best just as it was,
but it really was asking rather a lot of the engine. Now, stick back very
slowly—**very** slowly, or I shall loop or something. Speed down to 300,
280, 260, 240. Soon goes, doesn't it? But my Angle of Attack is
going up 2°, 6°, 8°, 12°. I'm climbing, too; but never mind—a little
more angle, and I won't climb. 150 m.p.h.—that's a quick change,
140, 130, 120. Stick back just a little more, 14°, 15°—90 m.p.h., 80,
70, 65. Try my controls now—aileron control not too good, is it?
Why didn't you give me some automatic slots at my wing tips, Designer?
No, perhaps you are right. Flaps? Oh, yes, Pilot; do you know I
forgot all about my flaps, I hardly ever use them up here. Yes, put
them down by all means—that slows me up. Steady, you must put
my nose down a bit, or I shall stall; I want that tail trim adjusting,
too—forward, that's right. 55, 53, 52, 51, 50. Steady at that—watch
the sensitive altimeter—am I losing height? No? Keep it at that.
Try my nose down a bit—speed 52, and losing height. Nose up a bit
—speed 50, 49½—steady, steady; no, I can't do it—I can't do it—
something is going to happen—I can't do it—my right wing's going
down—stick over to the left—quick!—no good, aileron didn't work—
no, even the elevator won't work. There's nothing for it—round **we**

PLATE L. "ABOVE THE CLOUDS"
(*By courtesy of "The Aeroplane."*)

go again, spinning merrily, round and round—that's the way—left rudder, stop the spin—stick forward, out of the stall—then ease me back. That shook you all a bit, didn't it? But it is just as well to know that I can get out of it. So my stalling speed is 50—no, dash it, what is it, Designer? 50 Indicated, or 58 True. So I can fly at 350 m.p.h. and I can fly at 58 m.p.h.—and all at 10,000 ft. But let us go up to fifteen thousand, Pilot. . . . Good!

Gliding

Now let us try some gliding experiments. Throttle down—right down, this time. No, you need not touch the stick—look! my nose drops automatically. Oh, what a relief!—no noise, no vibration, no slipstream—just God's pure air and that marvellous view of rolling clouds down below. This is real flight, the kind I enjoy best. I often think I ought to have been a sailplane. Now, Pilot, put me at my best gliding angle. Flaps up—that's right, I shall glide flatter then, or perhaps you might try about 10° of Flap. That's it—stick back a bit. Speed, 80 m.p.h. Angle of Attack, 4°. Now watch the rate at which I lose height and we'll ask our mathematical Designer to work out our gliding angle. Why, he's already done it. 1 in 15. What do you think of that? And your fathers used to talk about a mile per thousand feet, which was only 1 in 5. Now slow up a bit—stick back, that's right—75, 70, 65 m.p.h. Hold her at that. My nose is farther up now, Angle of Attack is 10°, but time my rate of descent—what does it work out at? Gliding angle of 1 in 5—just like the old days. Now, nose down a bit—more yet—80, 85, 90, 95 m.p.h. Try that Angle of Attack, 2°. Rate of descent? 1 in 5 again—but what a different attitude I'm in! Do you remember how your Instructor told you all about this in lectures? And now you see that it all really happens in practical flight.

Now for the final test—but take the flaps off first.

Nose-dive

Put my nose down steadily, and we will glide faster and faster. Gee, this is fun, isn't it! Watch that clock—150, 200, 250. Phew, what a wind coming up to meet us! And now my Angle of Attack is nought—no Lift, but what a Drag! 300—oh, my tail—what a downward load!—oh, my fuselage, what a pull at the top!—and the bottom feels like crumpling up—350. There's our record broken—but I feel like breaking myself. I'm sure that my wings are going to fold backwards soon. What's that, Designer—I could stand my terminal velocity? How much is that? 500 m.p.h. No, thank you—no, thank you—I'll take your word for it. This feels over the vertical already, and I'm sure something is going to happen soon. 400 m.p.h.—and off the clock. What's all that I heard about the speed of sound?—do you know, I think I am going to feel a shock wave or something soon! Look, Pilot, we are going into those clouds in about a thousandth of a second at this rate. Yes, I think so—stick back—slowly—**slowly —SLOWLY.** Gently does it at times like this. Oh, what aches and pains! Oh, my spars, my ribs, my skin—I feel about six times my usual weight! What's that, Designer? I **am**—but I can stand ten times my weight. Ah, but can **you**? What's that? . . . No reply? What do you say, Pilot? . . . No reply. You've all gone out this time—I've beaten the lot of you. That'll teach you to talk about *g*'s! only 200 m.p.h. now. Ah, you've woken up, Pilot. . . . Just as well, because I was about to stall—yes, stall at 200 m.p.h. Give me some engine—that's it. Oh, what a relief! What's that you say?—"and so say all of us"? Yes, once in a lifetime is quite enough of that. If all of you could have seen my rivets and welds, my nuts and bolts! On each of these my life—**and yours**—depended, and each was hanging on by the skin of its teeth. If just **one** had broken—where would we be now? However, all's well that ends well, and I congratulate you—all of you—you've made a good job of me, and I will endeavour to do you credit.

*   *   *   *   *

And so on

But here we are again at 10,000 ft., so let us have some fun.

> *For now is the time to tumble around,*
> *Ten thousand or more above the ground,*
>   *It's a pleasure to be alive ;*
> *With the engine roaring down we swoop,*
> *Then over the top in a graceful loop,*
>   *And down again in a dive.*
> *Then rolling round and round about,*
> *A stall and a spin, oh ! it makes you shout,*
> *And it turns your troubles all inside out,*
>   *And blows them away in the Air.*
>   *Oh ! it's great to be in the Air, my lad,*
>   *A care-free son of the Air, my lad,*
>   *And I am the King of the Air, my lad,*
>   *Yes, I am the King of the Air.*

APPENDICES

APPENDIX I

AEROFOIL DATA

*(Extracted, by permission, from " Handbook of Aeronautics,"
published by Sir Isaac Pitman & Sons, Ltd.)*

NOTES

1. The aerofoil sections, of which particulars are given in the following pages, have been chosen from among the thousand or more that have been tested, as being typical of the best that have been designed for particular purposes.

2. Although the values have been taken from standard tests they have been modified so as to bring them all into line, and simplified so as to correspond with the symbols and methods used throughout the remainder of the book. In thus modifying the figures the aim has been to bring out the principles even at the sacrifice of some degree of accuracy and so figures are given to fewer decimal places than in the official results. For the purpose of this book, nothing whatever is lost by this simplification, and while it is right and proper that official results should be given to the accuracy with which they can be measured, the student should remember that they are, after all, taken from experimental figures, and that there is a limit not only to the accuracy of such figures but even more so to the various corrections that have to be applied to them.

3. Unfortunately it is not possible to obtain results of all the aerofoils at the same Reynolds' Number, but for each aerofoil the approximate Reynolds' Number of the test has been given, and where alternative results are available those at the highest Reynolds' Number have been chosen.

4. Values of coefficients relate to aspect ratio 6 and have been corrected for wind-tunnel interference.

5. The values of L/D have been calculated by dividing C_L by C_D, but for this purpose C_L and C_D have been evaluated to a higher degree of accuracy than the approximate values given in the tables. The reader may find, therefore, that if he divides the approximate values of C_L by C_D he will get a slightly different value of L/D from the more correct one given in the tables.

6. It is not at present possible to give test results for the most modern high-speed bi-convex or double-wedge sections and, even if they could be given, it is doubtful whether the tests would have been made at sufficiently high Mach Numbers and Reynolds' Numbers to be reliable as a guide to full-scale performance.

7. For the benefit of those readers who would like to sketch out the shapes of the various aerofoils, the co-ordinates of the upper and lower surfaces are given for each aerofoil. The measurements are expressed as a percentage of the chord, negative values being below the chord line and positive values above it.

304

1. R.A.F. 15

Excellent general purpose aerofoil for use on biplanes

Designed during the First World War, but still unrivalled for its particular purpose.

Note the high maximum value of L/D ratio.

Shares, with the American Clark Y, the distinction of having been used on more types of aircraft than any other aerofoil section.

Approx. Reynolds' Number of test—$3\frac{1}{2}$ million.

Distance from L.E.	Upper Surface	Lower Surface
0	1·50	1·50
1·25	3·14	0·76
2·5	3·94	0·50
5	5·00	0·18
7·5	5·37	0·02
10	6·09	0·02
15	6·37	0·18
20	6·96	0·53
30	6·94	1·02
40	6·63	1·02
50	6·13	0·71
60	5·52	0·33
70	4·79	0·06
80	3·91	0·04
90	2·81	0·21
95	2·17	0·32
100	0·94	0·94

Angle of Attack	c_L	c_D	L/D	Position of C.P. Fraction of Chord
− 4°	− 0·14	0·014	− 10	—
− 2°	+ 0·02	0·008	+ 2	2·0*
0°	0·14	0·008	18	0·58
+ 2°	0·32	0·012	23·5	0·38
4°	0·46	0·020	24	0·34
6°	0·60	0·030	21	0·31
8°	0·76	0·044	18	0·30
10°	0·90	0·060	15	0·29
12°	1·04	0·076	13	0·29
14°	1·16	0·096	12	0·28
15°	1·22	0·110	11·5	0·28
16°	1·16	0·140	8	0·30
18°	1·02	0·210	5	0·37
20°	0·94	0·260	3	0·38

* The value of 2·0 means that the centre of pressure at this angle (− 2°) is two chords length behind the leading edge of the aerofoil, and there is therefore a very strong "Nose-down" moment. (See p. 75.)

2. R.A.F. 15 WITH SLOT

Shows the effect of a Handley Page slot on a thin section.

The slot has less effect on a thicker section.

Maximum lift of R.A.F. 15 is increased by nearly 50 per cent, while the stalling angle is delayed for about 11° by the use of the slot.

The slot is assumed to remain open in the position which gives the greatest increase in the maximum lift.

Approx. Reynolds' Number of test—200,000.

Angle of Attack	c_L	c_D	L/D	Position of C.P. Fraction of Chord
0°	0·04	0·056	0·5	—
2°	0·16	0·050	4	0·70
4°	0·34	0·050	7	0·45
8°	0·56	0·060	9·5	0·37
12°	0·90	0·080	11·5	0·34
16°	1·24	0·120	10	0·32
20°	1·50	0·174	8·5	0·31
24°	1·70	0·234	7·5	0·30
26°	1·76	0·270	6·5	0·30
28°	1·76	0·304	6	0·30
30°	1·64	0·344	—	—
34°	1·30	0·430	—	—

3. R.A.F. 28

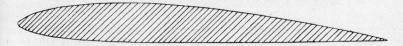

Excellent general purpose aerofoil for use on monoplanes
The monoplane counterpart of R.A.F. 15; designed at an early date
but still in use on some types of aircraft.
Approx. Reynolds' Number of test—6 million.

Distance from L. E.	Upper Surface	Lower Surface
0	0	0
1·25	1·37	− 1·26
2·5	2·17	− 1·68
5	3·14	− 2·23
7·5	3·85	− 2.55
10	4·44	− 2·76
15	5·38	− 3·04
20	6·00	− 3·13
30	6·64	− 3·11
40	6·70	− 2·86
50	6·27	− 2·51
60	5·40	− 2·07
70	4·28	− 1·60
80	3·02	− 1·11
90	1·63	− 0·64
95	0·91	− 0·42
100	0	0

Angle of Attack	C_L	C_D	L/D	Position of C.P. Fraction of Chord
− 4°	− 0·18	0·009	− 13	—
− 2°	− 0·04	0·008	− 3·5	—
0°	+ 0·16	0·010	15	0·48
+ 2°	0·32	0·013	23·5	0·38
4°	0·46	0·019	22·7	0·34
6°	0·60	0·028	20·5	0·31
8°	0·76	0·040	18·3	0·30
10°	0·90	0·056	16·2	0·29
12°	1·04	0·073	14·3	0·29
14°	1·17	0·094	12·7	0·28
16°	1·31	0·114	11·3	0·28
18°	1·38	0·142	10·0	0·28
20°	1·20	0·260	4·6	0·30
25°	1·00	0·395	2·5	0·37
30°	0·82	0·489	1·7	0·39

4. CLARK YH

Excellent American general purpose aerofoil

One of several modifications of Clark Y which shares with R.A.F. 15 the distinction of having been used on more types of aircraft than any other aerofoil section.

Clark Y, in its various forms, has been used on both biplane and monoplane, and even now is used as much as any other section for propeller blades.

Approx. Reynolds' Number of test—7 million.

Distance from L.E.	Upper Surface	Lower Surface
0	3·50	3·50
1·25	5·45	1·93
2·5	6·50	1·47
5	7·90	0·93
7·5	8·85	0·63
10	9·60	0·42
15	10·68	0·15
20	11·36	0·03
30	11·70	0
40	11·40	0
50	10·51	0
60	9·15	0
70	7·42	0·06
80	5·62	0·38
90	3·84	1·02
95	2·93	1·40
100	2·05	1·85

Angle of Attack	C_L	C_D	L/D	Position of C.P. Fraction of Chord
− 4°	− 0·09	0·010	− 10	—
− 2°	+ 0·05	0·009	+ 5·2	0·74
0°	0·20	0·010	19·3	0·40
2°	0·36	0·015	23·2	0·32
4°	0·51	0·022	23	0·295
6°	0·66	0·033	20·6	0·285
8°	0·80	0·045	17·7	0·275
10°	0·94	0·062	15·2	0·27
12°	1·06	0·083	13·3	0·27
14°	1·21	0·103	11·8	0·27
16°	1·33	0·125	11	0·265
18°	1·43	0·146	9·9	0·265
19°	1·36	0·170	8	0·275
20°	1·26	0·211	7	0·29
25°	0·97	0·324	2·9	0·33
30°	0·81	0·430	1·9	0·37

5. R.A.F. 34

One of the R.A.F. 30 series with which began a systematic attempt to analyse aerofoil characteristics by starting with a symmetrical section (R.A.F. 30), and modifying by curving the centre line (R.A.F. 31, 32, 33, etc.).

This particular section, R.A.F. 34, was designed to give a fixed Centre of Pressure and the figures show how nearly this has been achieved at angles of attack from 4° to 14°.

Results are given at two values of Reynolds' Number so as to give some indication of the differences that may occur, but it must be remembered that it is one of the pecularities of Reynolds' Number changes that the effects vary considerably on different sections (see Appendix III).

Distance from L.E.	Upper Surface	Lower Surface
0	0	0
1·25	1·98	− 1·62
2·5	2·82	− 2·14
5·0	4·11	− 2·81
10	5·83	− 3·53
15	6·97	− 3·91
20	7·72	− 4·16
25	8·14	− 4·26
30	8·32	− 4·32
35	8·27	− 4·33
40	8·08	− 4·32
45	7·74	− 4·26
50	7·21	− 4·11
55	6·59	− 3·93
60	5·87	− 3·69
65	5·13	− 3·43
70	4·31	− 3·09
75	3·49	− 2·71
80	2·70	− 2·30
85	1·95	− 1·85
90	1·26	− 1·34
95	0·64	− 0·76
100	0	0

Approx. Reynolds' Number of test—350,000.

Angle of Attack	C_L	C_D	L/D	Position of C.P. Fraction of Chord
− 4°	− 0·2	0·016	—	—
− 2°	− 0·06	0·012	− 6	—
0°	+ 0·06	0·010	+ 6·5	0·28
+ 2°	0·24	0·012	18·5	0·26
4°	0·40	0·020	20	0·265
6°	0·56	0·030	19	0·27
8°	0·72	0·042	17	0·265
10°	0·86	0·054	15·5	0·26
12°	0·94	0·070	13	0·25
14°	1·00	0·090	11	0·25
15°	1·02	0·104	9	0·26
16°	1·02	0·140	8	0·27
18°	0·96	—	—	—
20°	0·86	—	—	—

Approx. Reynolds' Number of test—$6\frac{1}{2}$ million.

Angle of Attack	C_L	C_D	L/D	Position of C.P. Fraction of Chord
$-4°$	-0.25	—	—	—
$-2°$	-0.10	0.009	-10	—
$0°$	$+0.06$	0.008	$+5.8$	0.323
$2°$	0.22	0.011	21.4	0.255
$4°$	0.36	0.017	22.8	0.250
$6°$	0.51	0.025	21.5	0.248
$8°$	0.68	0.034	19.9	0.248
$10°$	0.83	0.048	17.3	0.249
$12°$	0.97	0.065	14.8	0.250
$14°$	1.11	0.083	13	0.251
$16°$	1.24	0.105	11.7	0.253
$18°$	1.32	0.131	10	0.257
$20°$	1.28	0.175	7.2	0.266
$25°$	0.97	0.323	3	0.330
$30°$	0.74	0.397	2	0.347

6. GÖTTINGEN 387

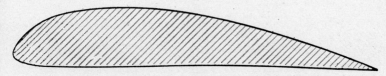

High Lift, thick section, for monoplane construction
Typical of German monoplane design in the days between the wars.

Distance from L.E.	Upper Surface	Lower Surface
0	3·78	3·78
1·25	6·53	1·43
2·5	7·91	0·93
5	9·89	0·40
7·5	11·32	0·15
10	12·40	0·03
15	13·84	0
20	14·71	0·05
30	15·34	0·23
40	14·85	0·38
50	13·47	0·50
60	11·54	0·57
70	9·21	0·58
80	6·58	0·49
90	3·61	0·28
95	2·02	0·16
100	0·25	0·25

Angle of Attack	C_L	C_D	L/D	Position of C.P. Fraction of Chord
− 8°	− 0·08	0·014	—	—
− 6°	+ 0·06	0·012	5	—
− 4°	0·20	0·014	13·5	0·73
− 2°	0·32	0·020	18	0·50
0°	0·48	0·026	18	0·40
+ 2°	0·62	0·038	16·5	0·38
4°	0·78	0·050	15	0·33
6°	0·94	0·068	14	0·30
8°	1·06	0·086	12·5	0·30
10°	1·18	0·108	11	0·31
12°	1·28	0·134	10	0·30
14°	1·32	0·162	8·5	0·32
16°	1·34	0·196	7	0·33
18°	1·32	0·230	6	0·34
20°	1·30	0·270	5	0·34

7. R.A.F. 48

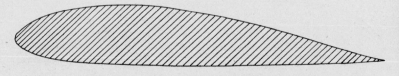

(*a*) Without flap.   (*b*) With flap.

One of the R.A.F. 40 series, being a modification of the symmetrical R.A.F. 40 which is of 15 per cent thickness as compared with the 13 per cent of R.A.F. 30.

(*a*) Shows the results of the plain aerofoil section.

(*b*) Shows the effect of a 10 per cent split flap in the fully lowered position.

Notice how the flap—

(i) Increases C_L at all angles of attack.

(ii) Increases C_D at all angles of attack.

(iii) Completely spoils the L/D ratio, making it nearly constant at about 6 throughout the flying range.

(iv) Causes the C.P. to be further back at positive angles of attack.

Approx. Reynolds' Number of tests—

Plain aerofoil—7 million.

Flapped aerofoil—$3\frac{1}{2}$ million.

Distance from L.E.	Upper Surface	Lower Surface
0	0	0
1·25	2·60	− 1·65
2·5	3·65	− 2·34
5	5·20	− 3·16
7·5	6·39	− 3·69
10	7·30	− 4·03
15	8·63	− 4·41
20	9·53	− 4·58
30	10·40	− 4·56
40	10·20	− 4·33
50	9·38	− 3·90
60	7·94	− 3·36
70	6·05	− 2·65
80	4·02	− 1·83
90	1·95	− 1·00
95	1·05	− 0·60
100	0	0

Angle of Attack	C_L		C_D		L/D		Position of C.P. Fraction of Chord	
	(a)	(b)	(a)	(b)	(a)	(b)	(a)	(b)
− 4°	− 0·14	+ 0·53	0·009	0·119	− 11·5	+ 4·6	—	0·595
− 2°	0	0·69	0·008	0·128	+ 0·5	5·3	—	0·51
0°	+ 0·16	0·84	0·010	0·141	13·3	5·8	0·515	0·47
2°	0·32	0·99	0·015	0·157	21·4	6·3	0·38	0·44
4°	0·46	1·13	0·021	0·176	21·6	6·4	0·335	0·415
6°	0·60	1·28	0·031	0·197	19·9	6·5	0·31	0·40
8°	0·76	1·42	0·044	0·219	17·7	6·5	0·30	0·385
10°	0·91	1·56	0·058	0·243	15·7	6·5	0·29	0·37
12°	1·04	1·70	0·075	0·270	14·2	6·3	0·285	0·36
14°	1·19	1·82	0·096	0·297	12·5	6·1	0·285	0·355
16°	1·33	1·94	0·117	0·326	11·2	6·0	0·28	0·35
18°	1·42	2·08	0·140	0·358	10·1	5·8	0·28	0·345
19°	1·42	2·14	0·166	0·376	8·6	5·7	0·285	0·345
20°	1·38	1·65	0·187	0·422	7·3	4·0	0·29	0·36
25°	1·21	1·29	0·288	0·516	4·2	2·5	0·32	0·40
30°	0·90	1·20	0·419	0·760	2·2	1·8	0·36	0·46

8. R.A.F. 89

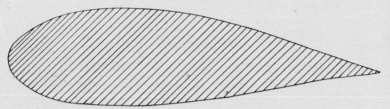

A really thick section (25 per cent), showing what happens when one goes too far!

Notice the poor value of C_L max. and the low maximum value of L/D.

Even thicker sections than this may come into their own if satisfactory means of controlling the boundary layer over the rear portion of the section are discovered.

Approx. Reynolds' Number of test—$4\frac{1}{2}$ million.

Distance from L.E.	Upper Surface	Lower Surface
0	0·50	0·50
1·25	4·20	− 3·00
2·5	5·72	− 4·39
5·0	7·78	− 6·16
7·5	9·30	− 7·37
10	10·49	− 8·33
15	12·20	− 9·57
20	13·35	− 10·34
30	14·29	− 10·71
40	14·06	− 10·24
50	13·01	− 9·22
60	11·12	− 7·67
70	8·56	− 5·67
80	5·76	− 3·72
90	2·91	− 1·87
95	1·55	− 1·01
100	0·01	− 0·01

Angle of Attack	C_L	C_D	L/D	Position of C.P. Fraction of Chord
− 4°	− 0·17	0·014	− 12·2	—
− 2°	− 0·03	0·013	− 1·7	—
0°	+ 0·12	0·013	8·8	0·50
2°	0·26	0·016	15·3	0·35
4°	0·39	0·021	17·7	0·31
6°	0·52	0·030	17·0	0·285
8°	0·64	0·041	15·4	0·27
10°	0·74	0·054	13·7	0·265
12°	0·83	0·072	11·6	0·26
14°	0·90	0·094	9·7	0·26
16°	0·94	0·119	7·9	0·265
18°	0·95	0·153	6·3	0·275
20°	0·94	0·185	5·2	0·275
25°	0·90	0·273	3·2	0·30
30°	0·80	0·340	2·5	0·32

9. N.A.C.A. 0012

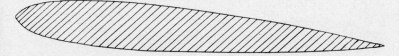

An American symmetrical section, rather similar in shape and characteristics to the British R.A.F. 30.

Notice the good values of L/D over a wide range of angles, and the almost constant position of the C.P. at about 24 per cent of the chord.

Approx. Reynolds' Number of test—5½ million.

Distance from L.E.	Upper and Lower Surfaces
0	0
1·25	1·89
2·5	2·61
5·0	3·56
7·5	4·20
10	4·68
15	5·34
20	5·74
30	6·00
40	5·80
50	5·30
60	4·66
70	3·67
80	2·62
90	1·45
95	0·81
100	0·02

Angle of Attack	C_L	C_D	L/D	Position of C.P. Fraction of Chord
− 4°	− 0·31	0·012	− 24·8	—
− 2°	− 0·16	0·010	− 19·3	—
0°	0	0·007	+ 0·4	0·32
2°	+ 0·17	0·010	19·3	0·235
4°	0·32	0·012	24·8	0·23
6°	0·47	0·019	23·7	0·23
8°	0·61	0·029	21·0	0·235
10°	0·77	0·043	18·3	0·235
12°	0·92	0·057	16·1	0·24
14°	1·06	0·075	14·2	0·24
16°	1·19	0·096	12·6	0·24
18°	1·31	0·116	11·2	0·245
20°	1·43	0·142	10·1	0·245
21°	1·48	0·155	9·6	0·24
22°	0·99	0·261	3·8	0·30
25°	0·81	0·314	2·6	0·32
30°	0·64	0·380	1·8	0·33

10. N.A.C.A. 23012

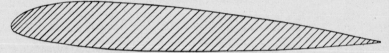

An American section that has been used with great success on high-performance sailplanes.

Approx. Reynolds' Number of test—$4\frac{1}{2}$ million.

Distance from L.E.	Upper Surface	Lower Surface
0	0	0
1·25	2·67	− 1·23
2·5	3·61	− 1·71
5·0	4·91	− 2·26
7·5	5·80	− 2·61
10	6·43	− 2·92
15	7·19	− 3·50
20	7·50	− 3·97
25	7·60	− 4·28
30	7·55	− 4·46
40	7·14	− 4·48
50	6·41	− 4·17
60	5·47	− 3·67
70	4·36	− 3·00
80	3·08	− 2·16
90	1·68	− 1·23
95	0·92	− 0·70
100	0	0

Angle of Attack	C_L	C_D	L/D	Position of C.P. Fraction of Chord
− 4°	− 0·20	0·011	− 18·5	—
− 2°	− 0·06	0·008	− 7·0	—
0°	+ 0·09	0·009	+ 11·2	0·325
2°	0·23	0·010	23·3	0·27
4°	0·39	0·016	24·6	0·255
6°	0·53	0·023	21·5	0·25
8°	0·68	0·036	18·9	0·245
10°	0·83	0·049	16·7	0·245
12°	0·98	0·064	15·1	0·245
14°	1·13	0·080	13·7	0·24
16°	1·27	0·103	12·4	0·24
18°	1·40	0·126	11·0	0·24
19°	1·46	0·142	10·2	0·24
20°	1·16	0·206	5·7	0·27
22°	1·05	0·244	4·3	0·29

APPENDIX II

UNITS AND DIMENSIONS

As was explained in Chapter I the difficulties of mechanics, and the mistakes that are made in calculating numerical examples, are largely due to the doubt and confusion about units. Teachers of mechanics have their own pet systems; books, schools, universities, even nations differ in the systems that they adopt, and specialist workers in different subjects maintain that only one system is suitable for their particular work—so we have engineering units, scientific units, and so on. When, on top of this, they all use different symbols for the same quantities, it is hardly surprising that the student becomes bewildered.

The system that has been used throughout this book is that now generally adopted by aeronautical engineers in the English-speaking world. We have made no other claim for it; and we do not propose to to do so, partly because that seems sufficient argument for its use **in this book,** and partly because the purpose of this appendix is to attempt to clarify the position as regards units, and that can never be done if we try to justify one system at the expense of the others.

Many readers of this book will have learnt a different system, at school may be, or in a university, or in the Services or elsewhere; or they may have read other books using other units. The aim in this short note is to make it easy for them to translate from one system to another and, even more important, to realize that the principles of the subject remain the same whatever system of units or symbols is adopted.

C.G.S. and FT. LB. SEC. Systems

The first point of controversy is, of course, between the Metric and the Anglo-American system, or, to avoid nationalities, let us say between the Centimetre-Gramme-Second and the Foot-Pound-Second system. At least we can be thankful for small mercies—that the unit of time is common to both!

As was explained in Chapter I, this seemingly important issue is not really serious so far as teaching and learning is concerned. In a perfect world two such systems could never co-exist; they involve such a waste of time, and money, and patience, and everything else, that one of them obviously ought to be abolished without a moment's delay. But which? Again, there is little doubt that if the decision were to be made according to democratic principles, it is our own system that would go.

But this is not a perfect world, and there is not the slightest sign of any general agreement on this subject, so it looks as though we must accept the two systems, whether we like it or not; and in spite of all the disadvantages of having two systems it is, after all. **only a question of conversion and not of understanding.** A centimetre, an inch, a foot, a mile, are all measures of length, and the fact that there are 2·54 cm. in one inch takes no more understanding than that there are 12 inches in a foot. But when some people say that a pound is a mass, and other people say that a pound is a force, and when both lots of people emphasize that forces and masses are quite different things—it does make you think, and wonder, and become confused.

317

Units of Force, Mass and Acceleration

If we could decide on our units of force, mass and acceleration, then the real difficulties of understanding would disappear, and we should begin to get the right answers when solving problems. But, alas, we cannot agree, and at least three sets of units are used within the Foot-Pound-Second system; so the next best thing is to try to see clearly what the differences are.

As was explained in Chapter I, there is kept in London a certain lump of metal which is defined as **One-Pound-Mass.**

The acceleration of the **One-Pound-Mass** under the influence of the **One-Pound-Force** is found, by experiment, to be approximately **32·2 ft. per sec. per sec.** This is called "g," but it must always be remembered that g **stands for an acceleration, i.e. that in itself it has the units ft./sec./sec.,** and that its numerical value is different at different parts of the earth.

Now let us go back to Newton's Second Law which gives us the relationship—

$$\text{Force} \propto \text{Mass} \times \text{Acceleration}$$

If we wish to make the coefficient of proportionality 1 and so write this as—

$$\text{Force} = \text{Mass} \times \text{Acceleration}$$

we must so arrange our units that—

One Unit of Force = One Unit of Mass × One Unit of Acceleration

This can be done in various ways. Suppose we accept the unit of acceleration as 1 ft./sec./sec., then it is only a question of what force acting on what mass produces this acceleration. Since 1 lb. force acting on 1 lb.-mass produces 32·2 ft./sec./sec., clearly **either** 1/32·2 lb.-force acting on 1 lb.-mass, **or** 1 lb.-force acting on 32·2 lb.-mass would produce 1 ft./sec./sec.

From this argument we can devise the following systems—

1. **Unit of Force = 1/32·2 lb.-force. This is called a Poundal.**
   Unit of Mass = 1 lb.-mass.
   Unit of Acceleration = 1 ft./sec./sec.

If we use these units consistently, and the formula

$$F = Ma$$

all will be well.

Possible objections to this system are that the poundal is rather a small force (about ½ oz.) and, what is rather more important, it is never used in everyday life. It could be, but it is not. Who buys apples, or weighs himself, in poundals?

1*a*. These objections can be overcome by a slight modification of this system. The poundal is the force which would produce in a mass of 1 lb. an acceleration of 1 ft./sec./sec., and therefore 1 lb.-force (which produces an acceleration of 32·2 ft./sec./sec., in the same mass) is equal to 32·2 poundals.

Therefore if we write the formula as—

$$F = \frac{Ma}{32\cdot2}$$

we can use—

Unit of Force = 1 lb.-force.
Unit of Mass = 1 lb.-mass.
Unit of Acceleration = 1 ft./sec./sec.

Note that in this system **32·2 is merely a number** (numerically equal to the acceleration of gravity in London expressed in ft. sec. units).

This method is clumsy from the formula point of view, there is the confusion between the two different units both called pounds, and the 32·2 appears rather meaningless. It is, however, a method of convenience, and after all we do use the pound in everyday life both for mass and weight.

2. **Unit of Force = 1 lb.-force.**
Unit of Mass = 32·2 lb.-mass. This is called a Slug.
Unit of Acceleration = 1 ft./sec./sec.

Again, if we use these units consistently, and the formula—

$$F = Ma$$

all will be well.

This system has been used throughout this book and, for good or ill, has been generally adopted in aeronautical work. Unfortunately the slug as a mass is as unfamiliar as the poundal as a force.

3. There is yet another way out—and some people will say that that is just about what it is!

By a little ingenuity we can avoid the unit of mass altogether and use the weight of the body instead. But we must be very careful because we certainly cannot say that Force = Weight × Acceleration. This is sheer nonsense because Force and Weight are the same kind of thing, so obviously Force and Weight × Acceleration cannot be the same kind of thing!

But if we divide the weight of a body by g, i.e. the acceleration of gravity at the place where the weight is measured, then W/g is a fixed quantity, not variable like W, and it does in fact represent the mass of the body.

So we must change our formula to—

$$F = W/g \cdot a$$

and our units are—

Units of both F and W = 1 lb.-force.
"g" is the accleration of gravity, at the place concerned, in ft./sec./sec. (it is an acceleration, not just a number as in 1a).
a is again in ft./sec./sec.

This system has many advocates. It is sometimes called the Engineers' system—though many Engineers hate it! It is used extensively on the Continent even for aeronautical work. One objection to it is the absence of the fundamental mass, and, in the aeronautical formula, of the density (ρ).

Application to Lift Formula

These systems as applied to the Lift Formula would be as follows—

1. $L = C_L \cdot \frac{1}{2}\rho \, V^2 \cdot S$

L in poundals. ρ in lb.-mass per cu. ft.

1a. $$L = \frac{C_L \cdot \frac{1}{2}\rho \, V^2 \cdot S}{32 \cdot 2}$$

L in lb.-force. ρ in lb.-mass per cu. ft.   32·2 merely a number.

2. $L = C_L \cdot \frac{1}{2}\rho \, V^2 \cdot S$

L in lb.-force. ρ in slugs per cu. ft.

3. $L = C_\mathrm{L} . \tfrac{1}{2} W/g \, V^2 . S$

L in lb.-force. W in lb.-force per cu. ft. g in ft./sec./sec.

In all systems V in ft./sec., S in sq. ft., and C_L is a number with no units.

Summary

All these methods are theoretically sound, and of course each has a counterpart in the metric system; so there is plenty of choice. All, if used consistently, will give correct answers. It is just a question of convenience, or convention, or what you will.

Dimensions

From all the confusion and chaos of units it is a real pleasure to turn to a brighter subject—that of Dimensions. In this we get to fundamentals, the fog clears away and, strange as it may seem, we find that everyone agrees. We may scratch each other's eyes out about the units of force, or mass, or whatever it may be, but we have no doubt about the dimensions of these or other quantities. Here then is common ground, but it is more than that; it is no exaggeration to say that a proper understanding of dimensions is a definite aid to the learning of mechanics in general and of the mechanics of flight in particular.

It was stated earlier in this appendix that it matters little whether we measure length in centimetres, inches, feet or miles, or any other unit of length for that matter, all are distances or **lengths** and nothing else— all have in common the dimension L.

Seconds, minutes, hours, years—all these are **times**—all have in common the dimension T.

And then there are masses, slugs or whatever it may be—M.

Yes, there are lots of other things, velocities, accelerations, forces, energy, momentum, lift, drag and all the rest of it. But have you ever realized how many of these things are just combinations of the fundamental dimensions, M, L and T.

Velocity, for instance, is distance divided by time, i.e. L/T.

Acceleration is velocity divided by time or $L/T/T$, i.e. L/T^2.

Force is Mass $\times$ Acceleration or $M \times L/T^2$, i.e. ML/T^2.

Work is Force $\times$ Distance or $ML/T^2 \times L$, i.e. ML^2/T^2.

Energy is, by definition, the same as Work, i.e. ML^2/T^2.

Area is, of course, $L \times L$, i.e. L^2.

Volume is $L \times L \times L$, i.e. L^3.

Pressure is Force divided by Area or $\dfrac{ML}{T^2}/L^2$, i.e. $\dfrac{M}{LT^2}$.

Density is Mass divided by Volume, i.e. M/L^3.

Momentum is Mass $\times$ Velocity, i.e. ML/T.

Power is Work divided by Time, i.e. ML^2/T^3.

and so on.

All these apply whatever system of units is used.

Application of Dimensions to the Checking of Formulae and Equations

The principle of Dimensions has been applied in many ways in aeronautics, not least in helping to elucidate the problems of scale effect and Reynolds' Number (which are dealt with in Appendix III), but there is an application which is particularly valuable to the student and that is in the checking of formulae and equations.

In using a formula or equation we are all too inclined to think of it simply as a means of substituting numbers and getting an answer, and in our hurry to get that answer we often overlook the physical meaning of the formula or equation.

For instance, $v = u + at$.

v **is of course a velocity.** Well, **a velocity can only be equal to a velocity,** it cannot be a length, or a mass, or an apple or orange, or anything except a velocity.

Therefore $u + at$ **must also be a velocity.**

But if two separate items when added together make a velocity, **each of them must in itself be a velocity ;** a distance added to a velocity cannot make a velocity, nor a time added to a distance, but only a velocity to a velocity. So not only must $u + at$ be a velocity, **but** u **must be a velocity,** and at **must be a velocity.**

The dimensions of velocity are L/T.

Both v and u in the formula are of course simple velocities, i.e. have the dimensions L/T.

What of at? i.e. acceleration $\times$ time, i.e. $L/T^2 \times T = L/T$.

We have rather laboured this extremely simple example, but after a little practice it becomes second nature to make checks of quite complicated equations in this way.

To take a few more simple examples—

$$s = ut + \tfrac{1}{2}at^2$$

s is a distance (dimension L), ut must be a distance, $\frac{1}{2}at^2$ must be a distance.

$$ut = \text{vel.} \times \text{time} = L/T \times T = L$$
$$\tfrac{1}{2}at^2 = \text{accel.} \times \text{time}^2 = L/T^2 \times T^2 = L$$

What of our old familiar friend $F = Ma$?

F is a force, i.e. ML/T^2.

Ma must be a force. Ma is mass $\times$ accel. $= ML/T^2$.

All so simple after all that fuss about units.

Notice that $\dfrac{Ma}{32 \cdot 2}$ has exactly the same diemnsions as Ma since $32 \cdot 2$ is just a number.

Or take $F = \dfrac{W}{g} \times a$, a different form of the same formula—

$$\dfrac{W}{g} \times a \text{ must be a force like } F$$

W is a force, i.e. ML/T^2.

g and a are both accelerations, L/T^2.

So $\dfrac{W}{g} \times a$ is $\left(\dfrac{ML}{T^2} \div \dfrac{L}{T^2} \right) \times L/T^2 = \dfrac{ML}{T^2}$.

Notice that g is an acceleration, not just a number.

An even more familiar friend—by the end of the book at any rate—

$$L = C_{\text{L}} \cdot \tfrac{1}{2}\rho V^2 \cdot S$$

Lift is a force, so $C_{\text{L}} \cdot \frac{1}{2}\rho V^2 \cdot S$ must be a force.

What is C_{L}? Well, let us see.

ρ is M/L^3. V is L/T. S is L^2.

$\therefore \rho V^2 S$ is $M/L^3 \times L^2/T^2 \times L^2$, i.e. ML/T^2, i.e. a Force.

Therefore C_{L} **has no dimensions,** it is called **a non-dimensional coefficient,** it is merely a number and has the great attraction that it is independent of the system of units. C_L will have the same value if any consistent system, whether c.g.s. or ft. lb. sec., is used.

Some coefficients have dimensions as, for instance, to take an interesting one from the aeronautical point of view, the coefficient of viscosity, μ, that forms part of the Reynolds' Number (see Appendix III). This is defined as: The force per unit area divided by the relative velocity and multiplied by the thickness of the fluid layer.

Force per unit area is $ML/T^2 \div L^2$ or M/LT^2.

Relative velocity is simply a velocity, L/T, being the difference in velocity at the two sides of the layer.

Thickness of the layer is of course L.

So the dimensions of μ are—

$$\frac{M}{LT^2} \div \frac{L}{T} \times L = \frac{M}{LT}$$

which means that the units (in the system used in this book) are slugs per foot per second.

It is admittedly not easy to get a physical conception of what that means—but it means something, it is not just a number.

Finally, let us examine the Reynolds' Number itself—

$$\text{i.e. } \frac{\rho\,VL}{\mu}$$

The dimensions of this will be—

$$M/L^3 \times L/T \times L \times \frac{LT}{M}$$

which all cancels out!

So the Reynolds' Number is itself non-dimensional, while the coefficient, μ, used to find it has dimensions.

If the student takes the trouble to check all formulae and equations by their dimensions, he will soon become accustomed to their use. He will then realize their other applications and, most important of all, he should never again be scared by the problems of units.

APPENDIX III

SCALE EFFECT AND REYNOLDS' NUMBER

THIS Appendix is an amplification of the short note given about Scale Effect in Chapter II (p. 43). It may be of interest to those readers who would like to know more about a fascinating branch of the subject, but one that is not essential to the understanding of the remainder.

There are few of us who have not at some period of our lives played with models. To some it is just a passing fancy of childhood days, a cheap and safe way of playing at the real thing; to others it is a more serious hobby, one that persists through boyhood to manhood, sometimes even to old age, but always as a hobby, something quite apart from their daily work; to others it becomes a study, their job in life. It is as a study that we are interested in it here, and a very fascinating study it is. Much can be learnt from models, whether they be model locomotives, model ships, or model aeroplanes; but we must beware of certain traps, because otherwise we shall jump to wrong conclusions from our experiments with models.

The first difficulty in making a model is to make it accurate; that is part of the fascination. The smaller we make the model, the more difficult it is to make it accurate. For that very reason, curious creatures that we are, we delight in making small models, or in admiring the skill of those who are more patient and more clever than ourselves in making them. But clever though these small models may be, the attainment of real accuracy becomes a more practical proposition as the size of the model is increased, and in aeronautical work, for this reason among others, we like our models to be large.

Now, the majority of serious experiments on aeronautical models are done in wind tunnels. The air in a wind tunnel does not behave in quite the same way as the free air in which we fly; there are various reasons for this, but the most important one is that the air is constrained by the wind tunnel walls. The constraint affects the airflow, and the airflow affects the forces on the model and so may lead us to wrong conclusions. The obvious moral is to make the tunnel large compared with the model.

So our second difficulty about model work is that we need large wind tunnels. Large models, and much larger tunnels. Thus we find firms and even nations vying with each other to produce larger and larger tunnels. These large tunnels need enormous power and the cost is prodigious—but the race goes on.

But, however large our models, however large our wind tunnels, we shall still have to use models that are smaller than real aeroplanes, and it is very improbable that we shall be able to obtain the actual speeds of flight in these large wind tunnels. And so we shall continue to be faced with the third and greatest problem, that of **scale effect.**

By means of photography, or by a scale drawing, we can reproduce a large body on a small piece of paper. A map is a good example. By trick photography we can make a small body appear large, or a large body small. In cinematography we can do even more; we can adjust both the size of a body and the speed at which it moves, and so make it appear to move slower or faster than it really does. But it is not so easy to play about with forces and accelerations. A model ship tossing on a real sea does not look real, nor does a collision between two model cars, nor does the crash of a model aeroplane—however clever the faking in a film, critical members of the audience can always spot the use of models designed to deceive them.

Why is this? Well, there are various ways of looking at it, and it is all really part of our problem of scale effect. Consider a $\frac{1}{10}$th scale model. All the linear dimensions are $\frac{1}{10}$th of those of the real thing, but the areas are $\frac{1}{100}$th; and if it is constructed of the same materials, its mass is but $\frac{1}{1000}$th of the real thing. So it is to scale in some respects, but not in others. This is one of the difficulties in trying to learn from flying models of aeroplanes; unless we are very careful in adjustment of the weights, we will get completely false results as regards behaviour in manoeuvre, spinning, crashes, and so on. It is all a question of adjustment, and another thing we must remember is that we fly model aeroplanes in full-size air, and sail model boats in full-size water; we do not adjust the air and the water to suit the models!

This is not a new problem. More than a hundred years ago a physicist, named Reynolds, was experimenting with the flow of fluids in pipes, and he made the important discovery that the flow changed from streamline to turbulent when the velocity reached a value that was inversely proportional to the diameter of the pipe. The larger the pipe, the less the velocity at which the flow became turbulent, e.g. if 20 ft. per sec. was the critical velocity in a pipe of 1 in. diameter, then 10 ft. per sec. would be the critical velocity in a pipe of 2 in. diameter. This illustrates the principle, but really the discovery was of much wider application than this. It did not only apply to the critical velocity, nor only to the diameter of the pipe, but to the flow past any body placed in the stream. If the velocity multiplied by some linear dimension of the body, e.g. the diameter in the case of a sphere, came to the same value, then the flow pattern would be the same.

We must emphasize this importance of the flow pattern. Since the time of Reynolds there has been ample confirmation of his experiments, and we know that if we get the same flow pattern over a model as over a full-scale body, then our laws of aerodynamics are true and we can scale up the forces with confidence; in other words, there will be no error due to Scale Effect. For Scale Effect does not mean—as we might justifiably suppose it to mean—the effect of scale. The laws of aerodynamics, the speed squared law, the law of dependence on area and density, all the laws summed up in the fundamental formulae $L = C_L \cdot \frac{1}{2}\rho V^2 \cdot S$ and $D = C_D \cdot \frac{1}{2}\rho V^2 \cdot S$, these are all the effects of scale; perhaps we should call them the primary effects of scale. Scale Effect really means that these laws are not strictly true unless certain conditions apply, and the conditions are those founded on the experiments of Reynolds. If the conditions do not apply, then there are secondary effects of scale, errors are introduced, errors due to Scale Effect, and unfortunately these errors are apt to be erratic and difficult to predict.

To see how to avoid this Scale Effect, with its unpredictable errors, we must return to the principles discovered by Reynolds. The most simple of these is that we should keep the same value of Velocity multiplied by Size for the model experiment as for full-scale flight. This may be referred to as the **VL law,** L referring to some linear dimension of the body, usually taken as the chord in the case of a wing section, the diameter in the case of a disc, sphere, or streamline body. This law means that if we wish to experiment on a $\frac{1}{10}$th **scale model in order to forecast what will happen on the full-size aeroplane at 200 m.p.h., we should test the model at 2,000 m.p.h.**—thus keeping $V L$ the same in both cases.

This conclusion is somewhat alarming, the more so if we remember that we must also employ a large wind tunnel! In such a tunnel **we have never succeeded in obtaining a speed of anywhere near 2,000 m.p.h.,** indeed, it is doubtful whether we could even obtain 200 m.p.h. Furthermore, even if we could obtain this fantastic speed, **we should have run into even more serious problems, because the speed of sound would have been exceeded,** and for this reason the flow pattern would have changed completely, so we would have defeated our own ends. But that is not all; let us consider what the forces on the model would be. Because it is $\frac{1}{10}$th scale, the area is $\frac{1}{100}$th, so the forces would be divided by 100 compared with full scale; because we have 10 times the velocity, the forces should be multiplied by 100 (neglecting the effects of exceeding the speed of sound), so **the forces on the model would be equal to those on the full-scale aeroplane.** Imagine this small model wing supporting the same Lift as the real aeroplane!—it just could not be made strong enough to do it.

What then can we do? There does not seem much hope, unless it be to get as large a $V L$ as possible, and then trust that the error will be small, or perhaps we may be able to estimate how much the error will be and so make allowances for it. This is what we have tried to do, but it has not been altogether satisfactory. Let us consider an example. Suppose we wish to estimate the total drag of a large bomber at 200 m.p.h. We make a $\frac{1}{10}$th-scale model—it will be of considerable size, and we must have a much larger wind tunnel to test it in. We find its drag coefficient at, say, 50, 100, 150 and 200 m.p.h. We cannot get any more speed in the tunnel; we are lucky to get that. If there were no scale effect, the drag coefficient should be the same at the various speeds, but we find that it is, in fact, increasing, and the values are, say, 0·050, 0·051, 0·052, and 0·053. That seems simple. We draw a graph and plot the values of drag coefficient against $V L$; they lie on a straight line (they may, of course, lie on a curve; a straight line has been chosen to show the difficulties of even the simplest case). We can now extrapolate—a dangerous game! It is like forecasting what is going to happen in the future, as a result of past history. To interpolate is reasonably safe; that is only, as it were, to fill in gaps in past history, knowing what came before and what came after. But extrapolation is a very different matter. We can draw curves of wing loadings or of speeds of aeroplanes for the past forty years; the curves show definite trends; they show where we are going; they show— if we extrapolate—that in the year 2000 A.D. the wing loadings of aeroplanes will be more than 500 lb. per sq. ft., and maximum speeds will be over 1,000 m.p.h. But will they? That is the question. Maybe, maybe not. But to return to the drag coefficient—this is even worse than forecasting the future. At least we can feel sure that the wing loadings and speeds of 2000 A.D. will be higher than they are to-day. Not so with our drag coefficient. From 50 m.p.h. to 200 m.p.h. it had gone up steadily by 0·001 for each 50 m.p.h., so at 2,000 m.p.h. it should be 0·089. Now, 2,000 m.p.h. for the $\frac{1}{10}$th-scale model is the same VL as 200 m.p.h. for the full-scale aeroplane, so if the drag coefficient is 0·089 for the model at 2,000 m.p.h. it should be 0·089 for the full-scale aeroplane, and so we should be able to calculate the total drag of the aeroplane. If, that's the rub. And this is where we may find the result even worse than trying to forecast history; we may find that the actual drag coefficient of the full-scale aeroplane is **even less than 0·050.** So it was deceiving us by going up, and then it went down again. That is the sort of thing that sometimes happens— sometimes, not always! If it happened always, we should at least know what to expect. The moral is, of course, to go as high up the scale as possible, to test at the highest possible values of VL, but we have already seen how far they are off full-scale values.

Is there any other solution? Yes, there is at least a partial solution, but we would not be able to guess at it unless we went a little deeper into the experiments of Reynolds. The VL law is sound so long as we use the same fluid for our model experiments as for full-scale flight; this, of course, we do—in the ordinary wind tunnel. But Reynolds found that if different fluids were used, other properties of the fluid affected the type of flow; these properties, as one might almost expect, were the density and the viscosity of the fluid. To cut a long story short, he eventually summed it all up, as we intend to do, by saying that if the quantity

$$\frac{\text{Density} \times \text{Velocity} \times \text{Size}}{\text{Viscosity}}$$

is kept constant, the flow pattern will be similar, and there will be no error due to Scale Effect. This quantity, written in symbols

$$\frac{\rho\, V L,}{\mu}$$

is called the **Reynolds' Number** of the test.

ρ is the density of the fluid in slugs per cu. ft. (0·0024 for air at ground level);

V is the velocity of the test in ft. per sec.;

L is a dimension of the body in feet (for aerofoils and aeroplanes the chord is taken as the standard dimension);

μ is the viscosity of the fluid (0·000000373 slugs per ft. per sec. for air at normal temperature and pressure—do not worry about the strangeness of the unit).

Now, this idea gives us new hope, in that it suggests using a different fluid for the model test. Consider water, for instance. Water is about 815 times as dense as air at ground level, and only 64 times as viscous. So we immediately have a factor of about 12·8, and instead of experimenting on a $\frac{1}{10}$th scale model at 2,000 m.p.h., we shall get the same Reynolds' Number at 2,000 m.p.h./12·8, i.e. at about 156 m.p.h. Unfortunately, this idea has only led us up the garden path. A little thought will make us realize that a large tunnel with a water flow of 156 m.p.h. is even more fantastic than 2,000 m.p.h. for air, and a little calculation will show that the forces on the model, instead of equalling those of the full-size aeroplane, would be about five times as great.

What next? We are nearly beaten, but not quite. It may be surprising, but it is a fact that by compressing air we have little or no effect upon its viscosity. This offers a real ray of hope at last. Suppose we compress the air to, say, 25 atmospheres—and this can be

done in the **Compressed Air Tunnels** in Great Britain and in the U.S.A.
—then we have a factor of 25 (as regards ρ), with no corresponding
increase in the viscosity, μ. Thus a $\frac{1}{10}$th-scale model can be tested at
2,000 m.p.h./25, i.e. at 80 m.p.h. A practical solution at last—or very
nearly so.

Why the qualification—very nearly so? Only because compressed
air tunnels are considerable and costly engineering undertakings, and
there seem to be very real limits to practicable sizes and speeds to be
obtained in them. There are not as yet more than a dozen such tunnels
in the world; in none of them could we test anything so large as a
$\frac{1}{10}$th-scale model of a large bomber, nor can we yet obtain speeds much
higher than 100 m.p.h. when the compression is as high as 25 atmospheres.
The modern tendency has been to reduce the compression ratio and
raise the velocity. Within such limitations, however, the compressed
air tunnel solves the problem, and it is particularly valuable for testing
new devices when we are anxious to avoid the uncertainty of Scale
Effect errors.

A small point to be kept in mind is that, although the density does
not effect the viscosity of air, the temperature does, and quite considerably. Unlike liquids, which become less viscous with rise in
temperature, air becomes more viscous, e.g. at 0° C. the viscosity of
air is 0·000000357 slugs/ft./sec., whereas at 100° C. it is 0·000000454
slugs/ft./sec. Any increase in viscosity will mean so much less benefit
from the increase in density; and therefore since the compression of
the air will tend to raise its temperature, we must take precautions
to cool it again.

If we work out the Reynolds' Number of tests that can be done on
models of the appropriate size in **atmospheric wind tunnels** (called
"atmospheric" to distinguish them from compressed air tunnels), we
will find that the Reynolds' Number varies **from about 100,000** for
small slow-speed tunnels **to about 1,000,000 or 1,500,000** for large
high-speed tunnels.

Similarly, the Reynolds' Number of **full-scale flight** varies **from about
2,000,000** for small slow-speed aeroplanes **to about 20,000,000** for large
high-speed aeroplanes.

The Reynolds' Number that can be attained in **compressed air tunnels**
varies from **about 7,000,000 to 12,000,000 or more** in the latest types.

These figures clearly illustrate the value of the compressed air tunnel,
it being the only tunnel which gives a Reynolds' Number even within
the range of modern full-scale flight. In all atmospheric tunnels there
is some risk of errors due to scale effect.

Let us see what sort of forces we may expect on the models used in
a compressed air tunnel. Taking again a $\frac{1}{10}$th-scale model and a speed
of 80 m.p.h., and compression to 25 atmospheres, the forces will be

$\frac{1}{100}$th (because of scale) $\times$ $\frac{80^2}{200^2}$ (because of speed) $\times$ 25 (because of

density), i.e. $\frac{1}{25}$th of the full-scale forces.

This is a great improvement on the full-scale force for the atmospheric
tunnel at 2,000 m.p.h. and five times the full-scale force for the water
tunnel at 156 m.p.h. It is interesting, however, because even these
forces, $\frac{1}{25}$th of the full-scale forces, are so large as to cause serious
distortions of the models unless they are made very strong.

Such is the problem of scale effect, the meaning of Reynolds' Number, and the reason for the large and expensive wind tunnels, and especially for the compressed air tunnel. It is a story that is very typical of progress in aeronautics, of new problems seemingly insoluble being solved by new applications of old ideas. It is a story that explains the varying reputation of the wind tunnel. At first, when the speeds in wind tunnels were as great as, or even greater than, the speeds of flight, wind tunnels gave good results, they won a good reputation and were blindly believed; then with progress in flight, practice outstripping theory, the speeds of flight far exceeding the speeds in wind tunnels, with scale effect at its worst and little understood, the wind tunnel was first mistrusted, then discredited, eventually de-bunked; then came the investigation into scale effect, the building of larger and better tunnels, then the compressed air tunnels, and once again a re-born faith in the wind tunnel, but this time with a full realization of its limitations.

Now, of course, we are faced with new wind-tunnel problems in connection with flight at and above the speed of sound. We have even got de-compressed air tunnels—but that is another story and maybe we shall be wise to leave the subject until more is known about it.

APPENDIX IV

GENERAL QUESTIONS

AND now, before you lay the book aside, consider the following questions. They will help you to correlate your theoretical and practical knowledge of the aeroplane. In some instances the answer has been given, either in the last chapter or in other parts of the book, but in others the answer is left to the reader himself.

The purpose of these questions is to stimulate thought on the subject rather than the attainment of any definite conclusion. The answer to some of the questions may be indefinite, or may depend on circumstances, and, for this reason, various lines of thought are sometimes suggested after the question.

(i) At a certain height in the atmosphere the pressure is half the pressure at ground level; will the density of the air—at this same height—be half the density at ground level? If not half, will it be more or less than half? (This question is a good test as to whether you understand the relationships of pressure, density, and temperature—and incidentally the answer is important in certain calculations on the performance of aircraft.)

(ii) You are asked to handicap an air race over a triangular course. Should the wind speed at the time of the race make any difference to your handicapping?

(iii) What have been the effects on rigging of the following tendencies in aeroplane design—

(a) replacement of biplanes by monoplanes?
(b) introduction of control tabs?

(iv) Suppose that the Riggers' Angle of Incidence of a monoplane were increased from 2° to 4°, what would be the effect on the flight of the aircraft? (Does the result depend on the type of aerofoil section? Consider the effects of increase of Lift, movement of Centre of Pressure, increase of Drag.)

(v) When turning near the ground from flying down wind to up wind, most pilots tend to bank too steeply. Can you explain why?

(vi) If, without making any elaborate structural alterations, you were allowed to modify a standard type of aeroplane to take part in a race, what modifications would you carry out? (Consider the reduction of both wing drag and parasite drag.)

(vii) What will be the result of too great a Riggers' Angle of Incidence on the left wing of an aeroplane? (Not such an easy question as it sounds. Consider the effect not only of increased Lift, but also of increased Drag on the left wing. Will the combination cause the aeroplane to tend to turn to the left or to the right?)

(viii) A pilot is flying an aeroplane which is very stable laterally, but not very stable directionally. A bump causes the right wing to drop. Describe the subsequent behaviour of the aeroplane if the pilot leaves it to its own devices.

(ix) Suppose the aeroplane of Question viii had been very stable

329

directionally, but not very stable laterally, what would have been its behaviour?

(x) What are the advantages claimed for the so called tricycle type of undercarriage?

(xi) What is a laminar flow aerofoil, and why so called?

(xii) What are the relative advantages and disadvantages of propulsion by (a) Jets, (b) Rockets, (c) Propellers?

(xiii) Explain all the advantages that would be gained from an aerofoil on which the centre of pressure remained stationary as the angle of attack was changed. (The full answer to this question covers both aerodynamic and structural problems, and it can be claimed that the weight of nearly every part of the aircraft is affected.)

(xiv) When an aeroplane was inclined to fly right wing heavy, a piece of cable was sometimes laid along the top surface of the right aileron at the trailing edge and faired with fabric. What did this do, and what is the modern equivalent of the idea?

(xv) Is it a good thing to raise the tail at the beginning of the take-off run?

(xvi) Explain two distinct ways in which a propeller may be used as an airbrake.

(xvii) Why is it more likely that an inexperienced pilot will stall during a turn than during straight flight?

(xviii) Why may it be necessary to "hold off" the bank during a continuous turn?

(xix) Is there the same need to hold off bank during (a) a gliding turn? (b) a climbing turn? Give reasons for your answers.

(xx) Will the stalling speed remain the same at all altitudes?

(xxi) Does the altimeter tell the pilot the correct height?

(xxii) Does the air speed indicator tell the pilot the correct speed?

(xxiii) What has the speed of sound got to do with flight?

(xxiv) What will be the position of the elevator trimming tabs (a) for high-speed flight? (b) for best climb?

(xxv) Does the position of the trimming tab affect the position of the main control surface?

(xxvi) What will be the effect of (a) a large dihedral angle; (b) a large fin, during a steep sideslip?

(xxvii) Explain how and why it is possible to turn a modern aeroplane without the use of the rudder.

(xxviii) What is an athodyd?

(xxix) Why is the attitude of an aeroplane very much tail-down when flying inverted?

(xxx) Will the gliding angle and the stalling speed be the same inverted as in normal flight? (Consider the efficiency of the aerofoil, and the angle of attack of the aerofoil and the aeroplane when in the inverted position.)

(xxxi) Discuss the relative advantages and disadvantages of a biplane as compared with a monoplane for—

(a) A fighting machine.
(b) A racing machine.
(c) A long-distance record breaker.

Consider the relative importance for each purpose of—manoeuvrability aerodynamic efficiency, structural efficiency, low resistance, field of view, stability, vulnerability, and so on. (This question cannot be fully answered without a consideration of the structural problems involved.)

(xxxii) Distinguish between a Helicopter and an Autogiro. Is either of these types likely to supersede the conventional aeroplane?

(xxxiii) What are the advantages claimed for the tail-first and the tail-less type of aeroplane?

(xxxiv) Success in modern air fighting depends largely on the ability to out-turn an opponent. What are the problems of making steep, high-speed turns?

(xxxv) Does it require the same power to fly at the same indicated air speed at different heights? If not, why not?

(xxxvi) Is the drag the same at the same indicated air speed at different heights? Explain your answer.

(xxxvii) Does it require the same power to fly at the same true airs peed at different heights? If so, why? If not, why not?

(xxxviii) Two aircraft turn at the same rate of turn, i.e. both complete a turn through 360° in the same time, but the radius on which A turns is twice the radius on which B turns. Assuming perfect turns, i.e. no slip or skid, which should have the greater angle of bank, or should both be the same?

(xxxix) Why is there a limit to the angle of bank at which a particular aeroplane can make a turn without slip or skid? Why is the limiting angle different for different types of aircraft?

(xl) An aeroplane is short of fuel and is trying to reach an airport; will it pay to throw overboard any unnecessary weight?

(xli) An aeroplane has run short of fuel and is trying to glide to an airport; will it pay to throw overboard any unnecessary weight? (Watch this one!)

(xlii) If split flaps are lowered to about 30°, will the take-off run be shorter? Will the aircraft be off the ground in less time? Will the speed of take-off be less? (This, too, takes quite a lot of thought—possibly experiment.)

(xliii) Does the air speed that gives the greatest rate of climb also give the steepest angle of climb?

(xliv) If the thrust is equal to the drag, what makes the aeroplane go forward? (Try explaining this to someone who doesn't believe it—you won't find it easy.)

(xlv) When a body is moving on a curved path, is there any force acting on it tending to make it go outwards? (Tricky!)

(xlvi) An open tube facing the air stream is placed at the mouth, at the throat, and at the exit of a venturi tube—will the total pressure on it be the same at all three positions? If not, why not?

(xlvii) Why is there more drag when flying at the minimum speed of level flight than at some higher speed? Does it also require more power?

(xlviii) Why should we fly with the minimum drag to get maximum range?

(xlix) Why do we fly at a lower speed for maximum endurance than for maximum range?

(l) Explain to the uninitiated what a "slug" is, and what are the advantages of such a unit. (See Appendix II.)

(li) What is meant by a Reynolds' Number of 1,000,000? Is this a high or a low value for a Reynolds' Number? (See Appendix III.)

(lii) What is a Mach Number? What is its significance? What is meant by the Critical Mach Number of an aircraft?

(liii) What is the difference in shape between a modern aerofoil section designed for very high speed and the older type of section?

(liv) An aeroplane slips inwards during a turn. What will happen to (a) a plumb-bob hung in the cockpit? (b) the bubble of an ordinary spirit level placed laterally across the cockpit? (Note that the spirit level is *not* the same as the ball indicator.)

(lv) Does the true air speed that gives the best rate of climb change with height? If so, in which direction?

(lvi) What about the indicated air speed for the best rate of climb?

(lvii) How will an increase of engine power affect the performance of an aeroplane? (Discuss the effects on minimum speed, maximum speed, rate of climb, ceiling, tight turns, take-off, etc.)

(lviii) Why is there a tendency to increase the number of blades in modern propellers?

(lix) Why does the lowering of flaps often affect the trim of an aeroplane? Why sometimes one way, sometimes another?

(lx) Describe various types of air brake.

(lxi) Is it ever possible to glide farther than one would otherwise do by gliding faster than the air speed that gives the flattest gliding angle, and then using the momentum so gained to float a long distance? (Watch this one!)

(lxii) Is the air speed that gives the flattest glide the same as the air speed that gives the longest time in the air? If not, why not?

(lxiii) Why is one more likely to meet compressibility effects at high altitudes?

(lxiv) The propeller of an aeroplane rotates clockwise (when viewed from behind). In which direction is the aeroplane likely to swing on take-off? (Consider the effects of torque reaction, slipstream, and gyroscopic action when the tail is raised.)

(lxv) What are the advantages of contra-rotating propellers?

(lxvi) Explain how it is possible for a component of the total reaction on an aeroplane wing to act along the chord towards the leading edge.

(lxvii). What parts of the aeroplane are under severe loads during a high-speed nose-dive?

(lxviii) If a fixed pitch propeller is removed from an aeroplane and placed on the shaft back to front, will it drive the aeroplane backwards or forwards?

(lxix) What is meant by a constant-speed propeller? What are its advantages?

(lxx) If a mass balance weight is shot away by enemy action, what precautions should the pilot take in flying the aeroplane?

(lxxi) A twin-engine aircraft is flying on one engine. Will its track (neglecting any wind effect) be parallel to its longitudinal axis? If not, which way will its nose be pointing? (Not so easy. Try to sketch the forces acting on the aeroplane. Remember that the pull of the engine on one side may be counteracted either by rudder or by banking the aeroplane, or by both methods.)

(lxxii) Explain what is wrong with the so-called "horizontal equivalent" explanation of the effect of dihedral angle.

(lxxiii). An extra load is carried some distance behind the centre of gravity of an aeroplane. What are the probable effects during flight?

(lxxiv) An aeroplane tows a glider behind it. Are we getting something for nothing? If not, why not?

(lxxv) Why is it not quite true to say that in a very steep bank the rudder fulfils the same functions as the elevators in level flight?

(lxxvi) During a certain manoeuvre the accelerometer which read 1 in level flight now reads 4. What does this mean?

(lxxvii) What is the difference between a high-speed stall and a shock stall?

(lxxviii) Explain why an increase in drag cannot reduce the stalling speed.

(lxxix) Why is the engine-assisted approach, which was once considered bad flying, now the standard method?

(lxxx) Discuss the balance of the main forces acting on a flying boat.

(lxxxi) What are the disadvantages of the slot, as compared with the flap, as a means of reducing landing speed?

(lxxxii) Why has induced drag become a relatively more important problem as aircraft have been improved?

(lxxxiii) In what circumstances are wing-tip vortices likely to be visible?

(lxxxiv) An aeroplane is at the top of a loop. In what direction, viewed from the rear, will the wing-tip vortex on the starboard wing be rotating?

(lxxxv) Will the vortex rotate in the same direction in inverted flight?

(lxxxvi) The propeller of an aeroplane rotates anti-clockwise (viewed from the rear). What will be the gyroscopic effect in a turn to the right?

(lxxxvii) Explain the significance of a high maximum value of $C_L^{\frac{3}{2}}/C_D$.

(lxxxviii) Explain why the thrust and torque force on a section of the propeller blade are not quite the same thing as the lift and drag on a section of aerofoil.

(lxxxix) In order to avoid scale effect, we ought to test a $\frac{1}{10}$th scale model at 2,000 m.p.h. in order to forecast the forces on a full-scale body at 200 m.p.h. What is scale effect? Why is this not a practicable proposition? What is the solution of the problem?

(xc) The wing section on a certain aeroplane is changed from a high-speed section to a high-lift section. The wing area, aspect ratio, etc., remain the same. How will the performance of the aeroplane be changed?

(xci) The aspect ratio of the wings of a certain aeroplane is changed from 6 to 1 to 10 to 1. The wing area, wing section, etc., remain the same. How will the performance of the aeroplane be changed?

(xcii) In order to fly across the Atlantic in the least possible time, does it pay to fly high or low? (This is a question that cannot be answered directly. Consider the effects of wind, true and indicated speed, and so on.)

(xciii) In order to fly across the Atlantic with the minimum expenditure of fuel, does it pay to fly high or low? (This is not the same problem, but similar considerations enter into it.)

(xciv) An aircraft has to carry a considerable extra load. What will be the main effects on performance? (Consider maximum speed, landing speed, range, endurance, rate of climb, ceiling, etc.)

(xcv) An aircraft, which has previously flown from aerodromes at sea-level, has to fly from high aerodromes and over high country. What will be the main effects on performance, and how do they compare with the effects in Question xciv?

(xcvi) Why has it been forecasted that bombers will soon be able to fly as fast as fighters?

(xcvii) Does some knowledge of the principles underlying the mechanics of flight help or hinder a pilot to fly an aeroplane and to execute various manoeuvres?

(xcviii) Do you think that jet propulsion will cause any radical differences in the design and performance of aeroplanes? If so, in what particular directions?

(xcix) Wing loadings are going up. Maximum speeds are going up. Is there likely to be any check, temporary or permanent, in the present trend?

(c) What do you expect will be the main improvements in aeroplanes during the next hundred years? (High speed?—Low speed?—Reliability?—Economy?—Safety?—Size?—Carrying capacity?)

APPENDIX V

NUMERICAL QUESTIONS

NOTE. The following numerical examples are given in order that the student may puzzle out some of the problems of flight for himself. It is recognized that, in order to solve some of the examples, assumptions must be made which can hardly be justified in practice, and these assumptions may have an appreciable effect on the accuracy of the answers; on the other hand, the benefit from solving such problems lies not so much in the numerical answers as in the considerations involved in obtaining them.

A few simple examples from ordinary Physics and Mechanics are included. The methods of solution of these have not been given in the text, but the student will surely be familiar with these basic subjects before he approaches a specialized branch such as the Mechanics of Flight.

CHAPTER I. MECHANICS

(In the following numerical examples assume g, the value of the acceleration of gravity, to be 32·2 ft./sec./sec., unless otherwise stated.

Density of water = 62·4 lb. per cu. ft.

Density of air = 0·077 lb. per cu. ft. at 14·69 lb. per sq. in. pressure and 15° C. temperature.

Specific gravity of Mercury = 13·6.)

1. A car is travelling along a road at 30 m.p.h. If it accelerates uniformly at 3 ft./sec./sec.—

    (a) What speed will it reach in half a minute?

    (b) How long will it take to reach 60 m.p.h.?

2. A train starts from rest with a uniform acceleration and attains a speed of 70 m.p.h. in 2 min. Find—

    (a) the acceleration;

    (b) the distance travelled in the first minute;

    (c) the distance travelled in the two minutes.

3. If a motorcycle increases its speed by 3 m.p.h. every second, find—

    (a) the acceleration in ft./sec./sec.

    (b) the time taken to cover ¼ mile from rest.

4. During its take-off run, a light aircraft accelerates at 4 ft./sec./sec. If it starts from rest and takes 20 sec. to become airborne, what is its take-off speed and what length of runway is required?

5. A boy on a bicycle is going downhill at 10 m.p.h. If his brakes fail and he accelerates at 2 ft./sec./sec., what speed will he attain if the hill is a quarter of a mile long?

6. Assuming that the maximum deceleration of a car when full braking is applied is 0·8g, find the length of run required to pull up from (a) 30 m.p.h., (b) 60 m.p.h.

7. A rifle bullet is fired vertically upwards with a muzzle velocity of 2,400 ft./sec. Assuming no air resistance, what height will it reach and how long will it take to reach the ground again?

8. The landing speed of a certain aircraft is 90 knots. If the maximum possible deceleration with full braking is 6 ft./sec./sec., what length of landing run will be required?

9. An athlete runs 100 yd. in 10 sec. Assuming that he accelerates uniformly for 25 yd. and then runs the remaining 75 yd. at constant velocity, what is his velocity at the 100 yd. mark?

10. An aircraft flying straight and level at a speed of 296 knots and at a height of 22,500 ft. above ground level drops a bomb. Assuming no air resistance, with what velocity will the bomb strike the ground? (For this question take "g" as 32 ft./sec./sec. Remember that the final velocity will have to be found by compounding the vertical and horizontal velocities.)

11. Two weights of 10 lb. each are attached to the ends of a rope and the rope is hung over a frictionless pulley. What is the tension in the rope?

12. One of the weights in Q. 11 is replaced by a 15 lb. weight. What is the tension in the rope when the system is released?

13. What force is necessary to accelerate a shell weighing 300 lb. from rest to a velocity of 2,000 ft./sec. in a distance of 12 ft.?

14. What thrust is necessary to accelerate an aircraft weighing 13,000 lb. from rest to a speed of 90 knots in a distance of 800 yd.?

15. A train weighing 250 tons is moving at 60 m.p.h. What retarding force will be required to bring it to rest in $\frac{1}{4}$ min.?

16. A 12-stone man is standing on a weighing machine which is on the floor of a lift. What will the weighing machine record when—

    (a) the lift is ascending with velocity increasing by 2 ft./sec./sec.?
    (b) the lift is ascending with velocity decreasing by 2 ft./sec./sec.?
    (c) the lift is descending with a constant velocity of 4 ft./sec.?

17. An engine weighing 50 tons is coupled to a train weighing 400 tons. What pull in the coupling will be required to accelerate the train up a gradient of 1 in 100 from rest to 30 m.p.h. in 2 min. if the frictional resistance is 15 lb./ton?

18. An aircraft weighing 10,000 lb. is diving vertically downwards at a speed of 600 m.p.h. The pilot operates the dive brakes at a height of 30,000 ft. and reduces his speed to 400 m.p.h. at 20,000 ft. If the average air resistance of the rest of the aircraft during the deceleration is 3,000 lb., what average force must be exerted by the dive brakes? (Assume the engine is throttled back and is not providing any thrust.)

19. A truck weighing one ton is pulled on a level track by a force 50 lb. in excess of the frictional resistance. How far will it travel from rest in 30 sec.?

20. A horizontal jet of water from a nozzle 2 in. diameter strikes a vertical wall. If the water is diverted at right angles and none splashes back, what force is exerted on the wall when the speed of the jet is 20 ft./sec.?

(*Note.* This type of problem is best solved by considering the product of mass and acceleration as a rate of change of momentum.)

21. A train is standing on an incline of 1 in 80. If the frictional resistance is 12 lb./ton, how far will it travel from rest in 15 sec.?

22. If the air resistance of a 2,000 lb. bomb is equal to $\dfrac{v^2}{800}$ lb. wt., where v is the velocity in ft./sec., what is the terminal velocity of the bomb?

23. An aircraft weighing 8,000 lb. has a take-off speed of 80 knots and a take-off run of 440 yd. in no wind conditions. If the thrust delivered by the engine is 3,000 lb. and the frictional resistance is 200 lb., what is the average aerodynamic resistance during the take-off?

24. What force is necessary to stop a 10 cwt. car in 35 ft. from a speed of 30 m.p.h.?

25. A solid shot weighing 2 lb. is fired from a barrel weighing 250 lb. with a muzzle velocity of 2,800 ft./sec. If the barrel is free to recoil against a resistance of 1,250 lb. wt., how far will the barrel move back when a shot is fired?

26. A fighter aircraft weighing 8,000 lb. is fitted with four cannon, each of which fires 600 rounds per minute with a muzzle velocity of 3,000 ft./sec. If each round weighs $\frac{1}{4}$ lb. and if all the recoil is taken by the aircraft, find the loss in speed that the aircraft would experience in a 5 sec. burst of fire.

27. An aircraft weighing 18,000 lb. is flying straight and level at 300 knots. What thrust is necessary to accelerate it to 450 knots in half a minute if the average air resistance of the aircraft between these speeds is 3,500 lb. wt.?

28. A rifle weighing 9 lb. fires a bullet weighing 1 oz. with a muzzle velocity of 2,400 ft./sec. Find the force a rifleman must exert on the butt of the rifle to limit the recoil to $1\frac{1}{2}$ in.

29. An aircraft is fitted with brakes capable of exerting a force of 2,000 lb. wt. and reversible pitch propellers capable of producing a backward thrust of 5,000 lb. wt. If the aircraft weighs 20,000 lb. and has a landing speed of 110 knots, find the minimum length of runway required for the landing run. (Neglect the effect of air resistance which will also help to decelerate the aircraft.)

30. An aircraft carrier is steaming at 20 knots against a head wind of 30 knots. An aircraft weighing 9,000 lb. lands on the deck with an airspeed of 90 knots. If the arrester gear must be sufficiently powerful to stop the aircraft in a distance of 35 ft. under these conditions, without any aid from brakes or air resistance, find the retarding force that the gear must exert.

31. A propeller 9 ft. in diameter revolves at 2,250 r.p.m. Find its angular velocity and the linear speed of the propeller tip.

32. The piston of an aircraft engine has a stroke of 6 in. and the engine runs at 3,000 r.p.m. Find the angular velocity of the crankshaft and the average speed of the piston.

33. Find the acceleration of the propeller tip in Q. 31.

34. Find the acceleration of the crankpins in the engine of Q. 32.

35. A stone weighing 2 lb. is whirled in a horizontal circle making 60 r.p.m. at the end of a string 3 ft. long. Find the pull in the string. If it is whirled in a vertical circle, what is the pull in the string (a) when the stone is at the top, (b) when the stone is at the bottom?

36. A gas turbine makes 20,000 r.p.m. Each blade weighs $\frac{1}{28}$ lb. and its Centre of Gravity is 15 in. from the axis of rotation. Calculate the centrifugal force due to each blade.

37. An aeroplane, weight 2,000 lb., is travelling at 100 m.p.h. on a horizontal circle of 80 yd. radius. What is the value of the Centrifugal Force?

38. What will be the correct angle of bank for the aeroplane in Q. 37?

39. At what speed (in miles per hour) is a bank of 45° required for an aeroplane to turn on a radius of 60 yd.?

40. An aeroplane weighs 2,300 lb. It is turning on a horizontal circle of radius of 300 ft. at an air speed of 90 m.p.h. Calculate—
  (a) The Centripetal Force exerted by the air on the machine.
  (b) The correct angle of bank.
  (c) The total lift normal to the wings.

41. Find the work required to lift a weight of 5 tons to a height of 100 ft. If this is done in 2 min., what horse power is being exerted?

42. Find the horse power required to propel a 6,000 lb. aircraft through the air at a speed of 200 m.p.h. if the air resistance is 900 lb. wt.

43. Find the horse power required to propel the same aircraft at 400 m.p.h. when the air resistance is 3,400 lb. wt.

44. A car weighing 15 cwt. can climb a gradient of 1 in 12 in top gear at 25 m.p.h. If the frictional resistance is 20 lb./ton, find the horse power developed by the engine under these conditions.

45. A 12,000 lb. aircraft is designed to climb from sea-level to 40,000 ft. in 10 min. at an angle of climb of 60°. If the rate of climb is constant and the air resistance is 1,500 lb., what h.p. must the engine deliver?

46. What h.p. is required of the engine in Q. 17 to enable it to achieve the performance stated?

47. A projectile weighing 2 lb. is fired from a gun with a muzzle velocity of 2,780 ft./sec. What is its kinetic energy? What will be its velocity when the K.E. has fallen to 60,000 ft. lb.?

48. The jet velocity of a certain gas turbine is 1,500 ft./sec. when the engine is stationary on the ground. If the mass flow of jet gases is 30 lb./sec., find the K.E. wasted to the atmosphere every minute.

49. A 6,000 lb. aircraft is taxying at 30 m.p.h. on a level perimeter track when its brakes fail. If the resistance to motion without the brakes is 200 lb. wt., how far will the aircraft run before coming to rest?

50. A block of wood weighing 150 lb. slides down a frictionless slope on to a rough level surface. The slope is 1 in 10 and is 30 ft. long. If the frictional resistance on the level surface is 10 per cent of the weight, how far will the block travel along the level surface?

51. Convert a pressure of 10 lb./sq. in. into inches of Mercury.

52. A rubber tube is connected to one limb of a U-tube containing Mercury. A man blows down the rubber tube until there is a difference of level of 2 in. in the U-tube. What pressure is he exerting in lb./sq. ft.?

53. What pressure (in lb./sq. in.) is produced by a head of 6 in. of Methylated Spirit (Specific Gravity, 0·78)?

54. The air speed in a wind tunnel is measured by a Pitot-Static tube which is connected to a U-tube containing water. At a certain speed the difference of pressure between the Pitot tube and the Static tube is found to be 3·5 in. of water. Express this difference of pressure in lb./sq. in.

55. A flat plate 1 sq. ft. in area is placed at right angles to an airstream and the total force on it due to the airflow was found to be 250 lb. If a round hole of 0·25 in. diameter is bored in the plate and connected to a U-tube containing Methylated Spirits of specific gravity 0·78, what would be the difference of the levels in the U-tube?

56. If a cubic foot of hydrogen weighs 0·0056 lb. at normal Temperature and Pressure and a cubic foot of air weighs 0·0807 lb. under the same conditions, what will be the lift of a balloon of 20,000 cu. ft. capacity?

57. In an experiment to determine the density of a certain alloy, a block of the alloy is weighed first in air and then in water. If the two weights were respectively 0·22 lb. and 0·19 lb., what is the density of the alloy in slugs/cu. ft. ?

58. An exhausted compressed air cylinder of 5 cu. ft. capacity weighs 128 lb. What will it weigh when filled with air at 225 atmospheres pressure and 15° C. temperature?

59. A decompression chamber has a capacity of 10.000 cu. ft. What mass of air will it contain if the pressure is reduced to 4·5 lb./sq. in. and the temperature reduced to − 10° C.?

60. A compressed air tunnel has a capacity of 78,000 cu. ft. and it is required to increase the pressure to 25 atmospheres and reduce the temperature to 0° C. for certain experiments. If the compressor pump will pass 750 cu. ft. of air at 17° C. and 14·69 lb./sq. in. pressure every minute, how long will it take to fill the tunnel with the correct amount of air?

61. Find the value of the resultant of two forces of 3·8 lb. and 19·0 lb. acting at right angles to each other.

62. An aeroplane wing is tested in a wind tunnel and in one particular test the vertically upward force is 20·5 lb. and the horizontal force is 2·1 lb. Find the resultant force on the wing and the angle between the resultant and the vertical.

63. Find the magnitude and direction of the resultant of the following forces acting at a point—

    10 lb. vertically upwards.

    6·8 lb. at 45° to the vertical.

    7·5 lb. at 190° to the vertical.

    4·5 lb. at 270° to the vertical.

(All angles to be measured in a clockwise direction.)

64. A car weighing 10 cwt. is standing on a curved race track which is banked at an angle of 30°. Find the frictional force between the track and the wheels of the car.

65. When flying straight and level very slowly a certain aircraft has its thrust line inclined upwards at 25° to the horizontal. If the thrust is 1,000 lb. (a) what force is being used to drive the aircraft through the air, and (b) what force is helping the lifting surfaces to keep the aircraft in the air.

66. The total force on a certain wing of an aeroplane in level flight is 7,500 lb. and is inclined at an angle of 84° to the horizontal. Find (a) the lift force (vertical component of the total force), (b) the drag force (horizontal component of the total force) and the ratio of the lift to the drag.

67. Two men are supporting a block of metal between them by two wires, each of which makes an angle of 45° with the horizontal. If the tension in each wire is 140 lb. what is the weight of the block of metal?

68. A pulley block weighing 56 lb. is supported from the roof of a building by two chains, one making an angle of 50° to the vertical, and the other 30° to the vertical. If the maximum weight to be carried by the pulley block is 3 tons, find the minimum breaking strains required for the chains.

69. Find (by drawing) the value of the resultant of two forces of 5 lb. and 10 lb. acting at a point at an angle of 60° to each other.

70. During a turn, the wings of an aircraft have to be banked so that they can provide the centripetal force as well as a vertical component

to balance the weight. If the weight of the aircraft is 6,000 lb. and the acceleration in the turn is 50 ft./sec./sec. find the force on the wings.

71. A uniform beam AB, 10 ft. long and weighing 60 lb., is supported at its ends and has the following weights suspended from it—

30 lb. at a point 3 ft. from A.

70 lb. at a point 6 ft. from A.

Find the reactions at A and B.

72. A uniform bar, 8 ft. long and weighing 40 lb., is hinged on a wall at one end and held at an angle of 45° to the vertical by a horizontal chain from the wall to the free end. If a weight of 65 lb. is hung on the bar 5 ft. from the hinge, what is the tension in the chain?

73. An electric motor does 150,000 ft. lb. of work in one minute. If the motor is running at 1,000 r.p.m. what is the torque on the motor shaft?

74. If the torque on the shaft of an aircraft engine is 3,000 lb. ft. when it is running at 2,600 r.p.m., what B.H.P. is being produced?

75. What B.H.P. will be produced by the engine in Q. 74 if the r.p.m. are increased to 3,600 and the torque is increased to 3,100 lb. ft.?

76. A uniform bar AB, 20 ft. long and weighing 75 lb., is loaded with three weights as follows—

50 lb. at a point 1 ft. from A.

25 lb. at a point 9 ft. from A.

20 lb. at a point 3 ft. from B.

Find the position of the centre of gravity of the system.

77. A uniform beam, AB, 5 ft. long and weighing 20 lb. has weights of 25 lb. and 5 lb. suspended from A and B respectively. Find the point about which the bar will balance.

78. The total weight of a certain aircraft is 8,000 lb. In order to find the position of the centre of gravity the proportion of the weight resting on the tail wheel is measured and is found to be 400 lb. If the tail wheel is 15 ft. horizontally behind the main wheels, how far horizontally behind the main wheels is the centre of gravity?

79. An aircraft was placed on three scales, one under each wheel. The scales recorded the following weights—

Port Main Wheel Scale, 2,300 lb.

Starboard Main Wheel Scale, 2,300 lb.

Tail Wheel Scale, 500 lb.

Horizontal distances were measured as follows—

Leading edge of mainplane to main wheel centre, 9 in. aft.

Leading edge of mainplane to tail wheel centre, 20 ft. aft.

Calculate the horizontal position of the centre of gravity with respect to the leading edge of the mainplane.

80. The weight of an aeroplane excluding the engine is 7,000 lb. and the weight of the engine is 2,000 lb. If the engine is moved a distance of 6 in. horizontally backwards, how far will the centre of gravity of the whole aircraft be moved?

CHAPTER II. AIR AND AIRFLOW—AIR RESISTANCE

(In the numerical questions on Air Resistance, unless otherwise stated, assume the following values of C_D. For a flat plate at right angles to the airflow, $C_D = 1.2$; for a cylinder, $C_D = 0.6$; for a streamline shape $C_D = 0.06$; for a Pitot Tube $C_D = 1.0$. Assume the density of air to be 0.0024 slugs/cu. ft. except where definite values are given. In the questions on the Atmosphere assume that atmospheric pressure is equivalent to 14·69 lb./sq. in., 760 millimetres of Mercury, 29·99 in. of Mercury and 1,013·2 millibars. For low altitudes one millibar change in atmospheric pressure can be assumed equivalent to 30 ft. change in altitude.)

81. The barometric pressure in the centre of a depression is 28·3 in. of Mercury. Convert this pressure into millibars.

82. At a certain height the barometric pressure is 24·4 in. of Mercury and the Temperature is 4° C. Find the density of air at this height, given that at 0° C. and 30 in. pressure the density is 0·0807 lb./cu. ft.

83. If one-fifth of the air (by weight) is oxygen, what will be the weight of oxygen in 1 cu. ft. of air at a temperature of − 30° C. and a pressure of 7 lb./sq. in.? (Assume that 1 cu. ft. of air at 15° C. and 14·69 lb./sq. in. weighs 0·077 lb.)

84. What is the total weight of the air in a room 40 ft. long, 25 ft. wide, and 12 ft. high? (Assume Standard Atmosphere sea-level conditions.)

85. What would be the total weight of air in the room mentioned in Q. 84 if the temperature rose from 15° C. to 25° C. and the pressure dropped from 29·99 in. to 29·0 in. of Mercury? (It should be assumed that the room is not air-tight, and that therefore air is free to enter or leave the room.)

86. From Fig. 18 read the Temperature, Pressure, and Density of the Air at sea-level. Taking these values and the corresponding values of Temperature and Pressure at (a) 10,000 ft., and (b) 40,000 ft., calculate the Density at these two heights on the assumption that Boyle's Law and Charles' Law are true for air. Compare the calculated values with the corresponding values given for the Density of the Standard Atmosphere in Fig. 18.

87. A fabric balloon with a maximum capacity of 30,000 cu. ft. is to be used for an ascent to 40,000 ft. above sea-level. What mass of hydrogen (density 0·0056 lb./cu. ft. at sea-level) should be put into the balloon so that the maximum volume is just reached at 40,000 ft.? (Assume Standard Atmosphere conditions.)

88. During a gliding competition a barograph was installed in a glider to measure the altitude reached. On landing, the minimum pressure recorded by the barograph was 13·97 in. of Mercury. Draw a graph of Pressure against Altitude from the values given in Fig. 18 and estimate the height reached by the competitor.

89. An aircraft is standing on an airfield 220 ft. above sea-level on a day when the barometric pressure at ground level is 1,004 mb. If the pilot sets the altimeter to read 220 ft. on this day, what will it read if the barometric pressure drops to 992 mb.?

90. An aircraft sets off from airfield A (126 ft. above sea-level) where the ground pressure is 1,010 mb. and flies to B (762 ft. above sea-level) where the ground pressure is 985 mb. If the pilot sets his altimeter (incorrectly) at 26 ft. at A, what will it read when he lands at B?

91. A certain four-stroke aero-engine with a swept-volume of 12 cu. ft. requires 30 lb. of air per second to deliver its maximum power at 3,000 r.p.m. What pressure ratio (ratio of outlet pressure to inlet pressure) of the supercharger is required if the maximum power is to be obtainable at 20,000 ft.? (Assume Standard Atmospheric conditions and assume that there is no temperature rise across the supercharger.)

92. A certain aircraft has a landing speed of 70 knots. A wind of

25 knots is blowing over the aerodrome. What is the ground speed of the aircraft when it touches down—

 (a) directly into wind?
 (b) at an angle of 30° to the wind?
 (c) at an angle of 60° to the wind?
 (d) directly down-wind?

93. A certain aircraft requires 80 m.p.h. air speed to become airborne. If it can accelerate at 6 ft./sec./sec. when running along the ground and if there is a wind of 25 m.p.h., calculate the length of run required when it takes off—

 (a) directly into wind;
 (b) at an angle of 30° to the wind;
 (c) at an angle of 60° to the wind;
 (d) directly down-wind.

94. A transatlantic air liner cruises at an air speed of 300 m.p.h. and uses 240 gal. of fuel per hour at this speed. In winter it is necessary to provide for a head-wind of 100 m.p.h. on the east to west trip. Calculate the cost per mile for (a) the east to west trip and, (b) the west to east trip under these conditions, assuming that the distance between airfields is 2,500 miles and the fuel is 2s. per gallon.

95. Calculate the cost per mile for each trip in summer when the head-wind is reduced to 60 m.p.h.

96. A and B are two places 400 miles apart. Find the total time taken by an aeroplane flying at an air speed of 250 m.p.h. to fly from A to B and back to A—

 (a) if there is no wind;
 (b) if the wind is blowing at 30 m.p.h. from A towards B;
 (c) if the wind is blowing at 30 m.p.h. at right angles to the line joining A and B.

97. If an aircraft carrier is steaming at 20 knots into a wind of 30 knots, calculate the deceleration required to bring an aircraft to a standstill in 50 ft. from point of touch-down if its landing speed is 80 knots.

98. A pilot is detailed to reach a destination 450 nautical miles away in one hour. He sets off at an air speed of 455 knots and after half an hour finds he has only covered 212 nautical miles. At what air speed must he travel for the remaining half an hour, to reach his destination on time?

99. If the pilot in Q. 98 flew at an air speed of 465 knots for the first half an hour, what air speed would be necessary for the remaining time to complete the journey in the hour?

100. An aircraft is taking part in a square search involving flying over the ground in the form of a square of 25 miles side. If the aircraft cruises at 160 m.p.h. air speed and there is a wind of 30 m.p.h. down one of the sides of the square, calculate the time of flight for each of the four sides.

101. A flat plate, area 6 sq. in., is placed in an exposed position on an aeroplane, the plate being at right angles to the direction of airflow. Find the Resistance of the plate when the aeroplane is travelling at 60 m.p.h.

102. What would be the approximate resistance if this plate were faired to streamline shape?

103. What would be the resistance of the flat plate of Q. 101 at 120 m.p.h.?

104. What will the resistance of a sphere, of radius 3 in., moving through air at 60 m.p.h.? ($C_D = 0.55$.)

105. What would be the resistance of the same sphere moving at the same speed through water?

106. A $\frac{1}{8}$th scale model of a body, when tested in a water tank at 20 ft./sec., had a resistance of $1\frac{1}{2}$ oz. Neglecting any "scale effect," what would be the resistance of the full-size body at 100 ft./sec. in air?

107. A wind of 15 m.p.h. causes a pressure of 1 lb./sq. ft. on a flat plate at right angles to it. What wind velocity would produce a total force of 250 lb. on 35 sq. ft. of a similar plate?

108. Of two exactly similar parts of an aeroplane, one is situated in the slipstream from the propeller, and the other is in an exposed position, but outside the effects of the slipstream. If the velocity of the slipstream is 1.4 times the velocity of the aeroplane, and if the resistance of the part outside the slipstream is 2.3 lb., what will be the resistance of the corresponding part within the slipstream?

109. The resistance of a body is being measured in a wind tunnel by means of the balance shown in Fig. 25. The distance x from centre of body to pivot is 2 ft. 6 in. In order to balance the resistance, the jockey weight of $1\frac{1}{2}$ lb. must be moved a distance y, of 11.3 in., from the pivot O. What is the resistance of the body? (Assume that the counterweight exactly balances the weight of the lever arm.)

110. The air resistance of the fuselage of an aircraft is 300 lb. at ground level at an air speed of 200 m.p.h. What will be the resistance of this fuselage at 250 m.p.h. at 20,000 ft., assuming the density of air at this height to be half what it is at ground level?

111. If the undercarriage of an aircraft has a frontal area of 4.8 sq. ft. and has a resistance of 107 lb. at a speed of 90 knots, what is the value of the drag coefficient?

112. A rough egg-shaped body with a circular cross-section 3 in. in diameter is tested in a wind tunnel at 120 m.p.h. and the air resistance is found to be 0.4 lb. What is the value of the drag coefficient?

113. The drag of a loop aerial on an aircraft was found to be 90 lb. at a speed of 220 knots. In an endeavour to reduce this as much as possible a fairing of 1 sq. ft. cross-section and having a drag coefficient of 0.11 was fitted to the aerial. By how much did this reduce the drag at this speed?

114. A $\frac{1}{5}$th scale model of an aeroplane is tested in a wind tunnel at a velocity of 80 ft./sec., and the resistance is found to be 12.5 lb. What will be the resistance of the full-size machine at 140 m.p.h.? (Neglect any "scale effect," and assume that the density is the same in each case.)

115. A $\frac{1}{10}$th scale model of an aircraft is tested in a wind tunnel and the air resistance is 16.2 lb. at a speed of 300 ft./sec. What would be the resistance of an $\frac{1}{8}$th scale model at a speed of 400 ft./sec.? (Assume the density of the air remains the same for both tests.)

116. An aircraft has a maximum speed of 500 m.p.h. in straight and level flight. By highly polishing all surfaces the drag coefficient of the aircraft is reduced from 0.065 to 0.062. Assuming the same propulsive effort is available, estimate the increase in maximum speed that this will produce.

117. A $\frac{1}{10}$th scale model of a hull of a flying boat is tested in a water tank and has a resistance of 30 lb. at a speed of 40 ft./sec. What would

be the resistance of the full-size hull in water at a speed of 50 m.p.h.?

118. A streamlined shape with a cross-sectional area of 16 sq. in. is tested in a compressed air tunnel at a speed of 80 m.p.h. and a pressure of 25 atmospheres. If the resistance is 3·9 lb., what is the value of the drag coefficient?

119. What would be the resistance of the same body in water at a speed of 10 ft./sec.?

120. A $\frac{1}{5}$th scale model has a resistance of 4 lb. when tested in a wind tunnel. What would be the resistance of a $\frac{1}{2}$-scale model at half the speed in air five times as dense?

121. If the drag coefficient of the flaps used on an aircraft is 0·92, what would be the drag of these flaps at 120 m.p.h. if their area totalled 20 sq. ft.?

122. An aeroplane is to be modified and in order to estimate the effect of the modification the drag of two models, one of the original aeroplane and one of the proposed modified type, is tested in a wind tunnel.

The model of the original is $\frac{1}{20}$th scale and when tested in air of density 0·0024 slugs/cu. ft. at 120 ft./sec. the drag is 15 lb.

The model of the modified type is $\frac{1}{16}$th scale and when tested in air of density 0·0020 slugs/cu. ft. at 100 ft./sec. the drag is 12 lb.

By what percentage will the modification raise or lower the drag coefficient of the aeroplane?

123. What velocity of airflow blowing into the open end of a Pitot tube would produce a pressure of 6 in. of methylated spirit greater than the atmospheric pressure? (S.G. of methylated spirit = 0·78.)

124. The resistance of a certain part of an aeroplane is 3·5 lb. when the aeroplane is flying at 85 m.p.h. near sea-level. What will be the resistance of this part at a height of 20,000 ft. if the "indicated" air speed is the same, i.e. 85 m.p.h.? (Assume the conditions of the International Standard Atmosphere.)

125. What will be the resistance of this part at 20,000 ft., if the "true" air speed is 85 m.p.h.?

126. If the static atmospheric pressure is 14·7 lb./sq. in. and the air density is 0·0024 slugs/cu. ft., what will be the pressure on the Pitot side of the diaphragm in an air speed indicator when the forward velocity of the aeroplane is 100 m.p.h.?

127. (a) If an aircraft stalls in straight and level flight at an indicated air speed of 100 m.p.h. at sea-level, at what true air speed will it stall at (i) 20,000 ft., (ii) 40,000 ft.? (Assume Standard Atmosphere conditions.)

(b) At what indicated air speed will it stall at (i) 20,000 ft., (ii) 40,000 ft.?

128. The landing speed of a certain aircraft at sea-level is 50 knots. At what speed would it land at an aerodrome situated at an altitude of 5,000 ft.? (Assume Standard Atmosphere conditions.)

129. An air speed indicator is being calibrated with a U-tube containing Mercury. Calculate the speed that corresponds to a difference of pressure of 40 millimetres of Mercury. (1 in. = 25·4 millimetres.)

130. An aircraft flying at 5,000 ft. runs into severe icing which blocks up the static tube but leaves the pitot tube open. The aircraft descends and approaches to land at sea-level with the static tube still blocked with ice. If the pilot approaches at a true speed of 60 knots, what speed will be indicated on the air speed indicator? (Assume Standard Atmosphere conditions.)

131. A venturi tube is so designed that the ratio of the diameter at the throat to the diameter at the mouth is 0·6. The velocity of airflow at the mouth is 80 knots and the static pressure there is 14·7 lb./sq. in. Find the static pressure at the throat, assuming that the air density is 0·0024 slugs/cu. ft. at both mouth and throat.

132. A venturi tube having the area of the mouth twice the area of the throat is placed in a 70 m.p.h. airstream. A pitot tube is connected to one side of a U-tube containing water, the other side being open to atmosphere. What will be the difference in levels in the U-tube when the pitot tube is placed (a) in the mouth, and (b) in the throat of the venturi tube?

133. What will be the difference in levels in the U-tube in Q. 132 if the pitot tube is replaced by a static tube and the static tube then placed (a) in the mouth, (b) in the throat of the venturi tube?

134. The diameter of the throat of a venturi is one-third of that of the mouth. What velocity of air at the mouth will be necessary to produce a decrease of pressure of 2 in. of Mercury at the throat when the normal atmospheric pressure is 30 in. of Mercury?

135. A venturi tube is placed in a 60 knot airstream and a static tapping is taken from the throat of the venturi and connected to the static side of an air speed indicator. If the ratio of the diameter at the mouth to the diameter at the throat is 1·6, what will the air speed indicator read if a pitot tube connected to the pitot side of the air speed indicator is placed (a) in the mouth, and (b) in the throat of the venturi tube?

136. What will the air speed indicator in Q. 135 read if the pitot tube is removed from the venturi tube and placed in the airstream alongside the venturi tube?

137. What will the air speed indicator in Q. 135 read if the pitot tube is removed from the airstream altogether and left lying in the open atmosphere?

138. What will the air speed indicator in Q. 135 read if a pitot tube is placed in the mouth of the venturi tube and connected to the pitot connection on the air speed indicator, while another pitot tube is placed in the throat and connected to the static connection on the air speed indicator?

139. What will the air speed indicator read if the two pitot tubes in Q. 138 are replaced by static tubes?

140. A double venturi tube is placed in a 50 m.p.h. airstream and a static tapping is taken from the throat of the small boost venturi and connected to the static side of an air speed indicator. A pitot tube is connected to the pitot side of the air speed indicator and is placed in the air stream alongside the venturi tube. The air speed indicator then records 300 m.p.h. The static tapping at the throat of the small boost venturi is then connected to one side of a U-tube containing Mercury, the other side being open to atmosphere. To what speed must the main airstream be adjusted if the difference in levels in the U-tube is to be 4 in.?

CHAPTER III. AEROFOILS—LIFT AND DRAG

(NOTE. Details of aerofoils, where required, should be taken from Appendix I.

Assume the air density to be 0·0024 slugs/cu. ft., except where otherwise stated.)

141. The table below shows the Lift Coefficient of a flat plate at angles of attack from 0° to 90°. A flat plate of 20 ft. span and 3 ft. chord is

tested in an airstream of velocity 100 ft./sec. Plot a graph showing how the lift of such a plate varies as its angle to the airflow is increased from 0° to 90°.

(a) What is the maximum Lift obtained?

(b) What would be the maximum Lift obtained from a R.A.F. 15 aerofoil of the same area under similar conditions?

Angle of Attack .	0°	5°	10°	15°	20°	30°	40°	50°	60°	70°	80°	90°
Lift Coefficient .	0	0·36	0·68	0·80	0·78	0·80	0·76	0·68	0·56	0·38	0·20	0

142. A rectangular flat plate, 6 in. by 3 ft. 6 in., is placed in an airstream and is inclined at an angle of 6° to the airflow. The atmospheric pressure is 14·70 lb./sq. in. The effect of the airflow is to reduce the pressure on the top of the plate by 0·15 lb./sq. in. and to increase the pressure on the lower surface by 0·06 lb./sq. in. What is the Lift and Drag of the flat plate? (Assume that the total Reaction is at right angles to the plate.)

143. If an aeroplane weighs 850 lb. and the wing area is 200 sq. ft., what is the "wing loading" in lb./sq. ft.?

Assuming that two-thirds of this lift is obtained by the decrease in pressure on the top surface, what will be the actual average pressure on the top surface of the wing? (Atmospheric pressure is 15 lb./sq. in.)

144. A Pressure Plotting experiment is carried out in a wind tunnel on a model aerofoil of chord 14 in., and large aspect ratio. Methylated spirit of specific gravity 0·83 is used in the manometer. The table below shows the distances of the holes a, b, c, d, etc., from the Leading Edge, and also the corresponding pressures recorded at these holes in inches of methylated spirit, the negative values representing pressures

	Distance from Leading Edge (in.)	Pressure, Ins. of Methylated Spirit
Upper Surface—		
Hole a . . .	0·2	− 9·0
,, b	0·8	− 8·0
,, c	1·6	− 7·5
,, d	2·9	− 6·0
,, e	4·2	− 4·4
,, f	6·0	− 3·0
,, g	8·5	− 2·5
,, h	11·5	−1·0
Lower Surface—		
Hole k .	0·6	+ 3·8
,, l	1·8	+ 3·9
,, m	3·5	+ 3·4
,, n	6·0	+ 2·2
,, o	9·0	+ 1·0
,, p	12·0	+ 0·3

below the static pressure in the tunnel. The air speed was 100 m.p.h. and the angle of attack 4°. Find the Lift Coefficient for the aerofoil at this angle of attack.

Note. Strictly speaking, from the data given, it is impossible to find the Lift coefficient because we do not know the shape of the aerofoil section. The pressures act perpendicular to the surface of the aerofoil and therefore we do not know the true direction of the pressure relative to the airflow and so we cannot find the Lift which, by definition, is that part of the total force which is at right angles to the airflow.

What we can do, however, is to find the **Normal Force**, i.e. the component of the total force **which is at right angles to the chord of the aerofoil.** From this we can calculate the Normal Force Coefficient which,

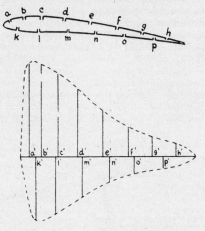

at this small angle of attack, will be of the same value as the Lift coefficient to at least two places of decimals.

The student is advised to work this question out because it will help him to understand several aspects of the subject. Proceed as follows—

Draw the chord line to some suitable scale, preferably on squared paper, marking off the position of each hole a', b', c', etc., as shown in the figure. (There is no need to incline the chord at 4°; exactly the same result will be obtained, rather more simply, if it is drawn horizontal.)

At each point set off a vertical line to some suitable scale to represent the pressure at the corresponding hole; the line should be upwards if the pressure is below atmospheric, and downwards if above atmospheric.

Draw a pressure distribution curve through the ends of these lines.

By one of the mathematical methods, or by counting the squares, or by using a planimeter, find the total area enclosed by this curve.

Divide the area by the length of the diagram, thus finding the average height; this represents the average pressure on the aerofoil—at right angles to the chord line—in inches of methylated spirit. (If the reader has worked on engines, he will recognize the similarity of this method to that of finding "mean effective pressure" from an indicator diagram.)

Convert the average pressure into lb./sq. ft. of wing area (S).

Then total force (normal to chord) = average pressure $\times S$.

This is called the Normal Force.

Just as Lift $= C_L \cdot \frac{1}{2}\rho\, V^2 \cdot S$, so Normal Force $= C_Z \cdot \frac{1}{2}\rho\, V^2 \cdot S$, where C_Z is called the Normal Force Coefficient.

Equating average pressure $\times S$ to $C_Z \cdot \frac{1}{2}\rho\, V^2 \cdot S$, the wing area (S) will cancel out, and taking ρ as $0 \cdot 0024$ slugs/cu. ft. and V (100 m.p.h.) as $100 \times \frac{88}{60}$, we can find C_Z which, as already explained, is very nearly the same as C_L.

145. Taking the values of the static pressures given in the table in Q. 144, find the speed of the airflow at each of the holes and construct velocity distribution diagrams for the upper and lower surfaces.

Note. The aerofoil acts like a venturi tube and Bernoulli's Principle (Static pressure + Dynamic Pressure = Constant) can be applied directly. At the leading edge the speed can be taken as the air speed in the tunnel and the static pressure as 14·69 lb./sq. in. Over the top surface the static pressure decreases, so the dynamic pressure and thus the speed of the airflow increases. On the under surface, the static pressure increases and the speed of the airflow decreases. The velocity distribution diagrams should be plotted with the aerofoil chord as abscissa (horizontal) and the velocity as ordinate (vertical), and the diagrams will be similar in shape to the pressure plotting diagrams. Assume the density of the air remains constant at 0·0024 slugs/cu. ft.

146. When the angle of attack of a certain aerofoil is 12°, the direction of the Total Reaction lies between the perpendicular to the chord line and the perpendicular to the airflow, being inclined at 8° to the latter (see figure). If the total Reaction is 150 lb., find its component in the direction *O C*.

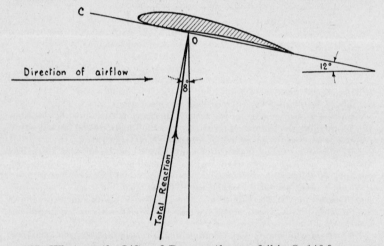

147. What are the Lift and Drag on the aerofoil in Q. 146 ?

148. If the Lift and Drag Coefficients of a flat plate at an angle of attack of 10° are 0·680 and 0·134 respectively, find the Lift and Drag of a flat plate of span 10 ft., aspect ratio 6 to 1, at a velocity of 100 ft./sec.

149. What is the Total Reaction on the flat plate of Q. 148 ?

150. At what angle is the Total Reaction inclined to the plate in Q. 148?

151. From the tables given in Appendix I, draw curves of Lift Coefficient against Angle of Attack for—

    (*a*) The "general purpose" biplane aerofoil section, R.A.F. 15.

    (*b*) The "high lift" section, Göttingen 387.

    (*c*) The "general purpose" monoplane section, R.A.F. 28.

    (*d*) The glider and sailplane section, N.A.C.A. 23012.

From your curves, write down the maximum Lift Coefficients of these four aerofoil sections.

(These curves should be drawn to the same scale so that comparisons can be made between the various sections. The student will find it useful to keep these curves, and also those in the following questions, as they will be valuable in solving other problems.)

152. Draw curves of Drag Coefficient against Angle of Attack for the four sections mentioned in Q. 151.
What are the minimum Drag Coefficients of these sections?

153. Draw curves of Lift/Drag ratio against Angle of Attack for the four sections mentioned in Q. 151.
In each case state the maximum value of this ratio and the Angle of Attack at which the maximum value occurs.

154. Draw graphs to show how the Centre of Pressure moves as the Angle of Attack is altered on the following aerofoil sections—

(a) Göttingen 387.

(b) R.A.F. 28.

(c) R.A.F. 34.

(d) N.A.C.A. 0012.

Which of these four sections gives the least movement of the Centre or Pressure over the ordinary angles of flight?

155. A model aerofoil section (span 12 in., chord 2 in.) is tested in a wind tunnel at a velocity of 60 m.p.h. The maximum lift obtained is 1·8 lb. Find the value of the maximum lift coefficient.

156. From the curves drawn for Q. 151, find the Lift of a R.A.F. 15 wing of area 250 sq. ft. at 80 m.p.h., the Angle of Attack being 4°.

157. What would be the Lift of the wing in Q. 156 if it had been of Göttingen 387 section?

158. A sailplane weighing 600 lb. is fitted with an N.A.C.A. 23012 section wing of area 412 sq. ft. From the graphs drawn in Q. 151 and 153, determine the indicated air speed at which it should be flown so that the wings are operating at the maximum Lift/Drag ratio.

159. Draw curves of Lift Coefficient, Drag Coefficient and Lift/Drag Ratio against Angle of Attack for the following—

(a) R.A.F. 48.

(b) R.A.F. 48 with 10 per cent Split Flap.

From these curves write down the values of the Maximum Lift Coefficient and the Maximum Lift/Drag Ratio for R.A.F. 48 with and without the flap.

160. Draw curves of Lift Coefficient, Drag Coefficient and Lift/Drag Ratio against Angle of Attack for the aerofoil R.A.F. 89. Compare the curves with those you have drawn for other sections and note the differences in the characteristics.

161. The area of an aeroplane wing is 435 sq. ft. If the aspect ratio is 6·5 to 1, what is the chord?

162. A rectangular monoplane wing has a span of 39 ft. and a chord of 6 ft. What is the Induced Drag Coefficient when the Lift Coefficient is 0·8?

163. What is the Induced Drag at 90 m.p.h. of a monoplane weighing 4,700 lb. and having a wing span of 52 ft.?

(This question may at first seem to have insufficient data, but it is quite easy if one remembers that Aspect Ratio = Span²/Area. Assume standard ground level air density.)

164. A monoplane weighs 3,000 lb. Its span is 30 ft. What is the Induced Drag at sea-level, at (i) 100 ft./sec. and (ii) at 200 ft./sec.?

165. What would be the Induced Drag of the monplane in Q. 164 at 40,000 ft. at (i) 200 ft./sec., and (ii) 400 ft./sec., the speeds being true air speeds? (Assume Standard Atmosphere conditions.)

166. What would be the Induced Drag of the monoplane in Q. 165 if the speeds were indicated air speeds?

167. An aircraft weighing 32,000 lb. is a monplane of 60 ft. span. Calculate the Induced Drag at sea-level at speeds ranging from 80 m.p.h. to 400 m.p.h. Plot the results in the form of a graph of Speed (abscissa) *v*. Induced Drag (ordinate).

(The student will find it useful to keep this graph as it will be referred to in later questions.)

168. Calculate the Horse Power required to overcome the Induced Drag of the aircraft at the speeds used in Q. 167 and plot the results in the form of a graph of Speed (abscissa) *v*. H.P. (ordinate).

169. The sailplane in Q. 158 has an Aspect Ratio of 8. Find the percentage reduction in Induced Drag that would result from increasing the Aspect Ratio to 12.

170. The following table gives the values of all the drag except Induced Drag (i.e. Form Drag + Skin Friction) of the aircraft in Q. 167 at various speeds at sea-level—

Speed . . .	80	120	160	200	240	280	320	360	400	m.p.h.
Form Drag + Skin Friction . .	400	900	1,600	2,500	3,600	4,900	6,400	8,100	10,000	lb.

Plot these values on the graph drawn in Q. 167, and construct a graph showing the variation of the Total Drag with speed. What percentage of the Total Drag is the Induced Drag at 120, 200, 280, 360 m.p.h. and at what speed is the Induced Drag exactly half the Total Drag? (*Note*. This speed is the speed for minimum Total Drag, i.e. the speed for Maximum Range. Keep these graphs, as they will be referred to in later questions.)

Chapter IV. Thrust

171. If a propeller on a stationary mounting blows back 60 lb. of air a second at a speed of 45 m.p.h., what thrust does it produce?

172. An aircraft engine is being tested on the ground prior to take-off. If the propeller has a diameter of 9 ft. and the slipstream has a velocity of 80 m.p.h. what thrust is being produced? (Assume sea-level conditions. In calculating the mass flow of air past the propeller take the average velocity of the air well in front of and behind the propeller, i.e. 40 m.p.h.)

173. What thrust will be produced by the propeller in Q. 172 when the aircraft is flying at 160 m.p.h. at 5,000 ft., if the velocity of the slipstream relative to the aircraft is now 180 m.p.h.? (Assume Standard Atmosphere conditions.)

174. A twin-engined aircraft with 10 ft. diameter propellers is flying at 10,000 ft. at a speed of 350 knots. If the aircraft weighs 18,000 lb. and has a lift/drag ratio of 5 to 1 under these conditions, what thrust is being produced and what is the velocity of the slipstream relative to the aircraft? (Assume Standard Atmosphere conditions.)

175. The jet velocity of a gas turbine on the ground is 1,300 ft./sec. If the mass flow is 42 lb./sec., what thrust does it produce?

176. An aircraft powered by two gas turbines is flying at 600 knots. If the jet velocity is 1,450 ft./sec. and the mass flow is 145 lb./sec. for each engine, what is the total thrust being developed?

177. What is the total Thrust Horse Power being developed by the gas turbines in Q. 176?

178. If a rocket can burn and eject 100 lb. of fuel per sec., what jet velocity is required to give a thrust of 5,000 lb.?

179. A rocket, the total weight of which is 50 lb., contains 20 lb. of combustible fuel. If all the fuel is burnt in 2 sec. and ejected with a velocity of 1,500 ft./sec. what thrust is produced? What would be the initial acceleration if the rocket were fired off vertically upwards?

180. An aircraft using the rocket assisted take-off system on an aircraft carrier weighs 9,000 lb. complete with rockets. It has a jet-engine capable of producing 3,000 lb. of Thrust and each rocket will produce 280 lb. of Thrust for 8 sec. If the carrier steams at 20 knots into a head wind of 25 knots, how many rockets will have to be fired to get the aircraft airborne in a distance of 200 ft. along the deck if the take-off speed is 80 knots and the average air and wheel resistance during take-off amounts to 1,680 lb.?

181. The pitch of a propeller is 8 ft. If the slip is 15 per cent when this propeller is running at 1,200 r.p.m., what is the speed of the aeroplane to which it is fitted?

182. The maximum speed of a certain light aeroplane is 80 m.p.h. when the engine is revolving at 3,000 r.p.m. If the pitch of the propeller is 2·9 ft., what is the percentage slip?

183. An engine develops 2,000 B.H.P. at 3,600 r.p.m. What is the Torque of the engine?

184. If the engine of Q. 183 is fitted with a propeller which has an efficiency of 83 per cent at an advance per revolution of 11 ft., what will be the thrust of the propeller?

185. When a certain aeroplane travels horizontally at an air speed of 300 knots, the engine develops 1,050 B.H.P. If the propeller efficiency at this speed is 87 per cent, find the Thrust of the propeller.

186. Find the Brake Horse Power of an engine which will drive a propeller, which is 80 per cent efficient, so as to give a Thrust of 720 lb. at 140 m.p.h.

187. The efficiency of a propeller is 78 per cent. At what forward speed will it provide a Thrust of 620 lb. when driven by an engine of 280 B.H.P.?

188. A propeller is making 2,600 r.p.m. on a machine travelling at 280 knots. The Thrust is 930 lb. and the Torque 1,900 lb. ft. What is the efficiency of the propeller?

189. The diameter of a propeller is 9 ft. The Blade Angle at a distance of 3 ft. from the axis is 23°. What is the Geometric Pitch of the propeller?

190. The Geometric Pitch of a propeller of 10 ft. diameter is to be 12 ft., and should be constant throughout the blade. Find the blade angle at distances of 2 ft., 3 ft., and 4 ft. respectively from the axis of the propeller.

CHAPTER V. LEVEL FLIGHT

191. An aeroplane weighs 3,500 lb. At a certain speed of straight and level flight the ratio of Lift to Drag of the complete machine is 7·5 to 1. If there is no force on the tail plane, what are the values of the Lift, Thrust, and Drag?

192. In a flying boat the line of Thrust is 5 ft. above the line of Drag. The boat weighs 4 tons. The Lift/Drag ratio of the complete machine

is 5 to 1 in straight and level flight. If there is to be no force on the tail, what must be the distance in front of the Centre of Gravity of the Centre of Pressure of the wings?

193. A large aeroplane weighs 18,000 lb. Owing to the nature of the design, it is necessary to have the line of Thrust 4 ft. above the line of Drag. In normal flight the Drag is 3,500 lb., and the Centre of Pressure on the Main Planes is 6 in. behind the Centre of Gravity. If the Centre of Pressure of the tail plane is 33 ft. behind the Centre of Gravity, what is the load on the tail plane?

194. In a certain aeroplane the line of Thrust is 4 in. below the line of Drag. The weight of the aeroplane is 3,300 lb., and the Drag is 520 lb. If it is required that the machine should be balanced without any load on the tail, what must be the position of the Centre of Pressure compared with the Centre of Gravity?

195. In a certain aeroplane the centre of Lift and the Centre of Gravity are in the same vertical straight line when in normal flight. If the Thrust (450 lb.) is 7 in. below the centre of Drag, what force must there be on the tail plane, which is 20 ft. behind the Centre of Gravity? The weight of the machine is 2,000 lb.

196. What force would be required on the tail plane of the aeroplane of Q. 195 if the centre of Lift had been 1 in. behind the Centre of Gravity?

197. When a certain aeroplane is in horizontal flight, the Thrust and Drag lie along the same line, which is 6 in. above the Centre of Gravity. The extreme positions of the Centre of Pressure for level flight are 1 in. in front of and 8 in. behind the Centre of Gravity. If the tail plane is 18 ft. behind the Centre of Gravity, what will be the load upon it in each case? (The weight of the aeroplane is 3,500 lb., and the Thrust required for both conditions is 700 lb.)

198. A jet aircraft weighing 13,000 lb. has its line of thrust 6 in. below the line of drag. When travelling at high speed, the thrust is 4,000 lb. and the Centre of Pressure is 1 ft. 6 in. behind the Centre of Gravity. What is the load on the tail plane which is 25 ft. behind the Centre of Gravity?

199. An aircraft weighing 5,500 lb. is flying straight and level at its maximum speed. The thrust line is horizontal and is 1 ft. above the drag line which passes through the Centre of Gravity. If the drag is 1,200 lb. and the Centre of Pressure is 2 ft. behind the Centre of Gravity, find the load on the tail plane which is 18 ft. behind and on a level with the Centre of Gravity.

200. When the aircraft in Q. 199 is flying at its minimum speed, the thrust line is inclined at 25° to the horizontal. If the Centre of Pressure is now a horizontal distance of 4 in. in front of the Centre of Gravity, what is the vertical load on the tail plane assuming that the drag (now 1,000 lb.) still acts through the Centre of Gravity?

201. An aircraft weighing 30,000 lb. is fitted with a R.A.F. 28 section wing of area 625 sq. ft. Taking the values of the lift coefficient from the graph drawn in Q. 151 calculate the indicated air speeds corresponding to the Angles of Attack from − 1° to + 25° in steps of two degrees. Draw the following graphs—

    (a) Indicated Air Speed (abscissa) v. Angle of Attack (ordinate).
    (b) Indicated Air Speed (abscissa) v. Lift Coefficient (ordinate).

At what speed must this aircraft fly to ensure that the wings are operating at the Angle of Attack giving the maximum Lift/Drag ratio? (Note that this speed will be the Aerodynamic Range Speed for this aircraft.)

202. If the aircraft in Q. 201 flies on a long trip and uses 3,000 lb. of fuel, to what value should the speed be altered to keep the wings operating at the angle of attack which gives maximum Lift/Drag ratio?

203. Draw a graph of the values of $C_L^{\frac{3}{2}}/C_D$ against Angle of Attack for the aerofoil section R.A.F. 28. What Angle of Attack gives the maximum value of $C_L^{\frac{3}{2}}/C_D$? Refer to the graphs drawn in Q. 201 and determine the air speed that corresponds to this Angle of Attack for the aircraft in question. Compare this air speed with four-fifths of the Range Speed found in Q. 201.

204. The aircraft in Q. 167 and Q. 170 is fitted with a 2,000 lb. bomb which is stowed internally. What is the new speed for Maximum Range? Compare the result with that obtained in Q. 170.

(*Note*. The Maximum Range Speed is that which gives the minimum Total Drag of the aircraft. The Total Drag curve is rather flat in this region, so it is difficult to estimate the minimum position accurately. A better method is to find the speed at which the Induced Drag is equal to all the other Drag (Form Drag plus Skin Friction), as this will also give the minimum Total Drag. All that is necessary in this question is to calculate the Induced Drag at the various speeds for this new condition and graph the results on the graph drawn in Q. 170. The intersection of the new Induced Drag curve and the old Form Drag plus Skin Friction curve will give the new Range Speed.)

205. The aircraft in Q. 167 is a twin-engined aircraft and on a certain flight one engine fails. The pilot continues flying with the propeller of the dead engine windmilling. This increases the Form Drag plus Skin Friction to the following values—

Speed . . .	80	120	160	200	240	280	320	360	400	m.p.h.
Form Drag + Skin Friction . .	500	1,125	2,000	3,130	4,500	6,140	8,010	10,140	12,520	lb.

What is the speed for Maximum Range under these conditions? (See note under Q. 204.)

206. The aircraft in Q. 204 is fitted with a 2,000 lb. torpedo instead of the 2,000 lb. bomb. The torpedo, however, has to be carried externally and this increases the Form Drag plus Skin Friction to the following values—

Speed . . .	80	120	160	200	240	280	320	360	400	m.p.h.
Form Drag + Skin Friction . .	460	1,030	1,830	2,860	4,120	5,600	7,320	9,270	11,440	lb

What is the speed for Maximum Range under these conditions?

207. Taking the values of the Total Drag at sea-level found in Q. 170, determine the H.P. needed to drive the aircraft through the air at speeds from 80 m.p.h. to 400 m.p.h. Graph the results and find the speed at which minimum H.P. is required, i.e. the speed for Maximum Endurance. Compare this speed with the Range Speed found in Q. 170.

208. From the graph drawn in Q. 207, read off the H.P. required at

sea-level to fly the aircraft at its Maximum Endurance Speed, and calculate the H.P. required for the same Indicated Air Speed at 5,000 ft., 10,000 ft. and 15,000 ft. above sea-level.

(*Note.* Remember that power depends on the True Air Speed. Assume Standard Atmosphere conditions as detailed in Fig. 18.)

209. The following table gives the fuel consumption of a twin-engined training aircraft at various speeds at sea-level. Draw graphs of Air Speed *v.* Gallons per Hour and Air Speed *v.* Air Miles per Gallon and determine the speeds for Maximum Range and Maximum Endurance.

True Air Speed .	90	100	110	120	130	140	150	160	170	m.p.h.
Gallons per Hour .	43·6	42·0	41·0	42·0	44·1	47·7	52·5	58·8	66·3	

210. Determine the speeds for Maximum Range over the ground for the aircraft in Q. 209 when flying—
   (*a*) Against a head wind of 50 m.p.h.
   (*b*) With a tail wind of 50 m.p.h.

211. If the aircraft in Q. 170 is to be propelled by jet engines instead of piston/propeller engines what will be (*a*) the speed for Maximum Range, (*b*) the speed for Maximum Endurance?

212. The following are the values of the fuel consumption of a jet propelled aircraft at 250 m.p.h. Indicated Air Speed at various altitudes—

Sea-level, 159 gallons per hour.
10,000 ft., 134 gallons per hour.
20,000 ft., 127 gallons per hour.
30,000 ft., 113 gallons per hour.

Calculate the Air Miles per Gallon for each altitude and plot a graph showing the variation of the Air Miles per Gallon with altitude. (Assume Standard Atmosphere conditions.)

Chapter VI. Gliding and Landing

213. When there is no wind, a certain aeroplane can glide (engine off) a horizontal distance of $1\frac{1}{2}$ miles for every 1,000 ft. of height. What gliding angle does this represent?

214. What will be the gliding angle and what will be the horizontal distance travelled per 1,000 ft. of height if the aeroplane of Q. 213 glides against a head wind of 20 m.p.h.? The air speed during the glide can be taken as 60 m.p.h., and the wind direction as horizontal.

215. The maximum value of the Lift/Drag ratio for a certain aeroplane is 5·5 to 1. Find the flattest possible gliding angle (in degrees) with the engine off.

216. An aeroplane glides, with the engine off, at an air speed of 80 m.p.h., and is found to lose height at the rate of 1,400 ft./min. What is the angle of glide? (Assume conditions of no wind.)

217. From the result of Q. 216, what is the value of the Lift/Drag ratio for this aeroplane on this glide?

218. At Angles of Attack of 1°, 4°, and 10° the values of the Lift/Drag ratio of a certain aeroplane, when gliding with the engine off, are 3·5, 8, and 4·5 respectively. What horizontal distance should a pilot be able to cover from a height of 10,000 ft. if he glides at each of these three Angles of Attack?

219. Draw a graph of the values of $C_L^{\frac{3}{2}}/C_D$ against Angle of Attack for aerofoil section N.A.C.A. 23012. What is the maximum value of $C_L^{\frac{3}{2}}/C_D$ and at what angle does it occur? Compare this Angle of Attack with that giving maximum Lift/Drag ratio (from the graph drawn in Q. 153).

220. At what speed must the sailplane of Q. 158 glide to ensure that the Angle of Attack of the wings is that giving the maximum value of $C_L^{\frac{3}{2}}/C_D$. Compare this speed with the maximum Lift/Drag ratio speed found in Q. 158.

221. A sailplane with an all-up-weight of 550 lb. has a Lift/Drag ratio of 24 to 1 when gliding for range at 40 m.p.h. Calculate the angle of glide and the sinking speed in ft./sec.

222. When flying with a heavier pilot, the all-up-weight of the sailplane of Q. 221 is 580 lb. At what speed must he fly to cover the same range (in still air) and what will be the sinking speed under these conditions?

223. When flying for endurance the sailplane of Q. 221 has a Lift/Drag ratio of 21·5 and a speed of 34 m.p.h. Calculate the angle of glide and the sinking speed, and compare these with the values found in Q. 221.

224. Find the minimum landing speed of an aeroplane of which the total weight is 1,100 lb., and the wing area 200 sq. ft. (The maximum lift coefficient of the aerofoil section is 1·0.)

225. When an aeroplane is fitted with an aerofoil having a maximum lift coefficient of 1·08, the minimum flying speed is 42 m.p.h. If, by the use of slots, the maximum lift coefficient can be increased to 1·60, what will be the minimum flying speed when fitted with slots?

226. It is required that a light aeroplane, of weight 850 lb., should land at 40 m.p.h. What wing area will be required if the following aerofoil sections are used—

   (a) R.A.F. 15.
   (b) Clark YH.
   (c) Göttingen 387.
   (d) R.A.F. 15 with slots.

227. From curves for R.A.F. 15 aerofoil, read the values of the lift coefficient at Angles of Attack of 3°, 8°, and 15°.

If an aeroplane, weight 1,000 lb., is fitted with this aerofoil, what air speed will be necessary for horizontal flight at each of these angles? (The effective wing area is 200 sq. ft.)

228. The total weight of an aeroplane is 3,000 lb., and the wing area is 400 sq. ft. The maximum lift coefficient of the aerofoil is 1·08. What will be the minimum speed of flight (in miles per hour)—

   (a) At sea-level?
   (b) At 10,000 ft. where the density is 0·00174 slugs/cu. ft.?

229. The total loaded weight of a two-seater aeroplane is 3,750 lb., and the corresponding minimum landing speed is 48 m.p.h. What will be the minimum landing speed if it is flown as a single-seater? (The reduction in weight in the latter case may be taken as 170 lb.)

230. The total loaded weight of an aeroplane is 2,300 lb. When R.A.F. 15 aerofoil section is used the minimum landing speed is 62 m.p.h. With a view to decreasing this landing speed, the following alterations are considered—

   (a) The fitting of slots, which will increase the maximum lift coefficient by 40 per cent.

(b) The fitting of variable camber flaps, which will increase the maximum lift coefficient by 30 per cent.

(e) A 20 per cent increase of wing area.

It is estimated that the increase in the total weight necessitated by these alterations would be (a) 50 lb., (b) 20 lb., (c) 100 lb. respectively. What will be the resulting reduction in landing speed which can be achieved by each of the three methods?

231. An aeroplane weighing 30,000 lb. has a wing loading of 55 lb./sq. ft. At 8° Angle of Attack the lift coefficient is 0·61. What is the speed, in knots, necessary to maintain horizontal flight at this Angle of Attack?

232. An aircraft is to be fitted with a N.A.C.A. 0012 aerofoil section. If the landing speed with flaps which increase the maximum lift coefficient by 60 per cent, is to be not more than 85 knots, what is the highest possible value of the wing loading?

233. An aircraft weighing 42,000 lb. is to be fitted with a R.A.F. 48 aerofoil section with 10 per cent split flap. If the area of the wing is to be 840 sq. ft., what will be the landing speed—

(a) with flap fully lowered?
(b) without flap?

CHAPTER VII. PERFORMANCE

(Note. Unless otherwise stated, assume Standard Atmosphere conditions.)

234. The total weight of a certain aeroplane is 2,700 lb., and the wing area is 300 sq. ft. R.A.F. 34 wing section is used. During the "take-off" the pilot allows the aeroplane to run along the ground with its tail up until it reaches a certain speed, and he then raises the elevators and so increases the angle of attack of the main planes to 12°, which just enables the aeroplane to leave the ground. What is the required speed?

235. What would have been the speed required for the aeroplane of Q. 234 if the pilot had allowed the aeroplane to continue running along the ground until it took off at an angle of attack of 4°?

236. An aeroplane of weight 3,000 lb. is climbing on a path inclined at 12° to the horizontal. If the Drag of the aeroplane is 500 lb., what is the value of the Thrust? (Assume the Thrust to be parallel to the path of flight.)

237. An aeroplane, weighing 1,200 lb., climbs at an angle of 10° to the horizontal with a speed of 85 m.p.h. along its line of flight. If the Drag on the aeroplane at this speed is 180 lb., find—

(a) The Horse Power used in overcoming Drag.
(b) The Horse Power used in overcoming the force of Gravity.

Hence find the total Horse Power required for this climb.

238. While climbing the air speed of an aeroplane is 85 m.p.h. along the flight path, while the vertical rate of climb is 2,000 ft./min. What is the angle of climb?

239. A jet aircraft climbs at an angle of climb of 15° at a speed of 200 knots. Calculate the rate of climb in ft./min.

240. An aircraft weighing 40,000 lb. requires 2,460 h.p. for level flight at a speed of 160 knots. If the maximum h.p. available is 4,800 h.p., what is the maximum possible rate of climb at this speed?

241. An aircraft weighing 10,000 lb. is powered by an engine capable of producing 2,000 B.H.P. Calculate the maximum angle of climb of this

aircraft at an airspeed of 130 knots if the propeller efficiency is 80 per cent and the drag of the aircraft at this speed is 1,500 lb.

242. An aircraft weighing 5,500 lb. has a normal climbing speed of 110 m.p.h. At this speed, it requires 280 h.p. to overcome the drag. With 15° of flap lowered the climbing speed is 85 m.p.h. and in this condition, the aircraft requires 290 h.p. to overcome the drag. What are the angle of climb and rate of climb in each case if the maximum power available from the propeller is 500 h.p.?

243. A jet aircraft weighing 13,000 lb. has a climbing speed of 250 knots. If the rate of climb is 9,000 ft./min. and the drag of the aircraft in this condition is 1,800 lb., find the thrust being delivered by the engines.

244. The following table gives particulars relating to a certain aeroplane of total weight 2,300 lb.—

Speed of level flight, m.p.h. .	45	50	55	60	65	70	75	80	85	90	95	100
Horse Power available from propeller	135	170	205	225	240	250	255	255	250	240	235	220
Horse Power required for level flight	250	115	95	90	110	125	150	175	215	240	300	350

Estimate—
(a) The minimum speed of level flight.
(b) The maximum speed of level flight.
(c) The best air speed for climbing purposes.
(d) The horse power available for climbing at this air speed.
(e) The maximum vertical rate of climb.

245. By throttling down the engine of the aeroplane of Q. 244 the Horse Power available is reduced by 30 per cent throughout the whole range of speed. Find the maximum and minimum speeds for level flight under these conditions.

246. If a certain aircraft requires 380 h.p. for level flight at 150 m.p.h. when the flying weight is 4,000 lb., what will be the corresponding speed (i.e. for same angle of attack) and horse power required when the flying weight is increased to 4,500 lb.?

247. An aeroplane weighs 3,000 lb. Its landing speed is 50 m.p.h. and the least horse power required to fly level is 40 h.p. at 80 m.p.h. If 500 lb. extra load is added, find the new landing speed, and the velocity and power required for minimum horse power in level flight, i.e. at same angle of attack as before.

248. The following table gives particulars of a certain aeroplane weighing 14,000 lb. which is designed for either piston engine/propeller or jet propulsion—

Speed of level flight in knots .	50	70	90	110	130	160	200	240	280	320	360	400	440
T.H.P. required for level flight .	2,000	750	580	540	540	640	910	1,340	2,000	2,870	4,000	5,500	7,500
T.H.P. available from propeller .	900	1,120	1,300	1,480	1,640	1,870	2,130	2,340	2,550	2,700	2,800	2,800	2,650
T.H.P. available from jet . .	660	950	1,200	1,500	1,750	2,170	2,720	3,260	3,800	4,340	4,900	5,450	6,000

Estimate the maximum and minimum speeds for level flight when the aircraft is propelled by the piston engine/propeller combination.

249. Estimate the maximum and minimum speeds for level flight when the aircraft in Q. 248 is propelled by the jet engine, and compare the speeds with those found in Q. 248.

250. Estimate the best climbing speed and rate of climb at this speed for the aircraft in Q. 248 when propelled by the piston engine/propeller combination.

251. Estimate the best climbing speed and rate of climb at this speed when the aircraft in Q. 248 is propelled by the jet engine. Compare these answers with those obtained in Q. 250.

252. When the weight of the aircraft in Q. 248 is increased by carrying an extra 2,000 lb. of fuel in overload tanks, the Horse Power required for level flight is increased to the following—

Speed of level flight, knots . . .	60	70	90	110	130	160	200	240	280	320	360	400	440
T.H.P. required for level flight . .	1,600	1,000	760	670	650	700	960	1,385	2,045	2,910	4,040	5,535	7,535

Estimate the maximum and minimum speeds for level flight in this condition when propelled by the piston engine/propeller combination.

253. Estimate the maximum and minimum speeds for level flight of the aircraft in Q. 252 when propelled by the jet engine.

254. The Drag of an aeroplane at sea-level at 200 m.p.h. is 2,500 lb. What will be the Drag at the same speed at 40,000 ft.?

255. What Thrust Horse Power will be required to overcome the Drag of the aeroplane in Q. 254 (a) at sea-level, (b) at 40,000 ft.?

256. The Lift produced by the wings of an aircraft travelling at 250 knots at sea-level is 15,000 lb. At what speed must the aircraft travel at 45,000 ft. to produce the same Lift at the same Angle of Attack of the wings?

257. What will be the Indicated Air Speed of the aircraft in Q. 256 at 45,000 ft.?

258. If the aircraft in Q. 256 has a Lift/Drag ratio of 10 to 1 when travelling at an Indicated Air Speed of 250 knots, calculate the Thrust Horse Power necessary to propel the aircraft at this Indicated Air Speed at (a) sea-level, (b) 45,000 ft.

259. When flying at its Endurance Speed of 160 m.p.h. an aircraft weighing 16,000 lb. has a drag of 3,000 lb. Calculate the Thrust Horse Power required to propel the aircraft at altitudes from sea-level to 45,000 ft. (at 5,000 ft. intervals) and construct a graph of—

Altitude (abscissa) v. Power Required (ordinate).

Estimate the altitude at which the Power Required is double that at sea-level.

260. The following table gives values at various altitudes of the maximum Thrust Horse Power available from the propeller fitted to the aircraft in Q. 259 when flying at the Endurance Speed—

Altitude ft. . .	0	5,000	10,000	15,000	20,000	25,000	30,000	35,000	40,000	45,000
T.H.P. Available .	2,750	2,810	2,870	2,930	3,000	2,800	2,630	2,460	2,325	2,180

NOTE. The Rated Altitude of the engine is 20,000 ft.

Estimate—

(a) the absolute ceiling of the aircraft;

(b) the service ceiling (the altitude at which the maximum rate of climb is reduced to 100 ft./min.).

261. If the engine fitted to the aircraft in Q. 259 uses fuel at the rate of 0·45 lb./B.H.P./hr., calculate the endurance of the aircraft (a) at sea-level, (b) at 30,000 ft., assuming that the aircraft has 2,160 lb. of fuel available for level flight and that the propeller efficiency is 80 per cent at both altitudes.

262. An aircraft weighing 30,000 lb. has a Range Speed of 200 m.p.h. Indicated Air Speed. At this speed the Lift/Drag ratio is 8 to 1 and the propeller efficiency is 82 per cent. If the fuel consumption is 0·42 lb. per B.H.P. per hour, calculate the Air Miles per Gallon of fuel at (a) sea-level, (b) 20,000 ft., (c) 40,000 ft. (Assume 1 gal. of fuel weighs 7 lb.)

263. If the aircraft in Q. 262 is propelled by jet engines at the same Indicated Air Speed, the fuel consumption is 0·56 lb. per lb. Thrust per hour. Calculate the Air Miles per Gallon of fuel at (a) sea-level, (b) 20,000 ft., (c) 40,000 ft. Compare these results with those obtained in Q. 262.

CHAPTER VIII. MANOEUVRES

264. Find the correct angle of bank for an aeroplane of weight 1,500 lb. taking a corner of radius 100 ft. at 60 m.p.h.

265. What will be the total Lift on the wings of the aeroplane in Q. 264 while taking this corner at the correct angle of bank?

266. An aircraft weighing 1,000 lb. does a steady 45° banked turn at 55 m.p.h. Calculate (a) the acceleration, (b) the force required to produce the acceleration, and (c) the wing loading of the aircraft if the wing area is 70·71 sq. ft.

267. If the aerofoil section used on the aeroplane of Q. 40 is R.A.F. 15, and if the total wing area is 250 sq. ft., calculate—

(a) The Angle of Attack required for normal horizontal flight at the same speed of 90 m.p.h.

(b) The Angle of Attack required to produce the necessary lift when turning the corner at this speed.

268. An aeroplane, weighing 2,500 lb., banks at an angle of 25° to make a horizontal turn. If the velocity while turning is 85 m.p.h., what is the radius of the turn?

269. If the stalling speed of an aeroplane in normal flight is 42 m.p.h., what will be its stalling speed when executing a correctly banked turn at 45° angle of bank?

270. Calculate the radius of turn and angle of bank of an aircraft doing a Rate 1 turn (180° per minute) at 600 m.p.h. What is the acceleration in multiples of g and if the aircraft weighs 11,000 lb., calculate the Lift force on the wings during the turn.

271. Calculate the loading on an aircraft in a correctly banked turn at angles of bank of 60°, 75°, 83°, 84°. (Note. The loading is expressed as a factor found by dividing the Lift force on the wings by the force on the wings in straight and level flight, i.e. the weight.)

272. Calculate the accelerations in multiples of g for each of the turns mentioned in Q. 271.

273. If the stalling speed of an aircraft is 60 knots in straight and level flight, what is the stalling speed in correctly banked turns at angles of bank of 45°, 60°, 75°, 83°, 84°?

274. Calculate the rate of turn of an aeroplane in degrees per minute

if the acceleration during the turn is $4g$ at speeds of 100 knots, 150 knots, 300 knots, 500 knots.

275. If the maximum loading a certain aircraft can sustain without structural failure is 8, what is the maximum angle of bank it can use in a correctly banked turn?

276. If the stalling speed of the aircraft in Q. 275 is 80 knots in straight and level flight, what will the stalling speed be in the turn at the maximum permissible angle of bank?

277. What will be the radius of the turn of the aircraft in Q. 275 when it is flying on the stall at its maximum permissible angle of bank?

278. What angles of bank are required for Rate 1 turns (180° per minute) at 100 knots, 200 knots, 300 knots, 400 knots?

279. What are the loadings on the aircraft in the turns in Q. 278?

280. An aircraft weighing 10,000 lb. completes a Rate 2 turn (360° per minute) at 250 m.p.h. What angle of bank is required and what Lift force must the wings provide?

281. If an aircraft stalls at 110 m.p.h. in straight and level flight, what will be the loading on the aircraft if it stalls in a turn at 246 m.p.h.?

282. What will be the radius of the turn in Q. 281 in which the aircraft stalls at 246 m.p.h.?

283. An aeroplane of weight 3,200 lb. performs a loop. If it is assumed that the top of the loop is in the form of a circle of radius 250 ft., what must be the speed at the highest point in order that the loads on the aeroplane may be the same as those of normal horizontal flight?

(If the centripetal force on the aeroplane at the top of the loop is just equal to the weight, then there will be no loads on the lift bracing, etc.; but if the centripetal force is double the weight, then the loads on the lift bracing will be the same as in normal flight, and the pilot will be sitting on his seat with the usual force, but upwards!)

284. If the terminal velocity of the aeroplane in Q. 283 is 420 m.p.h. a vertical nose-dive, what is its drag when travelling at this speed?

285. A spherical ball of weight 1 lb. and diameter 2 in. is dropped from an aeroplane. What will be its terminal velocity in air of density 0·00186 slugs/cu. ft.? (Take C_D for the sphere $= 0·8$.)

286. If, without any appreciable increase in weight, the ball is faired to streamline shape ($C_D = 0·044$), what will be the terminal velocity in air of the same density?

287. An aircraft weighing 13,000 lb. completes a vertical loop at 500 m.p.h. constant speed with a height range from top to bottom of the loop of 10,000 ft. What is the acceleration and, if the area of the wings is 400 sq. ft., what is the wing loading, (a) at the top of the loop, (b) at the bottom of the loop? (Assume that the loop is a perfect circle— this is very unlikely in practice although with jet aircraft it is more nearly attainable.)

288. An aircraft is in a vertical terminal velocity dive at 400 knots. If, in pulling out of the dive, it follows the arc of a circle, what will be the acceleration if the height lost is 5,000 ft.? What is the maximum loading during the pull-out?

289. What will be the acceleration and maximum loading of the aircraft in Q. 288 if the loss in height in the pull-out is only 2,500 ft.?

290. An aircraft completes a loop at a constant-speed of 200 m.p.h. in 15 sec. If the loop can be considered as a vertical circle, calculate

the radius of the loop and the maximum and minimum loadings during the loop?

CHAPTER IX. STABILITY AND CONTROL

(*Note*. Numerical questions on stability and control are too complex to be included in the scope of this book, nor is the solution of such problems in any way essential to the practical aeronautical engineer. Even in actual design work, such items as the amount of dihedral angle or the area of fin required are decided by empirical rules rather than by theoretical calculations on stability.)

CHAPTER X. HIGH-SPEED FLIGHT

(*Note*. In the following examples assume the speed of sound at sea-level under Standard Atmosphere conditions to be 1,120 ft./sec. = 764 m.p.h.)

291. Taking the values of the Temperature at various altitudes from Fig. 18, calculate the speed of sound at altitudes from sea-level up to 45,000 ft. Construct a graph of the Speed of Sound (abscissa) *v*. Altitude (ordinate).

292. An aircraft has a Critical Mach Number of 0·85. If the pilot cannot control the aircraft at higher Mach Numbers than this, what is the maximum permissible speed of the aircraft (*a*) at sea-level, (*b*) at 40,000 ft.?

293. What are the maximum indicated air speeds for the aircraft in Q. 292 (*a*) at sea-level, (*b*) at 40,000 ft.?

294. If the temperature at sea-level on a certain day rises to 25° C., what will be the maximum speed of the aircraft in Q. 292 at sea-level on that day?

295. A certain aircraft has a Critical Mach Number of 0·80 and a structural limitation which prevents it being flown at an indicated air speed greater than 502 m.p.h. At what altitude are these two speeds equal? (This example is best solved graphically.)

296. The following table gives the values of the Drag Coefficient of a thin aerofoil at various Mach Numbers—

Mach Number . .	0·6	0·7	0·8	0·9	1·0	1·1	1·2	1·3	1·4
Drag Coefficient . .	0·01	0·011	0·019	0·05	0·068	0·063	0·052	0·044	0·037
Mach Number. .	1·5	1·6	1·7	1·8	1·9	2·0			
Drag Coefficient .	0·032	0·028	0·026	0·024	0·022	0·021			

Calculate the Drag of the aerofoil at sea-level at these Mach Numbers taking the area of the aerofoil as 400 sq. ft., and plot a graph of Drag (ordinate) *v*. Mach Number (abscissa).

297. Calculate the Thrust Horse Power necessary to propel the aerofoil in Q. 296 at speeds corresponding to the Mach Numbers given, and plot a graph of T.H.P. (ordinate) *v*. Mach Number (abscissa). Compare the shape of this curve with that obtained in Q. 296.

298. Construct a graph similar to that in Fig. 185B for an aircraft which stalls at 130 m.p.h. at sea-level and has a Critical Mach Number of 0·85. Estimate the maximum height at which it can fly, assuming that it cannot fly at Mach Numbers higher than the Critical Mach Number.

299. Calculate the rise in temperature of the surface of an aeroplane travelling at 650 m.p.h. at sea-level. (Assume the $(v/100)^2$ formula given in Chapter X.)

300. A more general formula for the temperature rise is given by $\dfrac{M^2 T}{5}$ where M is the Mach Number and T is the absolute temperature of the air. Using this formula, calculate the speed required at 40,000 ft. to raise the temperature of the aircraft to 15° C.

APPENDIX II. UNITS AND DIMENSIONS

301. Write down the units (ft. lb. sec.) of the following quantities—

(a) Mass $\times$ Acceleration.

(b) ρ.

(c) $u^2 + 2as$.

(d) C_D.

302. Write down the units (ft. lb. sec.) of the following quantities—

(a) $\dfrac{W}{S}$

(b) $C_D \frac{1}{2}\rho V^2$.

(c) $\dfrac{V_s^2}{g} \times \dfrac{C_L \max.}{C_L}$

(d) $\frac{1}{2}\rho V^2$.

303. Write down the dimensions of the following expressions which are common in aerodynamics—

(a) $\dfrac{v^2}{gr}$

(b) $\dfrac{mv^2}{r}$

(c) $\dfrac{2\pi NQ}{33,000}$

(d) $\dfrac{2W}{C_L \rho Sg}$.

304. Write down the dimensions of the following—

(a) Wing loading.

(b) $\dfrac{C_L^2}{\pi A}$

(c) Angular velocity.

(d) $\dfrac{2W}{\rho S V^2}$

305. Bernoulli's Theorem is stated mathematically as—

$$p + \tfrac{1}{2}\rho V^2 = \text{constant}$$

What are the dimensions of the constant in this formula?

306. From the equation $\dfrac{P}{\rho} = RT$, where P = pressure, ρ = density and R is a dimensionless constant, find the dimensions of the temperature T.

307. The time of oscillation of a pendulum of length l is given by one of the following formulae—

(a) $T = 2\pi \sqrt{\dfrac{l^2}{g}}$

(b) $T = 2\pi \sqrt{\dfrac{g}{l}}$

(c) $T = 2\pi \sqrt{\dfrac{l}{g}}$

Find which one is correct by dimensional analysis.

308. The acceleration towards the centre of a body travelling in a circle can only depend on its weight, its velocity and the radius of the circle. Develop a formula for this acceleration by the system of dimensions.

309. The speed at which an aircraft flies depends on its weight, the area of its wings and the density of the air. Find a formula connecting these quantities by the system of dimensions.

310. The speed of sound in air is known to depend on the pressure and the density of the air. Find a formula connecting the speed of sound with these two quantities by the system of dimensions.

APPENDIX III. SCALE EFFECT

(*Note.* Assume the viscosity of air at 15° C. to be $3\cdot73 \times 10^{-7}$

slugs/ft./sec. Take the maximum length in the direction of motion for the length L in the Reynolds' Number formula.)

311. The viscosity of air varies with the temperature according to the formula—

$$\frac{\mu_1}{\mu_2} = \left(\frac{T_1}{T_2}\right)^{\frac{3}{4}}$$

where μ_1 and μ_2 are the viscosities at the absolute temperatures T_1 and T_2 respectively. Find the viscosity of air at $-25°$ C., $-5°$ C., $+5°$ C., and $+25°$ C.

312. An aircraft 36 ft. in length cruises at 160 m.p.h. at sea-level. Find its Reynolds' Number under these conditions. (Assume Standard Atmosphere conditions.)

313. What will be the Reynolds' Number of the aircraft in Q. 312 when it is flying at 20,000 ft. at the same speed?

314. What will be the Reynolds' Number of the aircraft in Q. 312 when it is flying at 20,000 ft. at an Indicated Air Speed of 160 m.p.h.?

315. The average length of the chord of a wing on a certain aircraft is 10 ft. Taking this as the length L, calculate the Reynolds' Number when flying at sea-level at 200 knots.

316. A $\frac{1}{10}$th scale model of the aircraft in Q. 315 is tested in a wind tunnel at 150 m.p.h. at 15° C. What is the Reynolds' Number of the test? (Assume the density of the air in the wind tunnel to be 0·0024 slugs/cu. ft.)

317. What will be the Reynolds' Number if the test in Q. 316 is conducted in a Compressed Air Tunnel in which the pressure is 10 atmospheres and the temperature 25° C.?

318. What must be the pressure in the Compressed Air Tunnel in Q. 317 if the $\frac{1}{10}$th scale model test is to have the same Reynolds' Number as the full-scale aircraft in Q. 315, assuming that the maximum speed of the tunnel under these conditions is 100 m.p.h. and the temperature is 25° C.?

319. By what percentage will the Reynolds' Number be raised or lowered if the temperature in the Compressed Air Tunnel in Q. 318 is reduced to 5° C. assuming that no more air is pumped into the tunnel during the cooling process?

320. If the weight of the aircraft in Q. 315 is 10,000 lb. what will be the Lift force on the model in Q. 318 assuming that both are operating at the same angle of attack?

321. Find the Reynolds' Number of a test conducted in a Decompressed Air Tunnel on an aerofoil of 18 in. chord at a Mach Number of 0·85, a temperature of 15° C. and a pressure of $\frac{1}{5}$th of an atmosphere. (Take the velocity of sound under Standard sea-level conditions to be 1,120 ft./sec.)

APPENDIX VI

ANSWERS TO NUMERICAL QUESTIONS

Chapter I

1. (a) 91·3 m.p.h.; (b) 14·7 sec.
2. (a) 0·856 ft./sec./sec. (b) 1,539 ft. (c) 6,156 ft.
3. (a) 4·4 ft./sec./sec. (b) 24·5 sec.
4. 54·5 m.p.h.; 800 ft.
5. 50·5 m.p.h.
6. (a) 37·6 ft.; (b) 150·4 ft.
7. 89,500 ft.; 2 min. 29·2 sec.
8. 1,926 ft.
9. 37·5 ft./sec.
10. 1,300 ft./sec.
11. 10 lb.
12. 12 lb.
13. 1,554,000 lb.
14. 1,943 lb.
15. 102,000 lb.
16. (a) 178·4 lb. (b) 157·6 lb.; (c) 168 lb.
17. 25,160 lb.
18. 13,680 lb.
19. 323 ft.
20. 16·94 lb.
21. 25·86 ft.
22. 1,266 ft./sec.
23. 1,083 lb.
24. 963 lb.
25. 1·56 ft.
26. 12·8 m.p.h.
27. 8,220 lb.
28. 310 lb.
29. 511 yd.
30. 18,240 lb.
31. 236 radians/sec.; 1,060 ft./sec.
32. 314 radians/sec.; 50 ft./sec.
33. 250,000 ft./sec./sec.
34. 24,680 ft./sec./sec.
35. 7·36 lb.; (a) 5·36 lb.; (b) 9·36 lb.
36. 6,080 lb.
37. 5,567 lb.
38. 70° 14′
39. 51·9 m.p.h.

40. (a) 4,149 lb.; (b) 61°; (c) 4,743 lb.
41. 1,120,000 ft. lb. 16·97 h.p.
42. 480 h.p.
43. 3,630 h.p.
44. 10·33 h.p.
45. 1,665 h.p.
46. 2,265 h.p.
47. 2,400,000 ft. lb. 1,390 ft./sec.
48. 62,900,000 ft. lb.
49. 902 ft.;
50. 30 ft.
51. 20·36 in.
52. 141·4 lb./sq. ft.
53. 0·169 lb./sq. in.
54. 0·126 lb./sq. in.
55. 61·6 in.
56. 1,502 lb.
57. 14·2 slugs/cu. ft.
58. 214·6 lb.
59. 258 lb.
60. 46 hr.
61. 19·37 lb.
62. 20·6 lb.; 5° 51′
63. 7·49 lb. at 352° 23′
64. 560 lb.
65. (a) 906·3 lb. (b) 422·6 lb.
66. (a) 7,459 lb.; (b) 784 lb.; 9·5.
67. 198 lb.
68. 3,417 lb.; 5,256 lb.
69. 13·2 lb.
70. 11,100 lb.
71. 79 lb.; 81 lb.
72. 60·6 lb.
73. 23·85 ft.
74. 1,485 B.H.P.
75. 2,122 B.H.P.
76. 8·03 ft. from A.
77. 1·5 ft. from A.
78. 9 in.
79. 31·6 in. aft.
80. 1⅓ in.

Chapter II

81. 955·9 mb.
82. 0·0647 lb./cu. ft.

83. 0·0087 lb.
84. 924 lb.

364

85. 863·6 lb.
86. (a) 0·057 lb./cu. ft.;
   (b) 0·019 lb./cu. ft.
87. 41·4 lb.
88. 19,700 ft.
89. 580 ft.
90. 776 ft.
91. 2·44 to 1.
92. (a) 45 kt.; (b) 48·35 kt.; (c)
   57·5 kt.; (d) 95 kt.
93. (a) 543 ft.; (b) 612 ft.; (c)
   817·5 ft.; (d) 1,976 ft.
94. (a) 2·4 shillings per mile;
   (b) 1·2 shillings per mile.
95. (a) 2·0 shillings per mile; (b)
   1·3 shillings per mile.
96. (a) 3 hr. 12 min.; (b) 3 hr.
   15 min.; (c) 3 hr. 13·5 min.
97. 25·7 ft./sec./sec.
98. 507 kt.
99. 497 kt.
100. 7·9 min. down wind; 9·5 min.
    across wind; 11·5 min. into
    wind.
101. 0·465 lb.
102. 0·023 lb.
103. 1·86 lb.
104. 1 lb.
105. 812 lb.
106. 2·97 oz.
107. 40·1 m.p.h.
108. 4·508 lb.
109. 0·565 lb.

110. 234 lb.
111. 0·804.
112. 0·219.
113. 71·8 lb.
114. 2,059 lb.
115. 45 lb.
116. 12 m.p.h.
117. 10,080 lb.
118. 0·085.
119. 0·92 lb.
120. 31·25 lb.
121. 684 lb.
122. 11·5% lower.
123. 97·1 m.p.h.
124. 3·5 lb.
125. 1·863 lb.
126. 14·88 lb./sq. in.
127. (a)   (i) 137·1 m.p.h.;   (ii)
    201·3 m.p.h.; (b) (i)
    100 m.p.h.; (ii) 100 m.p.h.
128. 54 kt.
129. 208 m.p.h.
130. 298 kt.
131. 13·67 lb./sq. in.
132. (a) 2·43 in.; (b) 2·43 in.
133. (a) Nil; (b) 7·3 in.
134. 26·2 m.p.h.
135. (a) 154 kt.; (b) 154 kt.
136. 154 kt.
137. 141 kt.
138. Nil.
139. 141 kt.
140. 55·9 m.p.h.

CHAPTER III

141. (a) 590 lb.; (b) 880 lb.
142. 52·6 lb.; 5·5 lb.
143. 4·25 lb./sq. ft.;   14·98 lb./sq.
    in.
144. 0·90
146. 10·47 lb.
147. 148·5 lb.; 20·9 lb.
148. 136 lb.; 26·8 lb.
149. 138·7 lb.
150. 88° 50′
151. 1·22; 1·34; 1·38; 1·46.
152. 0·0074;   0·012;   0·0078;
    0·008.
153. 24·2 at 3°; 18·5 at −1°;
    23·6 at 2·5°; 24·8 at 3·5°.

154. R.A.F. 34.
155. 1·162.
156. 1,890 lb.
157. 3,205 lb.
158. 40 m.p.h.
159. 2·14; 6·5: 1·43; 21·6.
161. 8·18 ft.
162. 0·031.
163. 125 lb.
164. (i) 268 lb.; (ii) 67 lb.
165. (i) 270 lb.; (ii)67·5 lb.
166. (i) 66·5 lb.; (ii) 16·6 lb.
169. 33⅓%.
170. 73·1%;   26·0%;   8·4%;
    3·2%; 154 m.p.h.

CHAPTER IV

171. 123 lb.
172. 1,050 lb.

173. 955 lb.
174. 3,600 lb.; 363 kt.

175. 1,696 lb.
176. 3,940 lb.
177. 7,250 T.H.P.
178. 1,610 ft./sec.
179. 466 lb.; 268 ft./sec./sec.
180. Four.
181. 92·7 m.p.h.
182. 19·1 %
183. 2,920 lb.-ft.

184. 1,383 lb.
185. 992 lb.
186. 336 h.p.
187. 132·1 m.p.h.
188. 85 %
189. 8·005 ft.
190. (a) 43° 40'; (b) 32° 28'; (c) 25° 31'.

CHAPTER V

191. 3,500 lb.; 467 lb.; 467 lb.
192. 1 ft.
193. 708 lb. Down.
194. 0·63 in. behind C.G.
195. 13·125 lb. Up.
196. 4·81 lb. Up.
197. 16·13 lb. Up; 134·6 lb. Down
198. 745 lb. Down.
199. 762·5 lb. Down.
200. 34·5 lb. Up.
201. 223 m.p.h.
202. 212 m.p.h.
203. 5½°; 181 m.p.h.

204. 159 m.p.h.
205. 145 m.p.h.
206. 153 m.p.h.
207. 117 m.p.h.
208. 1,064 h.p.; 1,149 h.p.; 1,247 h.p.; 1,348 h.p.
209. 135 m.p.h. for Range; 110 m.p.h. for Endurance.
210. (a) 148 m.p.h.; (b) 127 m.p.h.
211. (a) 205 m.p.h.; (b) 154 m.p.h.
212. 1·57 A.M.P.G.; 2·19 A.M.P.G. 2·70 A.M.P.G.; 3·60 A.M.P.G.

CHAPTER VI

213. 7° 12'.
214. 10° 46'; 5,258 ft.
215. 10° 18'.
216. 11° 28'.
217. 4·9.
218. 35,000; 80,000; 45,000.
219. 16·5 at 6°.
220. 33 m.p.h.
221. 2° 23'; 2·45 ft./sec.
222. 41 m.p.h.; 2·51 ft./sec.
223. 2° 40'. 2·32 ft./sec.
224. 46·2 m.p.h.
225. 34·5 m.p.h.

226. (a) 168·5 sq. ft.; (b) 143·9 sq. ft.; (c) 153·2 sq. ft.; (d) 115·4 sq. ft.
227. 0·39; 0·76; 1·22; 70·5 m.p.h. 50·5 m.p.h.; 39·9 m.p.h.
228. (a) 51·9 m.p.h.; (b) 61 m.p.h.
229. 46·9 m.p.h.
230. (a) 9 m.p.h.; (b) 7·4 m.p.h.; (c) 4·2 m.p.h.
231. 162 knots.
232. 58·5 lb./sq. ft.
233. (a) 83 kt.; (b) 101 kt.

CHAPTER VII

234. 60·9 m.p.h.
235. 93·4 m.p.h.
236. 1,124 lb.
237. (a) 40·8 h.p.; (b) 47·2 h.p.; 88·0 h.p.
238. 15° 30°.
239. 5,250 ft./min.
240. 1,930 ft./min.
241. 14° 32'.
242. 7° 51' 1,320 ft./min.; 9° 42' 1,260 ft./min.
243. 6,420 lb.
244. (a) 47 m.p.h.; (b) 90 m.p.h.; (c) 62 m.p.h.; (d) 139 h.p.; (e) 1,994 ft./min.

245. 80·3 m.p.h.; 49·8 m.p.h.
246. 159 m.p.h.; 454 h.p.
247. 54 m.p.h.; 86·5 m.p.h.; 50·4 h.p.
248. 312 knots; 59 knots.
249. 398 knots; 64 knots.
250. 172 knots; 2,950 ft./min.
251. 245 knots; 4,480 ft./min.
252. 309 knots; 67 knots.
253. 397 knots; 72 knots.
254. 617 lb.
255. (a) 1,333 T.H.P.; (b) 329 T.H.P.
256. 566 knots.
257. 250 knots.

258. (a) 1,150 T.H.P.; (b) 2,605 T.H.P.
259. 39,600 ft.
260. (a) 37,000 ft.; (b) 36,500 ft.
261. (a) 3 hours; (b) 1 hr. 50 min.

262. (a) 1·37 A.M.P.G.; (b) 1·37 A.M.P.G. (c) 1·37 A.M.P.G.
263. (a) 0·67 A.M.P.G.; (b) 0·91 A.M.P.G.; (c) 1·34 A.M.P.G.

CHAPTER VIII

264. 67° 25′.
265. 3,907 lb.
266. (a) 32·2 ft./sec./sec.; (b) 1,000 lb.; (c) 20 lb./sq. ft.
267. (a) 3° 43′; (b) 10° 6′.
268. 1,035 ft.
269. 49·9 m.p.h.
270. 3·18 miles; 55° 3′; 1·43 g.; 19,200 lb.
271. 2·0; 3·86; 8·2; 9·53.
272. 1·73; 3·73; 8·14; 9·51.
273. 71 kt.; 85 kt.; 118 kt.; 172 kt.; 185 kt.
274. 2,625°/min.; 1,750°/min.; 875°/min.; 525°/min.
275. 82° 49′.
276. 226 kt.

277. 571 ft.
278. 15° 21′; 28° 45′; 39° 27′; 47° 39′.
279. 1·04; 1·14; 1·29; 1·49.
280. 50° 2′; 15,570 lb.
281. 5·0.
282. 4,490 ft.
283. 86·5 m.p.h.
284. 3,200 lb.
285. 248 ft./sec.
286. 1,058 ft./sec.
287. 107·6 ft./sec./sec.; (a) 76 lb./sq. ft.; (b) 141 lb./sq. ft.
288. 91·2 ft./sec./sec.; 3·83.
289. 182·4 ft./sec./sec.; 6·66.
290. 700 ft.; 4·81; 2·81.

CHAPTER X

292. (a) 649 m.p.h.; (b) 562 m.p.h.
293. (a) 649 m.p.h.; (b) 279 m.p.h.
294. 660 m.p.h.
295. 10,000 ft.

298. 73,000 ft.
299. 42° C.
300. 854 m.p.h.

APPENDIX II

301. (a) lb.; (b) Slugs/cu. ft. or lb. sec.² / ft.⁴ (c) ft.²/sec.²; (d) Nil.
302. (a) lb./sq. ft.; (b) lb./sq. ft.; (c) ft.; (d) lb./sq. ft.
303. (a) Nil; (b) ML/T^2. (c) ML^2/T^3; (d) L.
304. (a) $\dfrac{M}{LT^2}$; (b) Nil; (c) $\dfrac{1}{T}$; (d) Nil.
305. M/LT^2.

306. L^2/T^2.
307. (c).
308. Acc. $= k\dfrac{v^2}{r}$ where k is a constant.
309. $V = k\sqrt{\dfrac{w}{\rho s}}$ where k is a constant.
310. $a = k\sqrt{\dfrac{P}{\rho}}$ where k is a constant.

APPENDIX III

311. 3·34 × 10⁻⁷ slugs/ft./sec. 3·54 × 10⁻⁷ slugs/ft./sec.; 3·63 × 10⁻⁷ slugs/ft./sec.; 3·83 × 10⁻⁷ slugs/ft./sec.
312. 54·3 × 10⁶.
313. 32·3 × 10⁶.
314. 44·2 × 10⁶.

315. 21·75 × 10⁶.
316. 1·415 × 10⁶.
317. 13·33 × 10⁶.
318. 24·5 atmospheres
319. Raised by 5·5%.
320. 446 lb.
321. 1·84 × 10⁶.

INDEX